FREE FROM UNCLE SAM:

AMERICA'S SECRET CASH GIVEAWAYS

Free From Uncle Sam:
America's Secret Cash Giveaways

CONTENTS

2008 [handwritten]

FREE FROM UNCLE SAM:

AMERICA'S SECRET CASH GIVEAWAYS

INTRODUCTION

You can collect $5,000... $10,000... $50,000... or more... from the U.S. Federal Government. Last year the Government handed out an astonishing 340 Billion Dollars to people just like you. This year the amount will be even higher.

The purpose of this book is to tell you about these government giveaways and how you can collect the money you qualify for. It covers red-hot government giveaways that could give you money to buy a condominium in Florida, money to start your own business, money to go to trade school, money to buy a new home, money to spruce up your home, money to study Spanish, money from Social Security regardless of your age or income... money for everything you can imagine!

FREE GIVEAWAYS — AMERICA'S BEST KEPT SECRET!

There are thousands of government programs and agencies and they have 340 billion dollars to give away to people who need help, or who want to change their lives, or want money for other reasons. This is money they have to give away by law!

These are little-known government programs that hand out cash, grants, assistance, help, housing, travel, health care, loan guarantees and subsidies and other giveaways — everything to make your dreams come true. And they're all spelled C-O-L-D C-A-S-H!

Many of these programs were created as part of the government's *War on Poverty* to help you and other Americans who need help. Or were slipped into the federal budget by Washington politicians to make themselves look good. Or help their fat cat friends. The government doesn't advertise these giveaways, so most people know nothing about them.

IT'S YOUR MONEY

The point is, you're entitled to apply for these dollars because:
1. You paid for these programs with your taxes all these years.
2. It's simply your money coming back to you as you deserve. Now it's your turn.

Cash Giveaways like these:

- **SOCIAL SECURITY: How you can qualify for a monthly retirement check** even if you never worked a day in your life, or paid any money into Social Security, or even nearly reached the age of 65.

- **MEDICAID: To qualify, you must be poor, Right?** Wrong! You can qualify even if you live in a million-dollar home and have money in the bank.

- **EMERGENCY BENEFITS:** The number to call to get a month's emergency aid.

- **EDUCATION:** Free government funding for your kid's college tuition. Doesn't require paying back one penny. And you get FREE books to boot.

To claim your share, simply choose the free money you're interested in, write or phone the government agency for an application, then apply, qualify and you could be receiving $thousands in free cash. Cash coming in to pay medical bills, education, buy a home, start a business.

Remember, however, you have to apply or you won't collect a cent. Because there are so many programs, you may feel it is just too much bother to look them all over to see which apply to your situation and needs. But this is the wrong attitude. Don't be lazy; this is real money you can be entitled to. Put in the needed time — the results could change your life.

I urge you: Don't just put this book away in a drawer. Actually use it to get the money you want.

GUIDE TO PROGRAM DESCRIPTIONS

The next seven chapters contain descriptions of government giveaway programs. Each program is headed by a descriptive name in large type. This is followed in smaller print by the official name of the government program and its official number. Followed by the description and details of the program.

SOURCES OF ADDITIONAL INFORMATION

The giveaways revealed in this book took countless hours of research to compile. Everything has been done to make it as accurate, easy-to-read, and up-to-date as possible. However, programs are improved, addresses and telephone numbers change— even as this book is being printed. So if you find you cannot contact an agency because it has a new phone number or some other change, the Appendix will show you how to get the latest information directly from a Federal agency set up to help you.

DON'T MISS OUT!

It's all here in this book, everything you need to collect your share of government giveaways. Now you can get your share of government money that is due you. So go get it!

Chapter 1
HOW TO COLLECT FAMILY ASSISTANCE AND SUPPORT

If you have financial or family problems, but don't know where to turn to look for help, there is a place where you can get help. The Federal Government.

To help out such people in need, Washington has set up what is called a federal "safety net." These are special programs established by Congress to help Americans who need temporary family assistance and social services. About one in five Americans is getting some type of assistance.

Among the federal agencies with major assistance programs are the Departments of Agriculture, Health and Human Services, and Labor. Each agency and program has its own rules and requirements. The purpose of this chapter is to show you how to collect what is coming to you.

DEPARTMENT OF HEALTH AND HUMAN SERVICES

The Department of Health and Human Services is the government agency most involved with welfare and public assistance. It's sub-agencies, such as the Administration for Children and Families and the Office of Family Assistance, administer the major Federal programs that support social services for children, youth and their families. These and the other important programs are **described** below.

Welfare—for Poor Families with Children

Temporary Assistance to Needy Families (TANF) (93.558)
(This program replaces Family Support Payments to States, Assistance Payments—"AFDC Maintenance Assistance") (93.560)

Description: Because many welfare families stay on welfare for long periods, even for two or three generations, the Federal Government recently passed new welfare reform legislation that substantially alters the old welfare program.

The new program is called Temporary Assistance to Needy Families (TANF). It provides assistance to needy families with children where the family includes a single, unemployed or incapacitated parent.

The emphasis of the new program is on moving people from welfare to economic self-sufficiency through work.

Each state develops it's own program and rules, but must get approval from the Federal Government. Most State's make welfare payments in the form of twice-a-month subsistence checks or direct vendor payments. They are made to cover costs for food, shelter, clothing, other necessary daily living needs and child care. In addition, payment may be made to provide temporary emergency assistance to certain families with children in emergency or crisis situations, in order to prevent destitution.

Unlike the old Welfare Program it replaces, which created an endless right to welfare, the new program emphasizes moving people from welfare to economic self-sufficiency through work. To do so, it places time limits on welfare eligibility. With certain exceptions, most families are limited to no more than 5 years of assistance under the Federal program.

In addition, most parents or caretakers receiving assistance under this program for more than 2 months may be required to participate in community service employment, and may be required to work after receiving 24 months of assistance.

Welfare recipients are eligible for Medicaid.

Eligibility Requirements: Needy families with children.

Financial Information: The amount of benefits you can receive varies, depending on your household income, and the State in which you live because each State decides the amount of benefits it will pay.

Based on the previous program's statistics, the new program should help about 4.7 million families comprising 13.1 million recipients. The average federally-contributed monthly payment per family was $385.

Who To Contact: *Headquarters Office*: Office of the Director, Office of Family Assistance, Administration for Children, Youth and Families, Department of Health and Human Services, 5th Floor, Aerospace Building, 370 L'Enfant Promenade, SW., Washington, DC 20447. (202) 401-9275. *Regional or Local Office*: Apply directly to your State or local welfare office. This office is often called the Department of Social Services. After filling out a form for aid, a department worker will take into consideration your family's income, resources and assets, and then determine how much you must have for housing, food and other necessities of life according to standards set by the State.

Child Care for Low-Income Families

Child Care and Development Fund (CCDF) (93.596) and Child Care and Development Block Grant (93.575)

Description: You may be able to get free or subsidized childcare for that part of the day when you are at work or in training. These two programs make grants to the States, which, in turn, give the money to local organizations to provide child care services to low-income families.

This is another government program that has changed because of recent welfare reform legislation. The newer program, **Child Care and Development Fund (CCDF),** will supercede the **Child Care and Development Block Grant** program. The purpose is to assist low-income families in obtaining subsidized child care so they can work or attend training/education in order to ultimately achieve independence from public assistance..

As an example of how the program works through the States, Pennsylvania has such a child care program funded by Federal block grants and the state. If you are a Pennsylvania resident and can't afford to work because of child care costs, this program could make work affordable, with the your weekly child care bill as low as $5.

Under Pennsylvania's program, you and your spouse/companion must be working at least 20 hours a week, three days a week. The child care must be necessary to allow you to work. Those leaving welfare and starting to work are given priority.

Under Pennsylvania's program, thousands of private child care providers enter in an agreement with Pennsylvania's Child Care Information Service. You may choose any provider who has or is willing to enter into such an agreement.

Most of the State's have similar programs.

Eligibility Requirements: Children under age 13 (or up to age 19, if disabled), who reside with a family whose income does not exceed 75 percent of the State median income for a family of the same size, and reside with a parent (or parents) who is working or attending a job-training or educational program; or are in need of, or are receiving protective services.

Financial Information: About $2.2 billion was funded for the two programs in the latest reported year.

Who To Contact: *Headquarters Office*: Child Care Bureau, Administration on Children, Youth, and Families, Administration for Children, Youth and Families, Department of Health and Human Services, 330 C Street, SW, Washington, DC 20447. (202) 690-6782. *Regional or Local Office*: Persons are encouraged to communicate with the Regional Administrators, Table 1a. *For more information about child care resources and referral agencies in your area*: Contact Child Care Bureau, ACYF. Phone: (202) 690-6782, Fax (202) 690-5600.

Hot Meals—for Senior Citizens
Special Programs for the Aging—Title III, Part C–Nutrition Services (93.045)

Description: This program provides grants to State Agencies on Aging to provide a hot or other appropriate meal at least once per day, five or more days per week, for older Americans. Meals may be served in congregate settings or delivered to the home. (In rural areas, a lesser frequency may be suitable.

Eligibility Requirements: Older individuals aged 60 and over and their spouses, and in certain cases, under age 60 if the individual is handicapped or disabled and resides with and accompanies an older individual

Financial Information: For the latest reported year, Congregate Nutrition Services totaled $378,412,000; Home Delivered Nutrition Services, $152,000,000.

Who To Contact: *Headquarters Office*: Mrs. Carol Crecy, Director, Office of State and Community Programs, Administration on Aging, Department of Health and Human Services, Washington, DC 20201. (202) 619-0011.

Regional or Local Office: Individuals needing assistance should contact the local welfare agency. This agency is often called the Department of Social Services.

In-Home Services for Frail Seniors
Special Programs for the Aging—Title III, Part D–"In-Home Services for Frail Older Individuals" (93.046)

Description: Under this program, money is given to the States to help pay for in-home services to frail older individuals so that they can continue to live at home. This includes in-home supportive services and personal care for victims of Alzheimer's disease and related disorders with neurological and organic brain dysfunctions, and to the families of such victims.

Eligibility Requirements: Individuals age 60 and older, especially older individuals with the greatest social needs and those with the greatest economic needs.

Financial Information: Last year, the Federal government share was $9,263,000.

Who To Contact: *Headquarters Office*: Mr. Edwin L. Walker, Director, Office of State and Community Programs, Administration on Aging, Department of Health and Human Services, Washington, DC 20201. (202) 619-0011. *Regional or Local Office*: Regional Administrator, Administration on Aging, Department of Health and Human Services, Regional Office (see Table 1j).

Job Training—If You Are Receiving Welfare
Job Opportunities and Basic Skills Training —"JOBS" (93.561)

Description: The goal of this program is to assure that needy families with children obtain the education, training, and employment that will help them avoid long-term welfare dependency. To help accomplish this goal, funding is given to the States, to federally-recognized Indian Tribes, and Alaska Native organizations to establish and operate JOBS programs that provide job-related education and training, including basic math and reading classes, job training programs, and on-the-job training.

In addition, the program provides reimbursement to JOBS participants for such work-related expenses as transportation and child care.

Beneficiary Eligibility: Welfare recipients and approved applicants, specifically those receiving Aid to Families with Dependent Children (AFDC) benefits or AFDC/Unemployed Parents benefits.

Financial Information: All States and Territories have approved JOBS and Supportive Services plans. A total of one billion dollars in federal funds is spent each year.

Literature: Information is available from Headquarters Office listed below.

Who To Contact: *Headquarters Office*: Office of the Director, Office of Family Assistance, Administration for Children and Families, 5th Floor, Aerospace Building, 370 L'Enfant Promenade, SW., Washington, DC 20447. (202) 401-9275. *Regional or Local Office*: Contact Administration for Children and Families regional offices (Table 1b).

Help in Collecting Child Support
Child Support Enforcement (93.563)

Description: About 4 million women are due child support payments from their children's' father but only about half of them get the full amount owed. Fathers in shocking numbers are refusing to pay child support.

This program was set up to help fight this problem by enforcing the collection of support payments owed by absent parents to their children. It also helps locate absent parents, establish paternity, and obtain child, spousal and medical support. It does this by funding State agencies which must provide enforcement services directly to eligible individuals.

Beneficiary Eligibility: All recipients of welfare, Foster Care Maintenance Payments, and Medicaid, for whom an assignment to the State for support rights has been made and who are in need of

such services; and any other individual who needs such services and who has applied for them.

Financial Information: $3.4 billion was funded for the program in the latest reported year.

Who To Contact: *Headquarters Office*: Gaile Maller, Office of Child Support Enforcement, Administration for Children, Youth and Families, Department of Health and Human Services, 4th Floor, 370 L'Enfant Promenade, SW., Washington, DC 20447. (202) 401-5368. *Regional or Local Office*: Regional Representative, Department of Health and Human Services. (See Table 1b for addresses and telephone numbers.)

Head Start
(93.600)

Description: The Head Start program is for preschool children from low-income families. It provides children with comprehensive educational, health, nutritional, social and other services to help them grow mentally, emotionally, socially, and physically. Included are Indian children on federally-recognized reservations, and children of migratory workers and their families.

Beneficiary Eligibility: Head Start programs are for children from low-income families. It serves children from birth up to the age when the child enters the school system. At least 10 percent of the total enrollment opportunities in each local Head Start program shall be available for children with disabilities.

Financial Information: Since 1965, Head Start has served about 19.4 million children from low-income families in 50 States, the District of Columbia, Puerto Rico, the Virgin Islands, and the Pacific Commonwealths. In the latest reported year, a total of $6,324,812,000 was awarded in the form of over 2000 grants.

Who To Contact: *Headquarters Office*: Head Start Bureau, 330 C Street, SW., Washington, DC 20447. Phone: (202) 205-8572. *Regional or Local Office*: Regional Administrator, Administration for Children and Families. (See Table 1a.)

Money and Help—for Refugees

Refugee and Entrant Assistance—State Administered Programs (93.566)

Description: This program subsidizes cash assistance, medical assistance, and social services provided to refugees, including Cuban and Haitian entrants, for resettlement throughout the country, (Refugees in the U.S. may be assisted regardless of national origin.) The Federal government funds State and local welfare and health agencies, and prescribes that the scope of assistance be similar to that in the regular domestic public assistance programs.

Beneficiary Eligibility: Persons for whom assistance is authorized are limited to refugees in alien status, with documentation from the Immigration and Naturalization Service (INS) as to refugee status, to certain Amerasian immigrants and their accompanying family members, and to Cuban and Haitian entrants with documentation from the INS.

Financial Information: In the latest reported year, $242,147,876 was allotted. Examples of the type of assistance provided: cash assistance for up to 8 months, employment services, English language training.

Literature: Various materials are available on request from the Office of Refugee resettlement, Administration for Children, Youth and Families, Department of Health and Human Services, Washington, DC 20447.

Who To Contact: *Headquarters Office*: Office of Refugee Resettlement, Administration for Children, Youth and Families, Department of Health and Human Services, 6th Floor, 370 L'Enfant Promenade, SW., Washington, DC 20447. (202) 401-4732. *Regional or Local Office*: Contact: Loren Bussert. Phone: (202) 401-4732.

Low–Income Home Energy Assistance

(93.568)

DESCRIPTION: Energy Assistance Block Grants are awarded to States and other jurisdictions, which then make payments directly to an eligible low-income household or, on behalf of such household, to an energy supplier to assist in meeting the cost of home energy.

See Chapter 3, page 119.

Money—for Refugees to Start a Small Business

Refugee and Entrant Assistance—Discretionary Grants (93.576)

DESCRIPTION: Project grants for demonstration projects that promote refugee self-sufficiency or address their special needs. State and local governments and private nonprofit organizations are eligible to apply for these funds, which they may then use for micro-financing to refugees engaged in small businesses activities.

See Chapter 2, page 75.

Money—to Americans Returning to the U.S. from Overseas Broke

U.S. Repatriate Program (93.579)

Description: Repayable loans to provide temporary assistance, care, and treatment to individuals after their return to the United States from travel in a foreign country due to physical or mental illness, destitution, or because of war, the threat of war, or a similar crisis. Assistance may include money for food, shelter, clothing, and transportation. It may also include payment for special services such as medical and psychiatric care, guidance counseling.

Temporary assistance is provided for up to 90 days from the date of arrival into the United States from travel abroad. Assistance is discontinued if applicant receives other resources or income prior to 90 days. Repatriate may request an extension of assistance beyond the normal limitation of 90 days.

Eligibility Requirements: U.S. citizens (certified by the Department of State) needing assistance because the repatriate is without other means of income. Also eligible are their dependents, spouses, parents, grandparents, unmarried minor children, unmarried adult children who are dependent because they are handicapped, and minor siblings.

Financial Information: About 200 citizens in the latest reported year. The amount and type of assistance provided is determined by a local social service agency according to that State's standards for the Aid to Families with Dependent Children program.

Literature: Brochure entitled "*Temporary Assistance for Repatriates*" is available from the Headquarters Office at no charge.

Who To Contact: *Headquarters Office*: Office of Refugee Resettlement, Administration for Children, Youth and Families, 370 L'Enfant Promenade, SW., Washington, DC 20447. Sue Benjamin, phone: (202) 401-4851. *Regional or Local Office*: None.

Application Procedure: Repatriate presents identification and signs repayment agreement.

Money—to Help You Adopt Children with Special Needs
Adoption Assistance (93.659)

Description: Under this program, adoption subsidy payments are made to support the adoption of hard-to-place children who meet the definition of special needs as specified in the law. All parents adopting special needs children are eligible. The subsidies are available from the time of adoption placement to age 18 (21 for certain handicaps).

Beneficiary Eligibility: You can receive adoption subsidy payments if you adopt:

1) children who are recipients or are eligible for Program **93.560** on page 7 and similar programs; or

2) children who have special needs, e.g., a special factor or condition which makes it reasonable to conclude that they cannot be adopted without adoption assistance

Financial Information: This program assists approximately 200,000 children per month.

Who To Contact: *Headquarters Office*: Jennifer Butler, Hembree, Children's Bureau, 330 C Street, SW., Washington, DC 20447. Phone: (202) 260-7684. *Regional or Local Office*: Contact Regional Administrator, Admin-istration for Children and Families (Table 1a).

Free Job Training For Teens in Foster Care
Independent Living (93.674)

Description: This program funds State and local programs to help teens and young adults who are in foster care make the transition to independent living. These programs provide skill development, and education or training related to independent living, but not room and board. The Independent Living program helps with job training, and with lessons in social skills, budgeting money, getting a high school equivalency diploma, drivers ed., job placement, career planning and more.

Beneficiary Eligibility: Youth age 16 and over, on whose behalf foster care maintenance payments are being made or were made and discontinued on or after their 16th birthday.

Financial Information: $200,000,000 was allotted last year..

Who to Contact: *Headquarters Office*: Terry Lewis, Deputy Associate Commissioner, Children's Bureau, Administration for Children and Families, P.O. Box 1182, Washington, DC 20013. Phone: (202) 205-8740. *Regional or Local Office*: Contact Regional Administration for Children and Families. (Table 1a.)

DEPARTMENT OF AGRICULTURE

Food Stamps
(10.551)

Description: The Food Stamp program gives low-income people food stamps which they can spend on food at grocery stores. They are available to low-income people no matter what there age or health.

The U.S. Department of Agriculture administers the Food Stamp Program. However, eligible households receive a coupon allotment from a state or local agency responsible for handling the program in their area. The allotment varies according to household size and income.

Disabled persons receiving Social Security Disability Insurance or Supplemental Security Income (SSI) can also receive food stamps. Food Stamps may also be used by certain elderly and handicapped persons, and their spouses, who cannot prepare their own meals to have meals delivered to them in their homes by authorized meal delivery services. Elderly persons and their spouses may also use Food Stamps to purchase meals in establishments providing communal dining for the elderly.

Beneficiary Eligibility: Households certified by local welfare officials to be in need of food assistance. These include:
- Most households who are receiving some form of welfare assistance;
- Persons who are unemployed, part-time employed, or working for low wages;
- Persons living on limited pensions.

Eligibility is based on family size, income, and level of resources. Able-bodied adults, with certain exceptions, must meet a work requirement.

Resource eligibility: Households may have up to $2,000 in cash, bank account or stocks (up to $3,000 if at least one person is age 60 or older); and a vehicle worth $4,650 or less or used for income-producing purposes or to transport a disabled family member or for training or education to prepare for work. Certain resources are not counted, such as a home and lot and the resources of people who receive Social Security Disability Insurance or SSI.

Income Eligibility: Households have to meet income tests unless all members are receiving welfare or SSI. Households that have income over the following limits generally cannot get food stamps.

People in Household	Gross Monthly Income Limits	Net Monthly Income Limits
1	$ 905	$ 696
2	1,219	938
3	1,553	1,180
4	1,848	1,421
5	2,162	1,663

Gross income includes all cash payments to the household. Net Income means gross income minus allowable deductions. *The following deductions are allowed*: A 20 percent deduction from earned income; a standard $134 deduction for all households; $200 for each child under age 2 and $175 for each other child; medical expenses paid out for elderly or disabled family members if more than $35 a month; legally owed child support payments; excess shelter, phone and utility costs which are more than half of the households income after other deductions.

Once the deductions are subtracted from income, many middle-class families become eligible for food stamps. It's been estimated that as many as 18 million Americans are eligible for food stamps but are not taking advantage of them.

Financial Information: Most applicants, if they qualify, have to wait 30 days to get food stamps. However, if you have very little money or can't pay your rent and utilities, you can get expedited (fast) service which means you get your food stamps within seven days of applying. You have to show: (1) you have under $100 in liquid resources and earn under $150 a month; or (2) your combined gross income and liquid resources are less than your monthly housing costs. *Range and Average of Financial Assistance*: The following are the maximum allotment levels:

Household Size	Maximum Allotment
1	$ 122
2	224
3	321
4	408
5	485

The allotments varies by income and family size, averaging $72.77 per month per person. There is a Food Stamp Program in every area in every State, with participation per month averaging over 17 million persons.

Literature: Available from the national office and the regional offices: "*Facts About the Food Stamp Program*" (in English and Spanish).

Who To Contact: *Headquarters Office*: Deputy Administrator, Food Stamp Program, Food and Consumer Service, Department of Agriculture, Alexandria, VA 22302. Contact: Bonny O'Neil, Acting Deputy Administrator, Food Stamp Program, (703) 305-2026. *Regional or Local Office*: See the Food and Consumer Service Regional Offices listed in Table 1c. *To Apply:* Apply at your local welfare office (often called the Dept. of Social Services). If you have questions, you can call the hot line for your state listed in Table 1l.

Free Food
Food Distribution—"Food Donation Program" (10.550)

Description: The objective of this program is to improve the diets of school and preschool children; the elderly; needy persons in charitable institutions; and other individuals in need of food assistance. To this end, the Department of Agriculture donates bonus food commodities to state agencies to distribute to qualifying outlets such as emergency feeding organizations, soup kitchens and food banks, schools, child and adult day care, charitable institutions, nutrition programs for the elderly, nonprofit summer camps and Summer Food Service for children. Individuals receiving such food may not be charged.

Beneficiary Eligibility:
1) Households in areas which participate in the Emergency Food Assistance Program (TEFAP), meeting Eligibility Requirements established by the State;
2) All children in schools, child care institutions, and summer camps which participate in the program may benefit from food donations.

Financial Information: Not applicable

Who To Contact: *Headquarters Office*: Food Distribution Division, Food and Consumer Service, Department of Agriculture, Alexandria, VA 22302. (703) 305-2680. Contact: Les Johnson, Director. *Regional or Local Office*: See Food and Consumer Service Regional Offices listed in Table 1c. *Application Procedure*: Heads of households apply to local welfare authorities (often called the Department of Social Services) on forms supplied by State or local office.

Free Breakfasts for School Children
School Breakfast Program (10.553)

Description: This program provides breakfast to students at participating public and private schools through high school grades. The schools serve free and reduced price meals to eligible students meeting income eligibility guidelines.

Beneficiary Eligibility: All students attending schools where the breakfast program is operating may participate—both needy and non-needy. Children from households certified to receive food stamps, the Food Distribution Program on Indian Reservations, Temporary Assistance for Needy Families (formerly known as Aid to Families with Dependent Children) and some children in Head Start Programs are automatically eligible for free meals.

Financial Information: In the most recent reported year, 4,543 million lunches were served and this is expected to increase by another 67 million next year.

Who To Contact: *Headquarters Office*: Director, Child Nutrition Division, Food and Consumer Service, Dept. of Agriculture, Alexandria, VA 22302. (703) 305-2590. Contact: Stanley Garnett, Director. *Regional or Local Office*: See Table 1c.

Free Lunch for School Children

National School Lunch Program (10.555)

Description: This program subsidizes the cost of providing lunch to students at participating public and private schools through high school grades. The schools serve free and reduced price meals to eligible students meeting income guidelines.

Beneficiary Eligibility: All students attending schools where the lunch program is operating may participate—both needy and non-needy. Children from households certified to receive food stamps, the Food Distribution Program on Indian Reservations, Temporary Assistance for Needy Families and some children in Head Start Programs are automatically eligible for free meals.

Financial Information: In the latest reported year, 4.4 billion lunches were served.

Literature: "*National School Lunch Program*," FCS-78, a fact sheet — no charge.

Who To Contact: Headquarters Office: Director, Child Nutrition Division, Food and Consumer Service, Dept. of Agriculture, Alexandria, VA 22302. (703) 305-2590. Contact: Stanley Garnett, Director. *Regional/Local Office*: Table 1c.

Free Milk for Children

Special Milk Program for Children (10.556)

Description: This program subsidizes the cost of providing milk to students in public and private schools of high school grade and under, public and private nonprofit nursery schools, child-care centers, settlement houses, summer camps, and similar nonprofit institutions devoted to the care and training of children. The milk is free or reduced in price to children meeting income eligibility guidelines.

Beneficiary Eligibility: All students attending schools and institutions in which this program is in operation may participate in the program.

Financial Information: In the latest reported year, 120,300,000 half-pints of milk were served.

Who To Contact: *Headquarters Office*: Director, Child Nutrition Division, Food and Consumer Service, Department of Agriculture, Alexandria, VA 22302. Contact: Stanley C. Garnett, Director. (703) 305-2590. *Regional/Local Office*: Table 1c.

Free Food for Infants, Tots and Pregnant Women

Special Supplemental Nutrition Program for Women, Infants, and Children—"WIC Program" (10.557)

Description: The purpose of the WIC Program is to provide at no cost supplemental nutritious foods, nutrition education, and referrals to health care to low-income pregnant, breastfeeding and new mothers, to infants, and to children to age five who are determined to be at nutritional risk. Federal funds go to State and local agencies that, in turn, distribute WIC food vouchers and program services. These stamps are in addition to any food stamps you are receiving.

WIC food vouchers can be used at grocery stores to buy milk, cheese, eggs, juice, cereals, beans and peanut butter. Women who breastfeed totally receive an extra set of vouchers for tuna and carrots. You can also get vouchers for iron-fortified infant formula and cereals for infants.

Beneficiary Eligibility: Pregnant women, breastfeeding and new mothers, infants, and children up to 5 years of age are eligible if:
- They are in need of the special supplemental foods supplied by the program because of nutritional risk; and
- They meet an income standard, or receive or have certain family members that receive benefits under the Food Stamp, Medicaid or Temporary Assistance for Needy Families Program.

If you breastfeed your baby, you can stay in WIC for a year after the baby's birth. If not, you can stay in WIC for 6 months. This rule is to encourage breastfeeding.

You qualify for WIC if your total monthly income is below the following:
- Family Size, 1 person: $1,288
- 2 persons: $1,735
- 3 people: $2,182

15

- 4 people: $2,629
- 5 people: $3,076

Unborn children are not counted in the total; a single pregnant woman counts as a family of one.

Financial Information: The average value of the vouchers is about $33 per person per month. In the latest reported year, approximately seven million women, infants and children received WIC benefits every month.

Who To Contact: Individual participants apply for WIC benefits at an approved local agency. *Headquarters Office*: Supplemental Food Programs Div., Food and Consumer Service, Dept. of Agriculture, Alexandria, VA 22302. Contact: Patricia Daniels, Dir. (703) 305-2746. *Regional/Local Office*: See Food and Consumer Service regional offices, Table 1c. Or call toll-free (888) WIC BABY to find WIC nearest program.

Free Meals to Children and Senior Citizens
Child and Adult Care Food Program (10.558)

Description: This program provides funding to eligible institutions so they can provide free meals and snacks to children and elderly or impaired adults in nonresidential day care facilities.

Eligibility Requirements: The program in child care institutions is limited to children 12 years old and younger, except for children of migrant workers, who may be up to 15, and individuals with disabilities, who if over 12, would be eligible to participate only in a center or home where the majority of those enrolled are 18 and younger.

In adult day care centers, functionally impaired adults 18 years of age and older, and adults 60 years of age and older, regardless of income, who are not residents of an institution are eligible. Spouses of participants can also get meals, no matter what their age.

Eligible public and nonprofit private institutions include day care centers, outside-school-hours care centers, settlement houses, recreation centers, family and group day care homes, Head Start programs, and institutions providing day care services to children with

disabilities. Also eligible are nonprofit centers which provide nonresidential adult day care, and private for-profit adult day care.

Financial Information: In the latest reported year, over 1.67 billion meals were served.

Literature: "*Adult Care, Food Program*" fact sheet is available at no charge.

Who To Contact: *Headquarters Office*: Director, Child Nutrition Division, Food and Consumer Service, U.S. Dept. of Agriculture, Alexandria, VA 22302. Contact: Stanley C. Garnett, Director. (703) 305-2590. *Regional/Local Office*: Table 1c.

Summer Food Service Program for Children
(10.559)

Description: The purpose of this program is to assist States, through grants-in-aid and other means, to conduct nonprofit food service programs for low-income children during the summer months and at other approved times, when area schools are closed for vacation.

It does this by disbursing funds to eligible service institutions (sponsors) which provide free and reduced-price meals during these periods to children in areas where at least 50 percent of the children meet the income eligibility criteria for free and reduced price lunches.

Meals may be served to children 18 and younger, and to individuals over 18 who participate in State approved programs for persons with disabilities.

Beneficiary Eligibility: Primarily, children from areas in which poor economic conditions exist. Also homeless children, regardless of location

Financial Information: In the latest reported year, over 136,000,000 meals were served.

Literature: "*Summer Food Service Program*" fact sheet is available at no charge.

Who To Contact: *Headquarters Office*: Director, Child Nutrition Division, Food and Consumer Service, U.S. Dept. of Agriculture, Alexandria, VA 22302. Contact: Stanley C. Garnett, Dir. (703) 305-2590. *Regional/Local Office*: Table 1c.

Free Food Commodities—to Needy Pregnant Women, Their Young Children, and Needy Seniors
Commodity Supplemental Food Program (10.565)

Description: Donation of supplemental foods to be distributed to low income pregnant, postpartum and breast-feeding women, infants, and children up to 6 years old, and elderly persons in order to improve their health and nutritional status. Under the program, commodities are distributed to State health, agriculture and other agencies, or federally recognized Indian organizations, which, in turn, distribute them to participating local public or private nonprofit agencies which make the food available to eligible beneficiaries. Donated foods can only be made available to eligible beneficiaries and can not be sold.

Beneficiary Eligibility: The following categories of persons are eligible under this program if they are income qualified under existing Federal, State, or local food, health, or welfare programs for low-income persons:
1) Infants; children up to age 6
2) Pregnant, postpartum or breast-feeding woman
3) Elderly persons 60 years old or older
4) At State agency discretion, persons determined to be at nutritional risk

Financial Information: In the latest report year, average monthly participation was approximately 95,419 women, infants, and children. Elderly projects served approximately 293,824 senior persons per month.

Who To Contact: Applicants should consult the office or official designated as the single point of contact in his or her State. *Headquarters Office*: Food Distribution Division, Food and Consumer Service, Department of Agriculture, Alexandria, VA 22302. Contact: Les Johnson, Director. (703) 305-2680. *Regional or Local Office*: See Food and Consumer Service regional offices listed in Table 1c.

$94 a Month—to Needy Persons in Puerto Rico to Buy Food
Nutrition Assistance For Puerto Rico (10.566)

Description: Cash money to households to purchase food. (This is an alternative to the Food Stamp Program to improve diets of needy persons living in Puerto Rico.)

Eligibility Requirements: Low-income individuals and families are eligible for benefits as determined by the Commonwealth of Puerto Rico.

Financial Information: Monthly data for the latest reported year: 1.08 million persons received benefits; benefits per person $94.39.

Who To Contact: *Headquarters Office*: Deputy Administrator, Food Stamp Program, Food and Consumer Service, Department of Agriculture, Alexandria, VA 22302. Contact: Bonny O'Neil, Acting Deputy Administrator, Food Stamp Program. Phone: (703) 305-2026. *Regional or Local Office*: Regional Administrator, Mid-Atlantic Regional Office, Food and Consumer Service, Department of Agriculture, Trenton, NJ 08691. Contact: Christopher Martin. (609) 259-5025. *Application Procedure:* Applicants should consult the office or official designated as the single point of contact in Puerto Rico for more information.

Free Food Commodities—to Needy Native Americans
Food Distribution Program on Indian Reservations (10.567)

Description: In order to improve the diets of needy persons in households on or near Indian reservations, Indian Tribal Organizations and State Distributing Agencies donate free foods to qualifying households. Food donations are provided by Dept. of Agriculture. Donated foods may not be sold, exchanged, or otherwise disposed of.

Beneficiary Eligibility: Households must be:
1) Living on an Indian reservation, or be Indian households living in a designated

area near an Indian reservation, or in Indian country for Oklahoma, and

2) Certified by local authorities as having inadequate income and resources. Upper limits of allowable income vary with family size.

Financial Information: Each month, approximately 121,495 needy persons in low-income households participate. 94 Indian tribal organizations and six States administer the program for 218 Indian Reservations.

Who To Contact: *Headquarters Office*: Les Johnson, Director, Food Distribution Division, Food and Consumer Service, Department of Agriculture, Alexandria, VA 22302. (703) 305-2680. *Regional or Local Office*: See Food and Consumer Service Regional Offices in Table 1c. *Application Procedure*: An applicant should consult the office or official designated as the single point of contact in his or her State for more information.

Free Emergency Food Commodities to Needy Persons

Emergency Food Assistance Program—Food Commodities (10.569)

Description: The Department of Agriculture provides food commodities to State and local agencies for distribution to needy persons or for use in preparing meals at congregate meal sites. The commodities are distributed to needy persons free of charge. All States are eligible to participate.

Beneficiary Eligibility: Needy individuals certified by local agencies on the basis of State eligibility standards. They may be the unemployed, welfare recipients, on SSI or Medicaid, or have low income. All individuals seeking food assistance at congregate meal sites are eligible.

Financial Information: Recipients get free food packages including cheese, butter, dry milk, corn meal, flour, honey, and other assorted items..

Who To Contact: *Headquarters Office*: Food Distribution Division, FCS, USDA, Room 502,

Park Office Center, 3101 Park Center Drive, Alexandria, VA 22302. Contact: Les Johnson, Director. (703) 305-2680. *Regional or Local Office*: See Food and Consumer Service Regional Office contacts listed in Table 1c. *Application Procedure*: Applicants should consult the office or official designated as the single point of contact in his or her State for more information.

Additional Food Coupons to Pregnant Women Already Receiving Food Stamps—to Use at Farmers Markets

WIC Farmers' Market Nutrition Program—"FMNP" (10.572)

Description: Subsidized Federal FMNP coupons are given to low-income, at-risk women, infants, and children to obtain fresh, nutritious unprepared foods (such as fruits and vegetables) from eligible farmers' markets. Under this program, Dept. of Agriculture grants are made to State health, agriculture and other agencies, or federally recognized Indian organizations. The participating State agencies, in turn, select Local FMNP farmers' markets based on the concentration of eligible WIC Program (**10.517**) participants and access to the market.

Beneficiary Eligibility: Federal FMNP coupons may be issued only to WIC participants — i.e., pregnant, postpartum or breast-feeding women; infants over 4 months of age; and children up to 5 years of age — or to persons who are on a waiting list to receive WIC benefits.

Financial Information: Not available. The FMNP program is in operation in at least 30 states.

Who To Contact: *Headquarters Office*: Supplemental Food Programs Division, Food and Consumer Service, Department of Agriculture, 3101 Park Center Drive, Room 540, Alexandria, VA 22302. Contact Debra R. Whitford, Branch Chief. Phone: (703) 305-2730. *Regional or Local Office*: See Food and Consumer Service regional offices, Table 1c.

Free Meals—for Homeless Children

Homeless Children Nutrition Program—National School Lunch Act (10.573)

Description: This program makes grants to State, city, county, and local governments, other public entities, and private nonprofit organizations to provide free breakfasts, lunches, suppers, and supplements throughout the year to homeless children under the age of 6 in emergency shelters.

Beneficiary Eligibility: All children under age 6 in emergency shelters where the Homeless Children Nutrition Program is operating are eligible for free meals without application.

Financial Information: In the latest reported year, 79 sponsoring organizations operated the program in numerous shelters.

Literature: "*Homeless Children Nutrition Program*", fact sheet — no charge.

Who To Contact: Headquarters Office: Director, Child Nutrition Division, Food and Consumer Service, United States Department of Agriculture, Alexandria, VA 22302. Contact: Stanley C. Garnett, Director. (703) 305-2590. *Regional or Local Office*: Table 1c.

DEPARTMENT OF HOUSING AND URBAN DEVELOPMENT

Construction Job Training for Youth

Opportunities for Youth—Youthbuild Program (14.243)

Description: The Youthbuild program provides funding assistance for a wide range of services to assist economically disadvantaged youth. The opportunities are designed to help disadvantaged young adults who have dropped out of high school to obtain the education and employment skills necessary to achieve economic self-efficiency.

It does this by providing disadvantaged young adults experience and training in the construction trades. Participants in the program get meaningful hands-on training in the construction and rehabilitation of housing by helping to build or rehabilitating housing for homeless and low income families in their community.

Beneficiary Eligibility: Very low income young adults, ages 16 to 24, who have dropped out of high school are eligible. The program emphasizes special outreach efforts to be undertaken to recruit eligible young women. The program permits exceptions for young adults who do not meet the program's income or education requirements but who have educational needs despite attainment of a high school diploma or its equivalent.

Financial Information: Funding this year: $60,000,000.

Who to Contact: *Headquarters Office*: Office of Economic Development, Department of Housing and Urban Development, 451 7th Street SW., Washington, DC 20410, Room 7134. (202) 708-2035. *Regional or Local Office*: None.

Money—for the Disadvantaged to Study Community Development

Community Development Work-Study Program (14.512)

Description: This program makes grants to institutions of higher education for the purpose of providing assistance to economically disadvantaged and minority students who are planning careers in community and economic development, community planning, and community management. Students must be full-time graduate students in these or related fields and participate in community development work-study programs.

Beneficiary Eligibility: Economically disadvantaged students who seek careers in community and economic development, community planning, community management or other related fields of study.

Financial Information: $3,000,000 is allocated this year. Average support per year is $30,000 for each graduate student.

Who to Contact: *Headquarters Office*: For application kits, contact HUD USER, P.O. Box 6091, Rockville, MD 20849. Phone: (800) 245-2691. Direct technical questions to Jane Karadbil, Office of University Partnerships, Department of Housing and Urban Development, Room 8110, 451 7th Street, SW., Wash. DC 20410. (202) 708-1537, ext. 5918. *Regional/Local Office*: None.

Work-Study Programs at Hispanic-Serving Community Colleges
Hispanic-Serving Institutions Work-Study Programs (14.513)

Description: This program awards funds to Hispanic-serving community colleges so they can assist economically disadvantaged and minority students who are enrolled full-time in an associate degree program in a community building academic program and participate in "Hispanic-Serving Institutions Work-Study Programs." The program is designed to provide entry for these

> **This program is not being funded this year.**

students to pre-professional careers in the community building field.

Eligible associate degree fields of study include community and economic development, community management, public administration, public policy, urban economics, urban management, urban planning, administration of justice, child development, and human services.

Beneficiary Eligibility: Economically disadvantaged and minority students who seek pre-professional careers in a community building field.

Financial Information: $2,000,000 is budgeted this year. Maximum support per student is $13,200 per year for two years.

Who to Contact: *Headquarters Office*: Jane Karadbil, Office of University Partnerships, U.S. Department of Housing and Urban Development, Room 8110, 451 7th Street, SW., Washington, DC

20410. (202) 708-1537, extension 218. *Regional or Local Office*: See Table 7c, Chapter 7.

DEPARTMENT OF LABOR

The Department of Labor has various programs to help the unemployed or underemployed develop employment skills so you can earn more money.

Salaried On-the-Job Training
Registered Apprenticeship Training (17.201)

Description: This program encourages industry and unions to set up apprenticeship and training programs. The Bureau of Apprenticeship and Training (BAT) registers apprentices and apprenticeship training programs in 23 States and Guam and other Pacific Islands. It also provides technical assistance and works closely with State Apprenticeship Councils (SACs) in the remaining 27 States, the District of Columbia, Puerto Rico, and the Virgin Islands, which register apprentices and programs in accordance with Federal standards.

Apprentices receive salaried on-the-job training. However, minimum wage standards don't apply. Special efforts are being made to increase the number of women and minority apprentices and to introduce the apprenticeship concept of training into new industries and occupations.

Beneficiary Eligibility: To be accepted into an apprenticeship training program, you must be at least 16 years old and must satisfy the apprenticeship program sponsor that you have sufficient ability, aptitude, and education to master the rudiments of the trade or occupation and to satisfactorily complete the related theoretical instruction required in the program.

Financial Information: In the latest reported year, over 360,511 apprentices received training in over 37,800 registered programs.

Literature: "*Equal Employment Opportunity in Apprenticeship and Training*"; "*The National Apprenticeship Program*"; "*Apprenticeship Past and Present*"; "*Apprentice Information*"; "*Apprenticeship*"; the Internet World Wide Web Home Page: http://www.doleta.gov/.

Who To Contact: *Headquarters Office*: Bureau of Apprenticeship and Training, Employment and Training Administration, Department of Labor, 200 Constitution Avenue, NW., Room N-4671, Washington, DC 20210. (202) 693-2796. *Regional or Local Office*: You are encouraged to communicate with the Bureau of Apprenticeship and Training Regional Directors. See Table 1d listing Bureau of Apprenticeship and Training Regional Offices.

Free Job Placement Services
Employment Service (17.207)

Description: The goal of this program is to place persons in employment by providing a variety of placement-related services without charge to job seekers and to employers seeking qualified individuals to fill job openings. For example, it maintains a nationwide computerized interstate job listing of hard-to-fill employer openings. Also available may be job search training or assistance, job counseling and testing services to job seekers.

Beneficiary Eligibility: Persons seeking employment. Veterans receive priority referral to jobs as well as special employment services and assistance, with disabled veterans receiving preferential treatment over other veterans. Handicapped workers are also entitled to special employment services.

Financial Information: Not applicable.

Literature: "*State and Local Area Labor Market Newsletters*" are available from State Employment Security Agencies. Available from Superintendent of Documents, U.S. Government Printing Office, Washington, DC 20402, are: "*Tips For Finding The Right Job*"; "*Guide for Occupational Exploration*"; "*Job Search Guide: Strategies for Professionals.*"

Who To Contact: *Headquarters Office*: Administrator, Office of Workforce Security United States Employment Service, Employment and Training Administration, Department of Labor, Washington, DC 20210. Phone: (202) 693-3046. Contact: Gay Gilbert. *Regional or Local Office*: Contact the nearest office of the State Employment Security Agency listed in Table 1e.

Money—if You Lose Your Job
Unemployment Compensation Insurance (17.225)

Description: If you lose your job through no fault of your own, you may receive regular unemployment insurance cash payments for up to 26 weeks. Benefits are available if you've been laid off, fired for a reason other than misconduct, or quit your job with good cause connected with the work. Examples of misconduct include violations of company policy, repeated unexcused absences or lateness, or insubordination.

Generally, absences for illness are not misconduct. Inability to do a job satisfactorily is also usually not considered misconduct.

If you quit a job for personal reasons — such as not liking the job — you would not be eligible for unemployment benefits.

The federal government administers the various State programs of unemployment insurance through Federal and State cooperation. It also administers payment of trade adjustment assistance; disaster unemployment assistance; unemployment compensation for Federal employees and ex-service members.

Even though the federal government administers the program, the various State agencies pay the actual cash benefits to eligible workers and fund it by collecting State unemployment taxes from employers.

Beneficiary Eligibility: All workers whose wages are subject to State unemployment insurance laws, Federal civilian employees, ex-service members, trade readjustment allowance for workers who become unemployed as a result of product imports, and workers whose unemployment is caused by a Presidentially-declared disaster. Individual State information and eligibility requirements are available from local employment offices.

Financial Information: Over $31 billion this year.

Literature: "*If Imports Cost You Your Job...Apply for Trade Adjustment Assistance*"; "*Unemployment Insurance, How It Works For You*"; "*If*

Disaster Strikes --- You Should Know About Disaster Unemployment Assistance"; "*Unemployment Insurance For Ex-Service Members*"; "*Unemployment Insurance For Federal Workers*"; "*Significant Provisions of State Unemployment Insurance Laws.*"

Who To Contact: *Headquarters Office*: Administrator, Office of Workforce Security, Employment and Training Administration, Department of Labor, Washington, DC 20210. Phone: (202) 693-3200. Contact: Cheryl Atkinson. *Regional or Local Office*: Local office of the State Employment Service (Table 1c); local office of the State Unemployment Insurance Service; Employment and Training Administration regional offices (Table 1f).

Part-Time Jobs for Low-Income Seniors
Senior Community Service Employment Program (17.235)

Description: Under this program, agencies and organizations receive grants to provide part-time work opportunities in community service activities for unemployed low-income persons who are 55 years of age and older. To the extent feasible, the program assists and promotes the transition of program enrollees into unsubsidized employment.

The individuals who are employed may be placed in work assignments at local service agencies (e.g., schools, hospitals, day care centers, park systems, etc.), or may be given work assignments in connection with community service projects. A portion of project funds may be used to provide participants with training, counseling, and other supportive services.

Beneficiary Eligibility: Adults 55 years or older with a family income at or below 125 percent of the poverty level.

Financial Information: In the latest reported year, 61,200 subsidized part-time jobs were funded.

Who To Contact: *Headquarters Office*: Div. of Older Worker Programs, Office of Adult Services, Employment and Training Administration, U.S. Dept. of Labor, Room N-5306, 200 Constitution Ave., NW., Washington, DC 20210. (202) 693-3842. *Regional or Local Office*: Not applicable.

Free Assistance and Training If You Lose Your Job Because of Increased Imports
Trade Adjustment Assistance—Workers (17.245)

Description: If you've been laid off because of a plant shut-down due to increased imports, this program provides adjustment assistance payments and job placement services. Under the program, State Employment Security Agencies (SESA's) administer the benefit payments. They do this through local offices that provide testing, counseling, and job placement services; job search and relocation assistance; training; and payment of weekly trade readjustment allowances. You must use up your State unemployment compensation benefits before collecting trade adjustment assistance.

Eligibility Requirements: Petitions for trade adjustment assistance must be filed with the Secretary of Labor by a group of three or more workers or by their certified or recognized union or by an official of the workers' firm. For workers to be eligible to apply for adjustment assistance, the Department of Labor must determine that:

1) a significant number or proportion of workers in such workers' firm, or subdivision of the firm, have become or will become totally or partially separated;
2) sales or production, or both, of such firm have decreased absolutely; and
3) increases of imports like or directly competitive with articles produced by such workers' firm were an important cause.

In addition, to be eligible for weekly trade readjustment allowance payments, you must: (1) have been employed with wages at a minimum of $30 per week by the import-affected firm for a least 26 of the previous 52 weeks including the week of total layoff; (2) your unemployment or underemployment must have begun on or up to two years after the impact date specified in the Secretary's certification as the beginning of the import-impacted unemployment or underemployment; and (3) be enrolled in or have completed an approved job training program, unless the determination is made that training is either not feasible or not appropriate, in which case a waiver of the training requirement may be issued.

Financial Information: After State unemployment compensation benefits run out, weekly allowance continues at the same level. Since April 1975, the Department of Labor issued certifications in almost 24,000 cases involving approximately 3.2 million workers.

Who To Contact: *Headquarters Office*: Edward A. Tomchick, Director, Division of Trade Adjustment Assistance, Employment and Training Administration, Department of Labor, 200 Constitution Ave., NW., Room C-5311, Washington, DC 20210. Phone: (202) 693-3560. *Regional or Local Office*: Regional offices of the Employment and Training Administration listed Table 1f, and local offices of affiliated State Employment Security Agencies, Table 1e.

Free Training—for Dislocated Workers
Employment and Training Assistance—Dislocated Workers (17.246)

Description: This program funds training and related employment services such as job search assistance, job development, placement assistance, supportive services, needs-related payments, and relocation assistance—to help dislocated workers obtain employment through training and related employment services using primarily a decentralized system of State and local programs.

Beneficiary Eligibility: Individuals who have been terminated or laid off or have received a notice of termination or lay-off and who are not likely to return to their previous industry or occupation, or who are long-term unemployed; individuals affected by mass layoffs, natural disasters, Federal government actions.

Financial Information: Not available.

Who To Contact: *Headquarters Office*: Employment and Training Administration, Department of Labor, Room N5426, 200 Constitution Avenue, NW., Washington, DC 20210. (202) 219-5577. *Regional or Local Office*: Contact appropriate Regional Employment and Training Office, Table 1f.

Free Job Training for Migrant Workers and Farmworkers
Migrant and Seasonal Farmworkers (17.247)

Description: This program is designed to offer a wide variety of services to migrant and seasonal workers. In order to help such farmworkers and their dependents get good, permanent jobs, farmworkers who suffer chronic seasonal unemployment and underemployment in the agricultural industry and their dependents may get such services as classroom training, on-the-job training, work experience, job development, job placement and resettlement assistance, education assistance, health services, and other supportive services.

Beneficiary Eligibility: Limited to those individuals and their dependents who have, during any consecutive 12 month period in the 24 months preceding their application for enrollment, been a seasonal farmworker, including a migrant farmworker, and (a) received at least 50 percent of their total earned income or (b) been employed at least 50 percent of their total time in farmwork, and (c) been identified as member of a family which receives public assistance or whose annual family income does not exceed the higher of either the poverty level or 70 percent of the lower-living-standard income level.

Financial Information: In the latest reported year, an estimated 40,000 persons received employment and training and supportive services.

Who To Contact: *Headquarters Office*: Division of Seasonal Farmworker Programs, Office of Adult Services, Employment and Training Administration, U.S. Department of Labor, Room N- 4645, 200 Constitution Ave., NW., Washington, DC 20210. Phone: (202) 693-3843. *Regional or Local Office*: Department of Labor Employment and Training Administration regional offices listed in Table 1f.

Free Job Training for the Severely Disadvantaged

Employment Services and Job Training—Pilot and Demonstration Programs (17.249)

Description: This program funds pilot projects that offer job training, related services, and job opportunities for economically disadvantaged persons who encounter special problems finding a job. This includes displaced homemakers, single parents, women, minorities, displaced workers, handicapped persons, ex-cons, persons with limited English-speaking ability and persons lacking educational credentials. The goal of the program is to prepare trainees for direct access to unsubsidized, stable, well-paying, and upwardly mobile job opportunities in the private sector;

The various pilot projects may offer different programs. For example, some concentrate on training workers to meet industry-wide skill shortages. Some provide training and apprenticeship opportunities. Other projects helps economically disadvantaged individuals establish and maintain small business ventures in their communities.

Beneficiary Eligibility: Generally limited to the economically disadvantaged, normally with further targeting by sex, age group, race, other demographic criteria, or according to employment barriers.

Financial Information: Annual allotment: approximately $23,717,000.

Who to Contact: *Headquarters Office*: Administrator, Office of Policy and Research, Employment and Training Administration, Department of Labor, 200 Constitution Avenue, NW., Washington, DC 20210. Contact: Steven Wandner. (202) 219-5677. *Regional or Local Office*: Not applicable.

Free Training for Teens and Unemployed Adults

Job Training Partnership Act (17.250)

Description: Under this Act, the States receive grants to establish training programs to prepare youth and adults facing serious barriers to employment for participation in the labor force. These programs provide job training and other services that will result in increased employment and earnings, increased educational and occupational skills, and decreased welfare dependency.

There are three separate programs:
1. **Title II-A** is the Adult Training Program for dislocated workers and other economically disadvantaged adults;
2. **Title II-B** contains a separate authorization for a summer youth employment and training program;
3. **Title II-C** is the Youth Training Program.

Services under titles II-A and II-C are targeted to the economically disadvantaged, but up to 10 percent of a local program's participants can be non-economically disadvantaged individuals who face employment barriers.

Beneficiary Eligibility:
1. **Title II-A - Economically disadvantaged adults** facing serious barriers to employment who are in special need of such training to obtain productive employment. Eligible are adults who are: basic skills deficient; school dropouts; recipients of cash welfare payments, including recipients under the JOBS program; offenders; individuals with disabilities; homeless.
2. **Title II-B - Economically disadvantaged youth** ages 14-21.
3. **Title II-C - In-School youth**: economically disadvantaged, ages 16-21 (or 14-21 if provided for in job training plan). Eligible are teens and young adults who are: basic skills deficient; have an educational attainment one or more years below grade level; pregnant or parenting; individuals with disabilities; homeless or run-away youth; offenders.

Title II-C - Out-of-school youth: economically disadvantaged, 16-21. The same eligibility standards apply as for **In-School youth**, with the exception of grade attainment and addition of a school dropout category.

Financial Information: In the latest reported year, funding for this program totaled $1.2 billion.

Information Contacts: *Headquarters Office*: Employment and Training Administration, Department of Labor, 200 Constitution Avenue, NW., Washington, DC 20210. Contact: James M. Aaron, Director, Office of Employment and Training Programs. (202) 219-5580. *Regional or Local Office*: Contact appropriate Regional Employment and Training Office in Table 1f.

Job Corps

Description: The Job Corps is a national residential job training and basic education program for unemployed and undereducated youth age 16 to 24. Accepted students usually live in one of more than one hundred Job Corps campuses throughout the U.S.

Students in the program receive: free basic education (leading to a GED-high school equivalency diploma if desired); English as a second language if needed; vocational skills training; work experience programs; counseling; meals and housing; health care; driver's education; $300 work clothing allowance the first year; up to $100 a month incentive-based allowance; up to $2,400 readjustment allowance upon graduation. Students can stay in the Corps for up to two years.

There are two main types of facilities:

Civilian Conservation Centers. There are 30 such centers operated by Federal agencies such as the U.S. Forest Service, Bureau of Reclamation, Fish and Wildlife Service and the U.S. Park Service.

Private Sector Centers. Major companies, large labor unions and nonprofit organizations operate more than 80 centers under contract with the Department of Labor. Here, vocational

training is provided in more than 100 trades in fields including

- Auto Repair Technician
- Bricklayer
- Building Maintenance
- Business Clerical
- Carpenter
- Cement Mason
- Computer Operator
- Cook Apprentice
- Data Entry Specialist
- Diesel Mechanic
- Electrician
- Home Health Aide
- Landscape Technician
- Nursery School Attendant
- Office Clerk
- Painter
- Plasterer
- Plumber
- Retail Sales Clerk
- Welder

...And many more!

Eligibility: Candidates for the Job Corps must:

- Be at least 16 and not yet 22 years old at time of enrollment.
- Be a U.S. citizen, national, or permanent resident.
- Be economically disadvantaged, living in a hostile environment not conducive to getting an education or a job.
- Be capable of succeeding in the Job Corps.
- Not be on probation, parole or under court supervision (unless special permission is granted).

Financial Information: Since 1964, 1.6 million at-risk youths have been successfully prepared for jobs, military service, or advanced educational opportunities. More than 68,000 students participate each year.

Who To Contact: *National Office*: Office of the Job Corps, U.S. Department of Labor, 200 Constitution Ave, NW, Room N4510, Washington DC 20201. (800) TRAIN YOU. *Regional or Local Offices*: See Table 1g.

OTHER PROGRAMS

Money—to Victims of Violent Crimes
Crime Victim Compensation (16.576)

Description: This program provides matching funds to States that have crime victim compensation programs that award compensation benefits to victims and survivors of criminal violence, including drunk driving and domestic violence. Compensation may be made for medical expenses, loss of wages attributable to a physical injury resulting from a compensable crime, funeral expenses.

Beneficiary Eligibility: Victims of crime that results in death or physical or personal injury and are determined eligible under the State victim compensation statute. State compensation statutes either declare that coverage extends generally to any crime resulting in physical or personal injury, or they list all specific crimes that can be covered.

Financial Information: In the latest reported year, the participating States received approximately $95 million.

Literature: For program information write to Office for Victims of Crime, Office of Justice Programs, Department of Justice, 810 Seventh Street, NW., Washington, DC 20531.

Who To Contact: *Headquarters Office*: Carol R. Watkins, Director, State Compensation and Assistance Division, Office for Victims of Crime, Department of Justice, Washington, DC 20531. (202) 514-4696. *Regional or Local Office*: None.

Emergency Food and Shelter
"Emergency Food and Shelter" National Board Program (83.523)

Description: The purpose of this program is to expand and assist local service organizations in order to provide emergency shelter, food, and supportive services for needy families and individuals for one month.

The range of local participant groups includes the American Red Cross, Catholic Charities, USA, Council of Jewish Federations, National Council of Churches, The Salvation Army and United Way of America. Also participating are thousands of independent nonprofits (such as Community Action Agencies and Food Banks and food pantries) which provide food and/or shelter services; and specialized groups such as domestic violence shelters, Native American organizations, organizations providing food or shelter to AIDs patients, handicapped individuals, the elderly, homeless veterans, teenage runaways, and many other groups with emergency needs.

Beneficiary Eligibility: People in need of such emergency services. Generally, emergency assistance can only be applied for once a year.

Financial Information: Over 11,000 social service agencies will pay approximately 300,000 rent/mortgage and utility bills to keep people in their homes, as well as provide millions of meals and nights of emergency shelter.

Who To Contact: *Headquarters Office*: Curtis Carleton, Federal Emergency Management Agency, Preparedness, Training and Exercises Directorate, Washington, DC 20472. Phone: (202) 646-4535. Sharon Bailey, Director, Emergency Food and Shelter Program, 701 North Fairfax Street, Suite 310, Alexandria, Virginia 22314. Phone: (703) 706-9660. *Regional or Local Office*: Contact the appropriate FEMA regional office (Table 3b, Chapter 3), or the State office responsible for coordinating the program's activities. *To Apply*, contact your local welfare office (often called the Department of Social Services). In larger cities, there are usually 24-hour hotlines or shelters to handle night and weekend emergencies.

Emergency Grants for Disaster Victims
Individual and Family Grants (83.543)

Description: This program provides funds for the necessary expenses and serious needs of disaster victims which cannot be met through other forms of disaster assistance or through other means such as insurance. Funds are provided to the States, which then make assistance available to households.

Eligible categories include: real property, personal property, medical, dental, funeral, and transportation. Costs which are ineligible include: improvements or additions to real or personal property, recreational property, cosmetic repair, business expenses, and debts incurred before the disaster.

Beneficiary Eligibility: Disaster victims in Presidentially-designated emergency or major disaster areas.

Families do not have to provide real or personal property estimates or receipts, but are asked to document expenditures for medical, dental, funeral, or transportation needs.

Businesses may be able to obtain assistance for real property, personal property and transportation (vehicle) categories by applying to the Small Business Administration (SBA) for a disaster loan. If SBA rules applicants ineligible for an SBA loan or if loan amounts are insufficient, SBA automatically refers the application to this program for consideration.

Financial Information: In the latest reported year, an individual or family may receive up to $13,100 from this program in each major disaster. The maximum grant is adjusted annually according to changes in the Consumer Price Index.

Who to Contact: *Headquarters Office*: Laurence Zensinger, Director, Human Services Division, Response and Recovery Directorate, Federal Emergency Management Agency, Wash. DC 20472. (202) 646-3685. *Regional/Local Office*: Table 3b, Chapter 3, for a listing of addresses for FEMA's Regional Offices. *Application Procedure*: Upon declaration of an emergency or major disaster, households may register an application for assistance with FEMA via (800) 462-9029 or by visiting a Disaster Recovery Center.

Emergency Housing Grants for Disaster Victims
Disaster Housing Program (83.545)

Description: Under this program, funds are granted to households affected by a disaster to enable them to address their disaster-created housing needs. Housing assistance may include:

1. Transient accommodations reimbursement
2. Home repair assistance
3. Mortgage and Rental Assistance.

In order to receive a grant, documentation and receipts are required to prove residency and ownership, damage to home caused by the disaster, and total estimated repair costs. Take pictures of your damages and make a detailed list of all damages. If you can, save all your damaged personal property until an inspector sees it.

Beneficiary Eligibility: Disaster victims in Presidentially-designated emergency or major disaster areas.

Financial Information: If your home or apartment is damaged so you can't safely stay there, FEMA Temporary Housing Assistance (rental assistance, mortgage and rental assistance) will give you a check for two or three month's rent, possibly longer. If you lost your job or business due to the disaster, FEMA may pay your rent or mortgage for up to 18 months.,

For damage claims, total repair costs cannot exceed the maximum allowable repair grant. FEMA will verify your damage information either by a visit or by comparison with a list of known damaged sites. The FEMA will decide what you qualify for an mail a check to your current address.

If you are low income, you can receive an Individual and Family Grant for up to $22,200 to meet your serious needs, for things like furniture, medical bills, car damage, and other personal property losses.

Who to Contact: *Headquarters Office*: Laurence Zensinger, Director, Human Services Division, Response and Recovery Directorate, Federal Emergency Management Agency, Washington, DC 20472. (202) 646-3685. *Regional or Local Office*: See Table 3b for a listing of addresses for FEMA's Regional Offices. *Application Procedure:* Upon declaration of an emergency or major disaster, households may register an application for assistance with FEMA via toll-free number (800) 462-9029 or other number that may be set up. For emergency shelter, clothing and food, you will usually be referred to the Red Cross or other agency or organization.

Part-Time Jobs For Senior Citizens
Foster Grandparent Program (94.011)

Description: This program serves two purposes: to provide part-time stipended "volunteer" jobs to income-eligible senior citizens age 60 and older; and to give person-to-person services to infants, children, or youth having special or exceptional needs. Foster Grandparents can serve in residential and non-residential facilities and in children's' own homes.

Beneficiary Eligibility: Foster Grandparents must be 60 years or older, with an income within certain limits and interested in serving infants, children, and youth with special or exceptional needs. (Special emphasis placed on terminally ill children, juvenile delinquents, pregnant teenagers, boarder babies and abused children.) Individuals who are not income eligible may serve as non-stipended volunteers under certain conditions.

Financial Information: The program cost $97,782,000 in the latest reported year. 309 community-based projects served over 89,000 children.

Literature: Foster Grandparent Program flyer.

Who To Contact: *Headquarters Office*: Foster Grandparent Program, Corp. for National Service, 1201 New York Avenue, NW., Washington, DC 20525. (202) 606-5000 ext. 181 and (800) 424-8867. *Regional or Local Office*: Corporation for National Service as listed in Table 4c, Chapter 4.

Part-Time Companion Jobs for Low-Income Seniors
Senior Companion Program (94.016)

Description: Under this program, agencies and organizations receive grants to provide paid part-time work opportunities for low-income senior citizens as "Senior Companions" who provide personal assistance and companionship to other seniors.

Senior Companions...
- provide companionship to other seniors in health care facilities;
- provide non-medical personal support to adults who, without support, might be inappropriately placed in a long-term care facility;
- help persons who have been discharged from health care facilities and other institutions;
- provide companionship to persons having developmental disabilities and other special needs.

Assignment of Senior Companions to adults may occur in residential and non-residential facilities and in their own homes.

Beneficiary Eligibility: Senior Companions must be age 60 or older, with an income within certain limits and interested in serving special-needs adults, especially the frail elderly, and must be physically, mentally, emotionally capable, and willing to serve on a person-to-person basis. Non-income eligible individuals may serve as non-stipended volunteers under certain conditions.

Financial Information: In the latest reported year, $41,669,000was spent serving 52,900 clients who benefited from having volunteer companions.

Literature: Senior Companion Program flyers.

Who to Contact: *Headquarters Office*: Senior Companion Program, Corporation for National Service, 1201 New York Ave., NW, Washington, DC 20525. (202) 606-5000, ext. 189 and (800) 424-8867. *Regional or Local Office*: Corporation for National Service as listed in Table 4c.

Negative Income Tax (Earned Income Tax Credit)
Internal Revenue Service (Publication 596)

Description: The Earned Income Tax Credit is a source of money for low-income working families. It is a special tax benefit the IRS gives to low income people who work and whose income does not exceed a specified amount. It reduces the amount of income tax you may owe, so if you qualify you will owe less tax or get a larger refund than they would without it or even get a check from the government.

In addition, the Earned Income Tax Credit can generate a refund above the withheld tax amounts. It can thus serve as a negative income tax and provide a real windfall to needy families. Even a worker who does not have to pay income tax can get a refund, but you must file a federal tax return to get the credit.

Eligibility: To qualify, you must work and have earned income. If you are married and file a joint return, you qualify if at least one spouse works and has earned income.

You may qualify if you have:
- Two children and your total earned income is less than $31,152;
- One child and your total earned income is less than $27,413;
- No children and your total earned income is less than $10,380.

Families with more than one child can receive up to $3,888. Families with one child can receive up to $2,353. Workers aged 25 to 64 with no children can receive up to $353.

So, for example, if you have two children under age 19 (under 24 if a full time student; any age if permanently disabled), and have earned income less than $31,152, you could qualify for the Earned Income Credit.

The credit can be taken by those who stop working during the year for any reason, even to go on Social Security Disability or Supplemental Social Security. The Earned Income Tax Credit does not effect the amounts of benefits received under these program or from Aid to Families with Dependent Children, Food Stamps, Medicaid or subsidized housing.

You don't have to wait for a tax return to be filed to begin collecting the credit. There's an advance payment option so that 60% of the credit can be received throughout the year in your paycheck.

Information: IRS publication 596 "*Earned Income Credit*."

Who to Contact: For general information, call any IRS office or call the IRS Information Line at (800) 829-1040. To get the tax form you will need in order to file and to receive free tax assistance, call the IRS at (800) 829-3676 and ask for VITA—Volunteer Income Tax Assistance.

Note: In conjunction with the federal Earned Income Tax Credit, many states also have an Earned Income Tax Credit provision—such as paying an extra 20% on top of the federal amount. Contact your state's income tax agency.

Federal Money—For Childcare
Child and Dependent Care Tax Credit

Description: The federal government's Child and Dependent Care Tax Credit provides tax relief if you are paying childcare so that you (and, if you're married, your spouse) can work, look for work, or train to work.

To be eligible for this credit, you must pay someone to take care of your child—who must be under 13—or take care of a disabled dependent or spouse. The tax credit is a direct offset against your income tax. It reduces your tax by a percentage of your childcare expense, the amount depending on your income.

In addition, the Child and Dependent Care Tax Credit can be partially refunded as cash to families who have no tax liability if you have more than two children. This money provides help to very-low-wage workers.

(In conjunction with the federal Child and Dependent Care Tax Credit, many states have a state child care tax provision. See **Money When You Stay Home and Take Care of Your Kids** below.)

These federal benefits are in addition to:
- The personal exemption of approximately $2,800 per child you get when filing your federal income tax.
- Up to an additional $600 direct tax reduction for each dependent child under 17 years old.

Beneficiary Eligibility: You're eligible regardless of income. Families who do not owe taxes can not claim the tax credit. But very low-income families with more than two children can receive a cash refund, even if they do not owe taxes.

Financial Information: The tax credit is available up to 30 percent of a limited dollar amount of employment-related child care expenses. Expenses are limited to $2,400 in child care expenses for one child, $4,800 for two or more children.

Information: You must fill out IRS Form-2441, "Child and Dependent Care Expenses." The form will walk you through the calculations.

Who to Contact: If you have questions about the Child and Dependent Care Tax Credit, call the National Women's Law Center, (202) 328-5160 or the Center on Budget and Policy Priorities, (202) 408-1080. You can also contact the Internal Revenue Service toll-free at (800) 829-3676.

Money When You Stay Home and Take Care of Your Kids
Relative Care Giver Cash Assistance Programs.

Description: Some of the States have Relative Care Giver Cash Assistance Programs. These programs provide families with a modest level of income support so that parents can raise their own children. The purpose of this aid is to help you stay at home with your kids.

Examples of some State programs include:

Florida's Relative Caregiver Assistance program helps relatives who are taking care of children who might otherwise have to go into the foster system. It pays you up to 82 percent of the foster care rate. *Who to Contact*: John Ratliff or Christina Zawisza at Children First, Nova Law School, (954) 262-6028.

Minnesota's Success Through Partnership program provides families a modest level of income support so you can raise your own children—up to 75 percent of what would be provided if you hired a child care provider. *Who to Contact*: Zoe Nicholie, (612) 296-6086.

In addition, many states have a state child care tax provision which can give you between $25 and $1,400 in tax benefits. These benefits can be in the form of tax credits or tax deductions.

Beneficiary Eligibility: Low-income families.

Who to Contact: National Women's Law Center, (202) 328-5160 or Child Car Aware Information

Hotline, (800) 424-2246. These services can direct you to child care resource and referral agencies in your community that can tell you about assistance programs in your area.

General Assistance from Your State

Description: General Assistance is the phrase commonly used for the State-local welfare programs offered by most States to low-income persons who are not covered by the federal welfare (AFDC, TANF) programs.

It may go by such other names in your state as welfare, county relief, home relief, general relief, public aid, public assistance, income maintenance, municipal aid

Most but not all States and localities have such programs. Their income and asset eligibility restrictions vary widely. And their payment amounts are lower than those paid under such federal programs as Supplemental Security Income (SSI).

Who to Contact: General Assistance payments are made by your local welfare office. This office is often called the Department of Social Services. Many applicants can also get Food Stamps.

General Medical Assistance

Description: General Medical Assistance is the phrase commonly used for the State-local programs that finance medical care for low-income persons who are not covered by the federal Medicaid program.

The larger, richer, more industrialized states give medical assistance substantially similar to Medicaid.

Who to Contact: Such medical care is provided through State and local welfare offices (often called the Department of Social Services), health departments, and public clinics and hospitals.

Free Local Hospital Care
Hill Burton Free Care Program

Description: The U.S. Department of Health and Human Service's "Hill-Burton Free Care Program" provides federal grants to modernize and expand private and public hospitals. In return, hospitals receiving such money agree to provide free or reduced charge medical services to eligible persons unable to pay because they are uninsured or underinsured. Not all hospitals participate in the program—just those that have received federal construction funds are required to participate.

Depending on the institution, participating hospital may provide such free or reduced-fee services as:
- Inpatient hospital care
- Low-income health clinics
- Outpatient departments
- Emergency room service
- Prescription drugs

Not all institutions provide all services or treat all medical conditions. But all participating hospitals and clinics must treat any patient needing emergency care, and admit if medically necessary, without regard to ability to pay, insurance coverage, or Medicare or Medicaid status.

Beneficiary Eligibility: Generally, persons with income below federal poverty levels are fully eligible, with partial bill reductions sometimes available on a sliding scale as income rises above this level.

Poverty Guidelines are based on a person's family size and income. Here are certain guidelines for 1998:
- 1 person family, $8,050
- 2 persons, $10,850
- 4 persons, $16,450
- 8 persons, $27,650.

Guidelines for Alaska and Hawaii are higher.

All Hill-Burton facilities give free care to eligible persons with incomes up to the poverty level. You may also qualify for free or reduced cost care at some facilities with incomes up to double (or triple for nursing home services) the poverty guidelines.

Financial Information: In the past two years, two million people received free or reduced charge care.

Who to Contact: *Headquarters Office*: Office of the Director, Division of Facilities Compliance and Recovery, HRSA, HHS, 12300 Twinbrook Pkwy., Ste. 520, Rockville, MD 20852; (301) 443-5656. *Toll Free Hotline*: The program has a 24-hour hotline available in English or Spanish to answer your questions: (800) 638-0742 ((800) 492-0359 for Maryland residents). *Participating Hospitals*: See Table 1i for a list of almost one thousand facilities. These include hospitals, nursing homes, clinics, etc. When applying for free Hill-Burton care, speak to the hospital's "charity care counselor," "financial counselor," "business office" or someone with a similar title who has the authority to forgive or reduce bills.

Free Educational Support for Homeless Children
Education for Homeless Children and Youth (84.196)

Description: The purpose of this program is to ensure that homeless children and youth have equal access to the same free, appropriate public education as other children. To accomplish this, the act provide activities for and services to identify these children and ensure that they enroll in, attend, and achieve success in school.

Under this act homeless students can receive a wide variety of special services including special coordinated education programs, free school supplies, summer tutoring enrichment programs. This is in addition to other services as free breakfast, lunch and milk that are funded separately.

Beneficiary Eligibility: Homeless children and youth in elementary and secondary schools (and homeless preschool children and the parents of homeless children).

Financial Information: $35,000,000 will be spent this year.

Who to Contact: *Headquarters*: Office of Elementary and Secondary Education, U.S. Department of Education, 400 Maryland Ave., SW., Washington, DC 20202-6132. Contact: Robert Alexander. Phone: (202) 260-0994. *Regional or Local Office*: Not applicable.

Free On-the-Job Literacy Training
Workplace Literacy Partnerships(84.198)

Description: In order to improve the productivity of the workforce by improving the basic education and skills workers need in today's economy, business, unions and government have teamed up to provide free literacy training in the workplace.

These programs offer workplace training in:
1) Adult literacy and other basic skills
2) Adult secondary education that may lead to the completion of a high school diploma;
3) English as a second language;
4) Upgrading or updating basic skills in accordance with changes in workplace requirements, technology products, or processes;
5) Speaking, listening, reasoning, and problem solving.

The program may even provide transportation and child care services during nonworking hours while you participate in a workplace literacy project.

Beneficiary Eligibility: Adults whose basic skills are inadequate in relation to job requirements.

Financial Information: Not available.

Who to Contact: *Headquarters Office*: Division of National Programs or Division of Adult Education and Literacy, Office of Vocational and Adult Education, U.S. Department of Education, 600 Independence Avenue, SW., Washington, DC 20202-7242. Contact: Liz Miller. (202) 205-9750. *Regional or Local Office*: Not applicable.

Free Basic Adult Education for Parents
Even Start—State Educational Agencies (84.213)

Description: This program, funded by the U.S. Department of Education, funds programs in the States to show parents how to become more involved in their children's education. Even Start programs provide adult basic education for their parents, including learning English, and helps

parents become partners with the schools in the education of their children.

The goal of the program is to help break the cycle of poverty and illiteracy, and improve the educational opportunities of low-income families, by integrating early childhood education, adult literacy or adult basic education, and parenting education into a unified family literacy program.

Beneficiary Eligibility: Parents eligible for participation under the Adult Education Act and their children aged birth through seven. Families must be in need of Even Start services, as indicated by a low-income level and low level of adult literacy or English language proficiency, or other need-related indicators.

Financial Information: Even Start has a budget of $99,600,000. In the latest reported year, more than 500 projects were funded in all States.

Who To Contact: *Headquarters Office*: Department of Education, Compensatory Education Programs, Office of Elementary and Secondary Education, 400 Maryland Ave., SW., Washington, DC 20202-6132. Contact: Patricia McKee. Phone: (202) 260-0826. *Regional or Local Office*: Not applicable.

Free Help for Migrant Workers to Get Their High School Degrees
Migrant Education—High School Equivalency Program (84.141)

Description: This program helps migrant workers and their older children to get high school equivalency diplomas and then to gain employment or enter an institution of higher education or other postsecondary education or training.

The program provides:
- Stipends
- Academic and support services, classroom instruction
- Counseling
- Health services
- Housing for on-campus residential programs
- Placement.

Beneficiary Eligibility: Migrant workers and their older children who are 16 and older or beyond the age of compulsory school attendance, and lacking a high school diploma. To be eligible the applicant or their parents must have worked a minimum of 75 days during the past 24 months in migrant or seasonal farmwork.

Financial Information: Approximately 6,000 students in 38 projects are being served. : The average Federal cost per student is $2,509

Who to Contact: *Headquarters Office*: Office of Migrant Education, Office of Elementary and Secondary Education, Department of Education, 400 Maryland Ave., SW., Room 3E317, Washington, DC 20202. Contact: Mary Suazo. Phone: (202) 260-1396. *Regional or Local Office*: Not applicable.

Free Legal Help
Legal Services Corporation

Description: The Legal Services Corporation is a non-profit corporation established by Congress to provide funding for civil legal assistance to low-income persons. It does not handle criminal cases.

Under the program, the actual legal representation is provided by local, independent legal services. They generally handle cases and matters affecting poor and low-income persons in the following general areas:
- **Family Law** (Divorce, Child Custody, Adoption, Domestic Violence Protection Orders)
- **Housing** (Landlord/Tenant Disputes, Lockouts, Evictions, Subsidized Housing, Foreclosures)
- **Consumer** (Bankruptcy, Debt Collection. Contract Dispute, Consumer Fraud)
- **Income Maintenance** (Reduction, Termination or Denial of AFDC, Food Stamps, Social Security Disability, SSI)
- **Health Law** (Health Insurance, Medicare, Medical Assistance, AIDS)
- **Employment Law** (Wage Claims, Unemployment Compensation)
- **Juvenile** (Neglect, Abuse, Custody Matters, Foster Care, Special Education Needs)

Free legal services lawyers know more about welfare, Medicaid, Food Stamps, SSI and other entitlement programs than almost anyone else in the community, and should be consulted when any entitlement or Social Security benefit is denied.

Eligibility: Generally, recipients must have an income at or below the federal poverty guidelines. And they must have a viable civil case that falls within the local services priority areas.

Maximum Gross Yearly Income: To qualify for free legal assistance, the maximum income of your family, depending on size, is:
- 1-person.....$12,588
- 2-people.....$16,963
- 3-people.....$21,338
- 4-people.....$25,713
- 5-people.....$30,088
- 6-people.....$34,463

The typical client is low income, unemployed or marginally employed, perhaps a victim of spouse abuse. There are also special programs for the elderly, migrant workers and Native Americans.

Emergency legal problems, e.g. domestic violence, evictions, foreclosures, receipt of summonses, are given priority.

Who to Contact: Headquarters Office: Legal Services Corporation, 750 First Street NE, 10th Floor, Washington, DC 20002-4250; (202) 336-8800; *Regional or Local Office*: Contact the nearest Legal Services or Legal Aid agency. The initial interview can often be done over the telephone to determine your financial eligibility and legal problem. See Table 1k for State and specialized links to local agencies.

Free Medicare
Qualified Medicare Beneficiary Program (QMB)

Description: Under this program, certain low-income persons do not have to pay Medicare premiums, coinsurance or deductibles. By enrolling in this special program, it pays all or some of their Medicare fees for them.

The federal government funds the program. It awards funds to State Medicaid programs which then may pay some or all of the Medicare expenses for you if you are elderly and poor, or disabled and poor and eligible for Medicare. What this means is that, depending on your income and the value of the things you own, you will not have to pay as much out of your pocket and could save hundreds if not thousands of dollars each year.

Eligibility: You must be entitled to Medicare, and your income must be at or below the national poverty level. Income includes, but is not limited to, Social Security benefits, pensions and wages, certain interest payments and dividends.

In addition, your total financial resources (such as bank accounts, stocks and bonds) and assets must be below certain maximums. However the home you live in, one automobile, home furnishings, personal jewelry and burial plots usually do not count as resources.

Financial Information: The program covers all costs you would normally have to pay yourself for individuals with income less than $716 gross per month and whose non-exempt resources are less than $4,000. It covers a husband and wife with less than $968 in gross income and no more than

$6,000 in non-exempt resources. You would only have to cover medical supplies and services not covered by Medicare, such as routine physicals, dental care, hearing aids and eyeglasses.

The program also helps if you have slightly higher earnings. Your State will pay your Medicare Part B premiums for you (putting about an extra $45 a month in your social security check) for individuals earning up to $940 and couples earning up to $1,266, with the same resource limits mentioned above.

Who to Contact: *Headquarters Office*: Health Care Financing Administration, 7500 Security Boulevard, Baltimore, Maryland 21244, (410) 786-3000; *Regional and Local Office*: Apply at a State, county or local medical assistance office (not a federal office). You can get the telephone number for your medical assistance office by calling HCFA's Medicare Hotline at (800) 638-6833. Give the operator the name of your State and county and explain that you want the telephone number of the nearest office that can help you file for assistance under the Qualified Medicare Beneficiary Program.

Table 1a: # ADMINISTRATION FOR CHILDREN AND FAMILIES:
REGIONAL STATE AND TRIBAL CHILD CARE ADMINISTRATORS

Region I (Boston)
Connecticut, Maine, Massachusetts, New Hampshire, Rhode Island, Vermont
(617) 565-1020

Region II (New York)
New Jersey, New York, Puerto Rico, Virgin Islands
(212) 264-2890

Region III (Philadelphia)
Delaware, District of Columbia, Maryland, Pennsylvania, Virginia, West Virginia
(215) 861-4000

Region IV (Atlanta)
Alabama, Florida, Georgia, Kentucky, Mississippi, North Carolina, South Carolina, Tennessee
(404) 562-2800

Region V (Chicago)
Illinois, Indiana, Michigan, Minnesota, Ohio, Wisconsin

(312) 353-4237

Region VI (Dallas)
Arkansas, Louisiana, New Mexico, Oklahoma, Texas
(214) 767-9648

Region VII (Kansas City)
Iowa, Kansas, Missouri, Nebraska
(816) 426-3981

Region VIII (Denver)
Colorado, Montana, North Dakota, South Dakota, Utah, Wyoming
(303) 844-3100

Region IX (San Francisco)
Arizona, California, Hawaii, Nevada, Trust Territories
(415) 437-8421

Region X (Seattle)
Alaska, Idaho, Oregon, Washington
(206) 615-2575

Table 1b: DEPARTMENT OF HEALTH AND HUMAN SERVICES

Region I
(Connecticut, Maine,
Massachusetts, New Hampshire,
Rhode Island, Vermont)
Maureen Osolnik
Room 2100
John F. Kennedy Federal Building
Government Center
Boston, MA 02203
(617) 565-1500

Region II
(New York, New Jersey, Puerto
Rico, Virgin Islands)
Anthony Marra
26 Federal Plaza, Room 3835
New York, NY 10278
(212) 264-4600

Region III
(Delaware, District of Columbia,
Maryland, Pennsylvania,
Virginia, West Virginia)
James Mengel
3535 Market Street, Room 11480
Gateway Building
Philadelphia, PA 19104
(215) 596-6492

Region IV
(Alabama, Florida, Georgia,
Kentucky, Mississippi, North
Carolina, South Carolina,
Tennessee)
Jim Brannon
101 Marietta Tower, Suite 1515
Atlanta, GA 30323
(404) 331-2442

Region V
(Illinois, Indiana, Michigan,
Minnesota, Ohio, Wisconsin)
Suzanne Krohn
105 West Adams, 23rd Floor
Chicago, IL 60603
(312) 353-5160

Region VI
(Arkansas, Louisiana, New
Mexico, Oklahoma, Texas)
Don Perkins
1301 Young Street,
Suite 1124
Dallas, TX 75202
(214) 767-3301

Region VII
(Iowa, Kansas, Missouri,
Nebraska)
Bobbie Mowery
601 East 12th Street, Room 210
Kansas City, MO 64106
(816) 426-2821

Region VIII
(Colorado, Montana, North
Dakota, South Dakota, Utah,
Wyoming)
Paul Denham
Federal Building
1961 Stout Street, Room 325
Denver, CO 80294-3538
(303) 844-3372

Region IX
(American Samoa, Arizona,
California, Guam, Hawaii,
Nevada, Northern Mariana
Islands, Trust Territories of the
Pacific Islands)
Emory Lee
Federal Office Building
50 United Nations Plaza, Room 431
San Francisco, CA 94102
(415) 437-8500

Region X
(Alaska, Idaho, Oregon,
Washington)
Elizabeth G. Healy
2201 Sixth Avenue, Room 1208
Seattle, WA 98121
(206) 615-2010

Table 1c: FOOD AND CONSUMER SERVICE

REGIONAL OFFICES

Western
(Alaska, American Samoa,
Arizona, California,
Commonwealth of the Northern
Marianas, Guam, Hawaii, Idaho,
Nevada, Oregon, Washington,
Freely Associated States of the
Pacific)
Dick Montoya
550 Kearny Street, Room 400
San Francisco, CA 94108
(415) 705-1310

Mountain Plains
(Colorado, Iowa, Kansas,
Missouri, Montana Nebraska,
North Dakota, South Dakota,
Utah, Wyoming)
Craig Forman
1244 Speer Boulevard, Suite 903
Denver, CO 80204
(303) 844-0300

Southeast
(Alabama, Florida, Georgia,
Kentucky, Mississippi, North
Carolina, South Carolina,
Tennessee)
Jerry Redding
61 Forsyth Street, SW,
Room 8T36
Atlanta, GA 30303-3415
404-562-1800

Midwest
(Illinois, Indiana, Michigan,
Minnesota, Ohio, Wisconsin)
Lawrence Rudmann
77 West Jackson Blvd., 20th Floor
Chicago, IL 60604-3507
(312) 353-6664

Northeast
(Connecticut, Maine,
Massachusetts, New Hampshire,
New York, Rhode Island,
Vermont)

Charles DeJulius
10 Causeway Street, Room 501
Boston, MA 02222-1068
(617) 565-6370

Mid-Atlantic
(Delaware, District of Columbia,
Maryland, New Jersey,

Pennsylvania, Puerto Rico, Virgin
Islands, Virginia, West Virginia)
Walt Haake
Mercer Corporate Park
300 Corporate Blvd.
Robbinsville, NJ 08691
609-259-5025

Southwest
Arkansas, Louisiana, New
Mexico, Oklahoma, Texas)
Judy Snow
1100 Commerce Street,
Room 5-A-6
Dallas, TX 75242
214-290-9800

Table 1d: BUREAU OF APRENTICESHIP AND TRAINING (BAT): REGIONAL OFFICES

Region I
(Connecticut, Maine,
Massachusetts, New Hampshire,
Rhode Island and Vermont)
BAT Region I Director
JFK Federal Bldg., Rm. 370
Boston, MA 02203
(617) 565-2288

Region II
(New Jersey, New York, Puerto
Rico and the Virgin Islands)
BAT Region II Director
USDOL/ETA/BAT
201 Varick Street, Room 602
New York, NY 10014
(212) 337-2313

Region III
(Delaware, Maryland,
Pennsylvania, Virginia and West
Virginia)
BAT Region III Director
USDOL/ETA/BAT
170 S. Indepemdence Hall Mall W.
Suite 815-East
Philadelphia, PA 19106
(215) 861-4830

Region IV
(Alabama, Florida, Georgia,
Kentucky, Mississippi, North

Carolina, and South Carolina,
Tennessee)
BAT Region IV Director
USDOL/ETA/BAT
61 Forsyth St., NW, Rm. 6T71
Atlanta, GA 30303
(404) 562-2335

Region V
(Illinois, Indiana, Michigan,
Minnesota, Ohio and Wisconsin
BAT Region V Director
230 South Dearborn Street,
Room 656
Chicago, ILL 60604
(312) 353-7205
(312) 353-5506 FAX

Region VI
(Arkansas, Louisiana, New
Mexico, Oklahoma and Texas)
BAT Region VI Director
Federal Building
525 Griffin Street, Room 311
Dallas, TX 75202
(214) 767-4993

Region VII
(Iowa, Kansas, Missouri, and
Nebraska)
BAT Region VII Director
USDOL/ETA/BAT

1100 Main Street, Suite 1040
Kansas City, MO 64105-2112
(816) 426-3856

Region VIII
(Colorado, Montana, North
Dakota, South Dakota, Utah, and
Wyoming)
BAT Region VIII Director
USDOL/ETA/BAT
1999 Broadway, Suite 1780
Denver, CO 80201
(303) 844-4791

Region IX
(Arizona, California, Hawaii, and
Nevada)
BAT Region IX Director
Federal Building, Room 815
71 Stevenson Street
San Francisco, CA 94105
(415) 975-4007

Region X
(Alaska, Idaho, Oregon and
Washington)
BAT Region X Director
1111 Third Avenue, Suite 830
Seattle, WA 98101-3212
(206) 553-5286

Table 1e: STATE EMPLOYMENT AGENCIES

Alabama
Dept. of Industrial Relations
Industrial Relations Building
649 Monroe Street, Room 204
Montgomery, AL 36130
(334) 242-8990

Alaska
Employment Security Division
Department of Labor
1111 West 8th Street, PO Box
25509
Juneau, AK 99802-5509
(907) 465-2712

Arizona
Department of Economic Security
1717 West Jefferson Street
PO Box 6123 (Site 010A)
Phoenix, AZ 85005
(602) 542-5678

Arkansas
Arkansas Employment Security
Department
PO Box 2981, Capitol Mall
Little Rock, AR 72203-2981
(501) 682-2121

California
Employment Development
Department
800 Capitol Mall, PO Box 826880,
MIC 83
Sacramento, CA 94280-0001
(916) 654-8210

Colorado
Dept. of Labor and Employment
1515 Arapahoe Street, Tower 2,
Suite 400
Denver, CO 80201-2117
(303) 620-4700

Connecticut
Connecticut Labor Department
Employment Security Division
200 Folly Brook Boulevard
Wethersfield, CT 06109
(860) 566-4384

Delaware
Secretary of Labor
Department of Labor
4425 N. Market Street, PO Box
9828
Wilmington, DE 19809-8109
(302) 761-8000

District of Columbia
Dept. of Employment Services
Department of Labor
500 C Street, NW, Room 600
Washington, DC 20001
(202) 724-7185

Florida
Department of Labor and
Employment Security
2012 Capitol Circle SE
Suite 303, Hartman Building
Tallahassee, FL 32399-2152
(850) 922-7021

Georgia
Department of Labor
Employment Security Agency
Sussex Place
148 International Boulevard, N.E.,
Suite 600
Atlanta, GA 30303
(404) 656-3011

Hawaii

Department of Labor and Industrial
Relations
830 Punchbowl St., Room 329
Honolulu, HI 96813
(808) 586-8812

Idaho
Department of Employment
317 Main Street
Boise, ID 83735-0001
(208) 334-6110

Illinois
Bureau of Employment Security
Department of Employment
Security
401 So. State Street, Suite 624
Chicago, IL 60605
(312) 793-9279

Indiana
Indiana Department of Workforce
Development
10 N. Senate Avenue, Room 302
Indianapolis, IN 46204
(317) 233-5661

Iowa
Division of Workforce
Development
Iowa Department of Economic
Development
1000 East Grand Avenue
Des Moines, IA 50319
(515) 281-5365

Kansas
Dept. of Human Resources
401 SW Topeka Boulevard
Topeka, KS 66603-3182
(913) 296-7874

Kentucky
Workforce Development Cabinet
Dept. of Employment Services
275 E. Main Street, 2nd Floor West
Frankfort, KY 40621
(502) 564-5331

Louisiana
Louisiana Department of Labor
Office of Employment Security
1001 North 23rd Street
PO Box 94094
Baton Rouge, LA 70804-9094
(504) 342-3013, 11

Maine
Department of Labor
20 Union Street, PO Box 309
Augusta, ME 04330
(207) 287-3788

Maryland
Division of Employment and
Training
Department of Labor, Licensing and
Regulation
State Office Building
1100 N. Eutaw St., Room 600
Baltimore, MD 21201
(410) 767-2400

Massachusetts
Department of Employment and
Training
Charles F. Hurley Bldg., 3rd Fl.
Government Center
Boston, MA 02114
(617) 626-6600

Michigan
Department of Labor
Michigan Employment Security
Agency
7310 Woodward Avenue
Detroit, MI 48202
(313) 876-5901

Minnesota
Dept. of Economic Security
390 North Robert Street
St. Paul, MN 55101
(612) 296-3711

Mississippi
Employment Security Commission
PO Box 1699, 1520 West Capital
Street
Jackson, MS 39215-1699
(601) 961-7400

Missouri
Department of Labor and Industrial
Relations
PO Box 504
Jefferson City, MO 65102-0504
(573) 751-4091

Montana
Dept. of Labor and Industry
PO Box 1728
Helena, MT 59624
(406) 444-4500

Nebraska
Job Service Division
Department of Labor
550 South 16th Street
PO Box 94600
Lincoln, NE 68509-4600
(402) 471-3405

Nevada

Nevada Employment Security
Division
500 East Third Street
Carson City, NV 89713-0001
(702) 687-4635

New Hampshire
Dept. of Employment Security
32 So. Main Street, Room 204
Concord, NH 03301
(603) 228-4000

New Jersey
Department of Labor
John Fitch Plaza, CN110
Trenton, NJ 08625-0110
(609) 292-2323

New Mexico
New Mexico Dept. of Labor
PO Box 1928
Albuquerque, NM 87103
(505) 841-8409

New York
Department of Labor
State Office Campus
Building 12, Room 500
Albany, NY 12240-0002
(518) 457-2741

North Carolina
Employment Security Commission
PO Box 25903
700 Wade Avenue
Raleigh, NC 27611
(919) 733-7546

North Dakota
Job Service North Dakota
Box 5507, 1000 E. Divide Ave.
Bismarck, ND 58506-5507
(701) 328-2836

Ohio
Bureau of Employment Services
145 South Front Street
PO Box 1618
Columbus, OH 43216-1618
(614) 466-2100

Oklahoma
Employment Security Commission
Will Rogers Memorial Office
Building
2401 North Lincoln

Oklahoma City, OK 73105
(405) 557-7200

Oregon
Employment Department
875 Union Street, N.E.
Salem, OR 97311
(503) 378-3208

Pennsylvania
Dept. of Labor and Industry
1700 Labor and Industry Bldg.
7th & Forster Streets, Rm. 1700
Harrisburg, PA 17121
(717) 787-3907

Puerto Rico
Bureau of Employment Security
505 Munoz Rivera Avenue
Hato Rey, PR 00918
(809) 721-2119

Rhode Island
Dept. of Employment & Training
101 Friendship Street
Providence, RI 02903-3740
(401) 277-3732
South Carolina
Employment Security Commission
PO Box 995
1550 Gadsden Street
Columbia, SC 29202
(803) 737-2617

South Dakota
Department of Labor
Kneip Building
700 Governors Drive
Pierre, SD 57501
(605) 773-3101

Tennessee
Dept. of Employment Security
Davy Crockett Tower, 12th Fl.
500 James Robertson Parkway
Nashville, TN 37245-0001
(615) 741-2131

Texas
Texas Workforce Commission
638 TEC Building
101 East 15th Street
Austin, TX 78701-0001
(512) 463-0735

Utah

Dept. of Employment Security
PO Box 45249, 140 E. 300 So.
Salt Lake City, UT 84145-0249
(801) 536-7432

Vermont
Department of Employment
Security and Training
PO Box 488, 5 Green Mountain
Drive
Montpelier, VT 05601-0488
(802) 828-4301

Virginia
Virginia Employment Commission
703 E. Main Street
Richmond, VA 23219
(804) 786-3001

Virgin Islands
Employment Security Agency
Virgin Islands Dept. of Labor
2131 Hospital Street, Christiansted
St. Croix, VI 00820
(809) 773-1994

Washington
Employment Security Dept.
212 Maple Park
PO Box 9046
Olympia, WA 98507-9046
(360) 902-9300

West Virginia
Bureau of Employment Programs
112 California Street, State Office
Building
Charleston, WV 25305-0112
(304) 558-2630

Wisconsin
Department of Workforce
Development
Box 7946, 201 East Washington
Avenue
Madison, WI 53707-7946
(608) 266-7552

Wyoming
Department of Employment
Employment Resources Division
PO Box 2760, 100 West Midwest
Casper, WY 82602
(307) 235-3254

Table 1f: EMPLOYMENT AND TRAINING ADMINISTRATION

REGIONAL OFFICES

Region I
(Connecticut, Maine,
Massachusetts, New Hampshire,
Rhode Island, Vermont)
Robert J. Semler
JFK Federal Building, Room E-350
Boston, MA 02203
(617) 565-3630

Region II
(Canal Zone, New Jersey, New
York, Puerto Rico, Virgin
Islands)
Marilyn K. Shea, Regional
Administrator
201 Varick Street, Room 755
New York, NY 10014
(212) 337-2139

Region III
(Delaware, District of Columbia,
Maryland, Pennsylvania,
Virginia, West Virginia)
Edwin G. Strong
PO Box 8796
Philadelphia, PA 19104
(215) 596-6336

Region IV

(Alabama, Florida, Georgia,
Kentucky, Mississippi, North
Carolina, South Carolina,
Tennessee)
Toussaint L. Hayes
Atlanta Federal Ctr., Room 6M12
61 Forsyth Street, SW
Atlanta, GA 30303
(404) 562-2092

Region V
(Illinois, Indiana, Michigan,
Minnesota, Ohio, Wisconsin)
Melvin Howard, Acting
230 South Dearborn St., Room 628
Chicago, IL 60604
(312) 353-0313

Region VI
(Arkansas, Louisiana, New
Mexico, Oklahoma, Texas)
Joseph C. Juarez
525 Griffin Street, Room 317
Dallas, TX 75202
(214) 767-8263

Region VII
(Iowa, Kansas, Missouri,
Nebraska)
William M. Hood
City Center Square
1100 Main Street, Suite 1050

Kansas City, MO 64106
(816) 426-3796

Region VIII
(Colorado, Montana, North
Dakota, South Dakota, Utah,
Wyoming)
Peter E. Rell
1999 Broadway Street, Suite 1780
Denver, CO 80202-5716
(303) 844-1650

Region IX
(American Samoa, Arizona,
California, Guam, Hawaii,
Nevada, Republic of Palau,
Federated State of Micronesia,
Commonwealth of Northern
Mariana Islands)
Armando Quiroz
71 Stevenson Street, 8th Floor
PO Box 193767
San Francisco, CA 94119-3767
(415) 975-4610

Region X
(Alaska, Idaho, Oregon,
Washington)
Michael Brauser
1111 Third Avenue, Suite 815
Seattle, WA 98101-3212
(206) 553-7700

Table 1g: REGIONAL JOB CORPS CENTERS

REGION 1 Main Office
Regional Director
U.S. Department of Labor, ETA
Office of Job Corps, Rm. E-350
John F. Kennedy Federal Bldg.
Boston, MA 02203
(617) 565-2166

Connecticut
Connecticut Job Corps Center
455 Wintergreen Avenue
New Haven, CT 06515
(203) 397-3775

Maine
Penobscot Job Corps Center
1375 Union Street
Bangor, ME 04401

(207) 990-3000

Loring Job Corps Center
RR#1 Box 1727
Limestone, ME 04750
 (207) 328-4212

Massachusetts
Grafton Job Corps Center
P.O. Box 575, 100 Pine St.
North Grafton, MA 01536
 (508) 839-9529

Sargent Shriver Job Corps Center
192 MacArthur Ave.
Devens, MA 01432
(978) 784-2610

New Hampshire
This state does not have a Job Corps
center. Contact the Regional Office
listed above for more information
about Job Corps.

Rhode Island
This state does not have a Job Corps
center. Contact the Regional Office
listed above for more information
about Job Corps.

Vermont
Northlands Job Corps Center
100-A Macdonough Drive
Vergennes, VT 05491
(802) 877-2922

REGION 2 Main Office
Regional Director
U.S. Department of Labor, ETA
Office of Job Corps
201 Varick Street, Room 897
New York, NY 10014-4811
(212) 337-2282

New Jersey
Edison Job Corps Center
500 Plainfield Avenue
Edison, NJ 08817-2587
(732) 985-4800

New York
Brooklyn Job Corps Center
585 DeKalb Ave.
Brooklyn, NY 11205
(718) 623-4000

Cassadaga Job Corps Center
8115 Glasgow Road
Cassadaga, NY 14718-9606
(716) 595-8760

Delaware Valley Job Corps Center
PO Box 846
Callicoon, NY 12723-0846
(854) 887-5400

Glenmont Job Corps Center
PO Box 993
Glenmont, NY 12077-0993
(518) 767-9371

Iroquois Job Corps Center
11780 Tibbets Road
Medina, NY 14103
(716) 798-7000

Oneonta Job Corps Center
Box 51A, R.D. #4
Oneonta, NY 13820-9325
(607) 433-2111

South Bronx Job Corps Center
1771 Andrews Avenue
Bronx, NY 10453-6803
(718) 731-7700

Puerto Rico
Arecibo Job Corps Center
PO Box 544
Garrochales, PR 00652-0540
(787) 881-2300

Barranquitas Job Corps Center
PO BOX 68
Barranquitas, PR 00794
(787) 857-5200

Ramey Job Corps Center

PO Box 250463
Aguadilla, PR 00604-0463
(787) 890-2030

REGION 3 Main Office
Regional Director
U.S. Department of Labor, ETA
Office of Job Corps
The Curtis Center, Suite 815 East
170 South Independence Mall West
Philadelphia, PA 19106
(215) 861-5500

Delaware
This state does not have a Job Corps center. Contact the Regional Office listed above for more information about Job Corps.

District of Columbia
Potomac Job Corps Center
No. 1 D.C. Village Lane, SW,
Washington, DC 20032
(202) 574-5000

Kentucky
Carl D. Perkins Job Corps Center
478 Meadows Branch Road
Prestonsburg, KY 41653
(606) 886-1037

Earle C. Clements Job Corps Ctr.
2302 U S. highway 60 E.
Morganfield, KY 42437
(270) 389-2419

Frenchburg Job Corps Center
HCR 68 - Box 2170, Hwy. 77
Mariba, KY 40322
(606) 768-2111

Great Onyx Job Corps Center
3115 Ollie Ridge Road
Mammoth Cave, KY 42259
(270) 286-4514

Muhlenburg Job Corps Center
3875 State Rte., Hwy 181 North
Greenville, KY 42345
(270) 338-5460

Pine Knot Job Corps Center
Hwy 27
Pine Knot, KY 42635
(606) 354-2176

Whitney Young Job Corps Ctr.
8460 Shelbyville Road
Simpsonville, KY 40067
(502) 722-8862

Maryland

Woodland Job Corps Center
3300 Fort Mead Road
Laurel, MD 20724
(301) 725-7900

Woodstock Job Corps Center
PO Box 300
Woodstock, MD 21163-0395
(410) 461-1100

Pennsylvania
Keystone Job Corps Center
PO Box 37
Drums, PA 18222
(570) 788-1164

Philadelphia Job Corps Center
4601 Market Street
Philadelphia, PA 19139
(215) 471-9693

Pittsburgh Job Corps Center
7175 Highland Drive
Pittsburgh, PA 15206
(412) 441-8700

Red Rock Job Corps Center
PO Box 218
Lopez, PA 18628
(570) 477-2221

Virginia
Blue Ridge Job Corps Center
PO Box 425
Marion, VA, 24354
(276) 783-7221

Flatwoods Job Corps Center
2803 Dungannon Road
Coeburn, VA 24230
(276) 395-3384

Old Dominion Job Corps Center
PO Box 278
Monroe, VA 24574
(434) 929-4081

West Virginia
Charleston Job Corps Center
1000 Kennawa Drive
Charleston, WV 25311
(304) 925-3200

Harpers Ferry Job Corps Center
PO Box 237
Harpers Ferry, WV 25425
(304) 728-5702

REGION 4
Regional Director
U.S. Department of Labor, ETA
Office of Job Corps
61 Forsyth St. NW

Atlanta, GA 30303
(404) 562-2372

Alabama
Gadsden Job Corps Center
600 Valley Street, PO Box 286
Gadsden, AL 35902
(256) 547-6222

Montgomery Job Corps Center
1145 AirBase Blvd.
Montgomery, AL 36108
(334) 262-8883

Florida
Gainesville Job Corps Center
5301 NE 40th Terrace
Gainesville, FL 32609
(352) 377-2555

Homestead Job Corps Center
12350 Southwest 285th St.
Homestead, FL 33033
(305) 257-3916

Jacksonville Job Corps Center
205 West Third Street
Jacksonville, FL 32206
(904) 353-5904

Miami Job Corps Center
3050 NW 183rd Street
Miami, FL 33056
(305) 626-7800

Georgia
Atlanta Job Corps Center
239 West Lake Avenue NW
Atlanta, GA 30314
(404) 794-9512

Brunswick Job Corps Center
4401 Glynco Industrial Park
Brunswick, GA 31525
(912) 264-8843

Turner Job Corps Center
2000 Schilling Avenue
Albany, GA 31705
(912) 838-8500

Mississippi
Batesville Job Corps Center
821 Highway 51 South
Batesville, MS 38606
(601) 563-4656

Gulfport Job Corps Center
3300 20th Street
Gulfport, MS 39501
(228) 864-9691

Mississippi Job Corps Center
PO Box 817
Crystal Springs, MS 39059
(601) 892-3348

North Carolina
Kittrell Job Corps Center
1096 US Hwy #1 South
Kittrell, NC 27544
(252) 438-6161

Lyndon Johnson Job Corps Ctr.
3170 Wayah Road
Franklin, NC, 28734
(828) 524-4446

Oconaluftee Job Corps Center
502 Oconaluftee Job Corps Road
Cherokee, NC 28719
(828) 497-5411

Schenck Job Corps Center
98 Schenck Drive, PO Box 98
Pisgah Forest, NC 28768
(828) 862-6100

South Carolina
Bamberg Job Corps Center
PO Box 967
Bamberg, SC 29003
(803) 245-6302

Tennessee
Jacobs Creek Job Corps Center
984 Denton Valley Road
Bristol, TN 37620-1430
(423) 878-4021

Memphis Job Corps Center
1555 McAlister Drive
Memphis, TN 38116
(901) 396-2800

REGION 5 Main Office
Regional Director
U.S. Department of Labor, ETA
Office of Job Corps
Federal Building, Room 676
230 South Dearborn Street
Chicago, IL 60604
(312) 353-1311

Illinois
Chicago Job Corps Center
3348 South Kedzie Avenue
Chicago, IL 60623
(773) 847-9820

Golconda Job Corps Center
Route 1 Box 104A
Golconda, IL 62938
(618) 285-6601

Joliet Job Corps Center
1101 Mills Road
Joliet, IL 60433
(815) 727-7677

Indiana
Atterbury Job Corps Center
PO Box 187
Edinburg, IN 46124
(812) 526-5581

IndyPendence Job Corps Center
17 West Market Street, Suite 400
Indianapolis, IN 46204
(317) 684-2555

Michigan
Detroit Job Corps Center
10401 East Jefferson Avenue
Detroit, MI 48214
(313) 821-7000

Grand Rapids Job Corps Center
110 Hall Street SE
Grand Rapids, MI 49507
(616) 243-6877

Flint-Genesee Job Corps Center
2400 North Saginaw Street
Flint, MI 48505
(810) 232-9102

Minnesota
Hubert Humphrey Job Corps Ctr.
1480 North Snelling Avenue
St Paul, MN 55108
(612) 642-1133

Ohio
Cincinnati Job Corps Center
1409 Western Avenue
Cincinnati, OH 45214
(513) 651-2000

Cleveland Job Corps Center
10660 Carnegie Avenue
Cleveland, OH 44106
(216) 795-8700

Dayton Job Corps Center
3849 Germantown Road
Dayton, OH 45418
(937) 268-6571

Wisconsin
Blackwell Job Corps Center
4155 County Hwy. H
Laona, WI 54541
(715) 674-2311

REGION 6 Main Office
Regional Director
U.S. Department of Labor, ETA
Office of Job Corps
Federal Building, Room 403
525 Griffin Street
Dallas, TX 75202
(214) 767-2567

Arkansas
Cass Job Corps Center
21424 N. Hwy 23
Ozark, AR 72949
(501) 667-3686

Little Rock Job Corps Center
2020 Vance Street
Little Rock, AR 72206
(501) 376-4600

Ouachita Job Corps Center
570 Job Corps Road
Royal, AR 71968
(501) 767-2707

Louisiana
New Orleans Job Corps Center
3801 Hollygrove Street
New Orleans, LA 70118
(504) 486-0641

Shreveport Job Corps Center
2815 Lillian Street
Shreveport, LA 71109
(318) 227-9331

New Mexico
Albuquerque Job Corps Center
1500 Indian School Road, NW
Albuquerque, NM 87104
(505) 346-2562

Roswell Job Corps Center
PO Box 5970, 57 G Street
Roswell, NM 88203
(505) 347-5414

Oklahoma
Guthrie Job Corps Center
3106 West University
Guthrie, OK 73044
(580) 282-9930

Talking Leaves Job Corps Ctr.
PO Box 1066
Tehlequah, OK 74465
(918) 456-9959

Treasure Lake Job Corps Center
Route 1, Box 30
Indiahoma, OK 73552
(405) 246-3203

Tulsa Job Corps Center
1133 North Lewis Avenue Tulsa,
OK 74110
(918) 585-9111

Texas
David L. Carrasco Job Corps Ctr.
11155 Gateway West
El Paso, TX 79935
(915) 594-0022

Gary Job Corps Center
PO Box 967
San Marcos, TX 78667
(512) 396-6652

Laredo Job Corps Center
PO Box 1819
Laredo, TX 78044
(956) 727-5147

North Texas Job Corps Center
PO Box 8003,
1701 North Church Street
McKinney, TX 75069
(972) 542-2623

REGION 7 Main Office
Regional Director
U.S. Department of Labor, ETA
Office of Job Corps
City Center Square
1100 Main Street, Suite 1000
Kansas City, MO 64105-2112
(816) 426-3661

Kansas
Flint Hills Job Corps Center
4620 Eureka Drive
Manhatten, KS 66503
(785) 537-7222

Iowa
Denison Job Corps Center
PO Box 610
Denison, IA 51442
(712) 263-4192

Missouri
Excelsior Spring Job Corps Ctr.
701 St. Louis Avenue
Excelsior Springs, MO 64024
(816) 630-5501

Mingo Job Corps Center
4253 State Highway T,
Puxico MO 63960-9585
(573) 222-3537

St. Louis Job Corps Center
4333 Goodfellow Boulevard

St. Louis, MO 63120
(314) 679-6200

Nebraska
Pine Ridge Job Corps Center
15710 Hwy. 385
Chadron, NE 69337
(308) 432-3316

REGION 8 Main Office
U.S. Department of Labor, ETA
Office of Job Corps
Federal Office Building
1999 Broadway, Suite 1720
Denver, CO 80202-5716
(303) 844-1630

Colorado
Collbran Job Corps Center
57608 Highway 330
Route 1 Box 12
Collbran, CO 81624
(303) 487-3576

Montana
Anaconda Job Corps Center
1407 Foster Creek Road
Anaconda, MT 59711
(406) 563-3476

Kicking Horse Job Corps Center
2000 Mollman Pass Trail
Ronan, MT 59864
(406) 644-2217

Trapper Creek Job Corps Center
5139 West Fork Road
Darby, MT 59829-5139
(406) 821-3286

North Dakota
Burdick JCC Job Corps Center
1500 University Avenue West
Minot, ND 58703
(701) 857-9900

South Dakota
Boxelder Job Corps Center
PO Box 110
Nemo, SD 57759
(605) 578-2371

Utah
Clearfield Job Corps Center
PO Box 160070
Clearfield, UT 84016-0070
(801) 774-4000

Weber Basin Job Corps Center
7400 South Cornia Drive
Ogden, UT 84405-9605
(801) 479-9806

Wyoming
This state does not have a Job Corps center. Contact the Regional Office listed above for more information about Job Corps.

REGION 9 Main Office
Regional Director
U.S. Department of Labor, ETA
Office of Job Corps
71 Stevenson Street, Suite 1015
San Francisco, CA 94105-3768
(415) 975-4680

Arizona
Phoenix Job Corps Center
518 South Third St
Phoenix, AZ 85004
(602) 254-5921

Fred G. Acosta Job Corps Ctr.
901 South Campbell Avenue
Tucson, AZ 85719
(520) 792-3015

California
Inland Empire Job Corps Center
3173 Kerry Street
PO Box 9550
San Bernardino, CA 92427
(909) 887-6305

Long Beach Job Corps Center
1903 Santa Fe Avenue
Long Beach, CA 90810
(562) 983-1777

Los Angeles Job Corps Center
1031 Hill Street
Los Angeles, CA 90015
(213) 748-0135

Sacramento Job Corps Center
3100 Meadowview Road
Sacramento, CA 95832
(916) 394-0770

San Diego Job Corps Center

1325 Iris Avenue, Building 60
Imperial Beach, CA 91932
(619) 429-8500

San Jose Job Corps Center
3485 East Hills Drive
San Jose, CA 95127-2970
(408) 254-5627

Treasure Island Job Corps Ctr.
655 H Avenue, Building 442,
Treasure Island,
San Francisco, CA 94130-5027
(415) 277-2400

Hawaii
Hawaii Job Corps Center
41-467 Hihimanu Street
Wimanalo, HI 96795
(808) 259-6010

Nevada
Sierra Nevada Job Corps Center
5255 Cocoa Avenue
Reno, NV 89506
(775) 972-5627

REGION 10 Main Office
Regional Director
U.S. Department of Labor, ETA
Office of Job Corps
1111 Third Avenue, Suite 960
Seattle, WA 98101-3212
(206) 553-7938

Alaska
Alaska Job Corps Center
750 Cope Industrial Way Palmer,
AK 99645
(800) 478-0531

Idaho
Centennial Job Corps Center
3201 Ridgecrest Dr.
Nampa, ID 83687
(208) 442-4500

Oregon
Angell Job Corps Center

335 N.E. Blodgett Road
Yachats, OR 97498
(541) 547-3137

Pivot Job Corps Center
2508 NE Everett
Portland, OR 97232
(503) 916-6170

Springdale Job Corps Center
31224 Hist Columbia River Hwy.
Troutdale, OR 97060
(503) 695-2245

Timber Lake Job Corps Center
59868 East Highway 224
Estacada, OR 97023
(503) 834-2291

Tongue Point Job Corps Center
37573 Old Highway 30
Astoria, OR 97103
(503) 325-2131

Wolf Creek Job Corps Center
2010 Opportunity Lane
Glide, OR 97443
(541) 496-3507

Washington
Cascades Job Corps Center
7782 Northern State Road
Sedro Wooley, WA 98284
(360) 856-3400

Columbia Basin Job Corps Ctr.
6739 24th Street, Building 2402
Moses Lake, WA 98837
(509) 762-5581

Curlew Job Corps Center
3 Campus Street
Curlew, WA 99118
(509) 779-4611

Fort Simcoe Job Corps Center
40 Abella Lane
White Swan, WA 98952
(509) 874-2244

Table 1h: FEDERAL EMERGENCY MANAGEMENT AGENCY

REGIONAL OFFICES

Region I (Boston)
Daniel A. Craig
Regional Director
442 J.W. Mc Cormack POCH

Boston, MA 02109-4595
(617) 223-9540

Region II (New York)
Joseph F. Picciano
Regional Director

26 Federal Plaza
New York, NY 10278-0002
(212)680-3600

Region III (Philadelphia)
Charlotte W. Herbert Mears

Regional Director
615 Chestnut Street
Philadelphia, Pennsylvania 10106
(215) 931-5608

Region IV (Atlanta)
Kenneth O. Burris, Jr.
Regional Director
3003 Chamblee-Tucker Road
Atlanta, GA 30341
(770) 220-5200

Region V (Chicago)
Edward G. Buikema
Regional Director
536 South Clark St.
Chicago, IL 60605
(312) 408-5500

Region VI (Dallas)
Ron Castleman
Regional Director
Federal Regional Center
800 N. Loop 288
Denton, Texas 76209
(940) 898-5399

Region VII (Kansas City)
Dick Hainje
Regional Director
2323 Grand Boulevard, Suite 900
Kansas City, MO 64108-2670
(816) 283-7061

Region VIII (Denver)
Regional Director
Denver Federal Center, Building
710, Box 25267

Denver, CO 80225-0267
(303) 235-4800

Region IX (Oakland)
Karen Armes
Regional Director
1111 Broadway, Suite 1200
Oakland, CA 94607
(415) 923-7100

Region X (Bothell)
John Pennington
Regional Director
130 228th Street, SW
Bothell, WA 98021
(425) 487-4600

Table 1i: # PARTICIPATING HILL–BURTON HOSPITALS AND MEDICAL CARE FACILITIES

ALABAMA
Autaugaville: Autaugaville Family Health Clinic, (334) 365-4524
Camden: Wilcox County Health Center, (205) 682-4515
Heflin: Cleburne County Nursing Home, (256) 463-2121
Mobile: USA Childrens & Womens Hospital, (334) 415-1000
Montgomery: John Knox Manor N.H., (334) 281-6336
Muscle Shoals: Northwest Ala. Rehab. Center, (256) 381-1110
Opelika: Achievement Center, (334) 745-3501
Tuscumbia: Colbert County Health Center, (256) 383-1231

ALASKA
Cordova: Cordova Community Hospital, (907) 424-8000
Pelican: Pelican Pub Health Center, (907) 735-2202
Wrangell: Wrangell General Hospital, (907) 874-3356

ARIZONA
Nogales: Mariposa Community Health Center, (520) 281-1550
Tucson: El Rio Santa Cruz Health Ctr., (502) 792-9890
Tucson: Handmaker Jewish Geriatric Center, (520) 881-2323
Williams: Williams Health Care Center, (502) 635-4441

ARKANSAS
Ash Flat: Sharp County Pub. Health Center, (501) 994-7364
Batesville: Independ. County Health Unit, (501) 793-2166
Clarksville: Johnson County Reg. Hospital, (501) 754-2060
Conway: Faulkner County Health Unit, (501) 327-6505
Des Arc: Prairie County Health Dept., (870) 256-4430
Fort Smith: Sebastian County Health Dept., (501) 452-8600
Jacksonville: Jacksonville Public Health Unit, (501) 982-5689
Melbourne: Izard County Public Health Center, (501) 368-7790
Mountain Home: Baxter County Pub. Health Ctr., (501) 425-3072
Rison: Cleveland County Nursing Home, (870) 325-6202
Salem: Fulton County Health Unit, (501) 895-3300
West Helena: Phillips County Health Center, (501) 338-3486

CALIFORNIA
Brawley: De Salud Del Pueblo, (760) 344-6471
Costa Mesa: Fairview Develpmntl. Mental Hosp./Unit., (714) 957-5101
Covelo: Round Valley Indian Health Center, (707) 983-2981
E. Palo Alto: Drew Health Foundation, (650) 328-5060
Fortuna: Lutheran Home For Aging, (707) 725-4467
Fresno: Sequoia Community Health Ctr., (209) 237-6193
Glendale: Glendale Adventist Med. Ctr., (818) 409-8000
Gridley: La Paloma Health Center, (530) 846-3693
Lone Pine: Southern Inyo Hospital, (760) 876-5501

Los Angeles: Alta Medical Senior Health Ctr., (213) 728-0411.
Los Angeles: L.A. Univ. So. Cal. Medical Center, (213) 343-8298
Los Angeles: L.A. Gay & Lesbian Health Center, (213) 993-7400
Napa: Napa State Mental Hospital/Unit, (707) 253-5454
Northridge: Northrdge Hsp. Medical Center, (213) 885-8500
Reseda: Jewish Home Aged, (213) 881-4411
San Diego: Logan Heights Family Health Center, (619) 234-8171
San Fernando: San Fernando Clinic, (818) 365-8086
San Francisco: Chinese Hospital, (415) 982-2400
San Francisco: San. Fran. Gen. Hosp. Med. Ctr., (415) 821-8200
San Francisco: Laguna Honda Hospital, (415) 664-1580
San Jose: Barbara Arons Pavilion Mental Hosp./Unit, (408) 299-6053
Torrance Harbor: Harbor UCLA Medical Center, (310) 222-2101
Truckee: Tahoe Forest Hospital, (916) 587-3541
West Hollywood: Partners Adult Day Health, (213) 883-0330

COLORADO
Antonito: Guadalupe Health Center, (719) 376-5426
Collbran: Plateau Valley Hsp. Dist., (303) 487-3565
Colorado Spgs: Comm. Health Ctr./Wahsatch Clinic, (719) 475-0783
Cortez: SW Memorial Hosp.-Via Grande Nsg. Hm., (970) 565-6666
Greeley: Sunrise Comm. Health Center, (970) 353-9403
San Luis: San Luis Health Center, (719) 672-3352

CONNECTICUT
Bridgeport: Rehab. Center Fairfield County, (203) 366-7551
Greenwich: Nathaniel Witherell Nursing Home, (203) 869-4130
Hartford: State Health Dept. Lab., (203) 566-5102
New Haven: Fair Haven Comm. Health Center, (203) 777-7411
Shelton: Hewitt Memorial Home, (203) 735-4671

DELAWARE
Delaware: Governor Bacon Health Center, (302) 834-9201
Newark: Floyd Hudson Service Center, (302) 368-6700
Wilmington: Emily P. Bissell Nursing Home, (302) 995-8475

DISTRICT OF COLUMBIA
Hospital For Sick Children, (202) 832-4400
Whitman Walker Clinic, (202) 797-3500

FLORIDA
Apopka: Florida Living Nursing Center, (407) 862-6263
Apopka: Apopka Family Health Center, (407) 886-6201
Belle Glade: C.L. Brumback Health Center, (561) 996-1600
Bradenton: Manatee County Health Dept., (941) 748-0666

Bronson: Levy County Public Health Unit, (904) 486-2101
Casselberry: Seminole County Public Health Ctr., (407) 331-4021
Clearwate: Clearwater Public Health Center, (813) 461-2727
Crystal River: Crystal River Aux. Pub. Health Ctr., (904) 795-6233
Daytona Beach: Volusia County Pub. Health Ctr., (904) 257-1700
Delray Beach: SE Palm Bch. Aux. Pub. Health Ctr., (407) 820-3125
Fernandina Bch: Nassau County Public Health Ctr., (904) 261-6191
Ft Lauderdale: Broward General Medical Center, (954) 355-4400
Ft Lauderdale: Comprehensive Care Center, *(954) 463-7313*
Immokalee: Collier County Health Dept., (941) 658-7300
Interlachen: Rural Health Center, (904) 684-4914
Jupiter: Jupiter Medical Ctr. Pavilion Nurs. Hm., (561) 744-4444
Macclenny: Baker County Public Health Center, (904) 259-6291
Miami: Jackson Memorial Hospital, (305) 325-7429
Panama City: Bay County Public Health Center, (904) 785-4384.
Pensacola: Escambia County Public Health Ctr., (850) 595-6500
Sarasota: Sarasota County Public Health Center, (813) 365-2020
St. Petersburg: Community Health Center Pinellas, (727) 821-6701
Tampa: Tampa Comm. Health Center, (813) 866-0950
Palm Beach: Jupiter Aux. Public Health Center, (561) 746-6751

GEORGIA
Americus: Magnolia Manor Methodist Nurs. Home, (229) 924-9352
Atlanta: A.G. Rhodes Nursing Home, (404) 688-6731
Atlanta: Sadie G. Mays Nursing Home, (404) 794-2477
Augusta: MCG Care Inc., (706) 721-3929
Buena Vista: Marion Community Hospital, (912) 649-2331
Columbus: Muscogee Manor Nursing Home, (706) 561-3219
Demorest: Habersham County Health Dept., (706) 778-7156
Flemington: Liberty County Public Health Center, (912) 876-2173
Hiawassee: Towns County Public Health Center, (706) 896-2265
Homer: Banks County Public Health Center, (404) 677-2296
Savannah: Memorial Medical Center, (912) 356-8496

HAWAII
Honolulu: Kokua Kalihi Valley Hospital Center, (808) 848-0976
Lihue: G.N. Wilcox Memorial Hospital Center, (808) 245-1175

IDAHO
Glens Ferry: Glenns Ferry Health Center, (208) 366-7416
Pierce: Pioneer Medical Clinic, (208) 464-2578

ILLINOIS
Carbondale: Shawnee Health Center., (618) 549-5302
Carrollton: Thos. H. Boyd Memorial Hospital, (217) 942-6946
Chicago: Englewood Neighborhood Hospital Center, (312) 744-7486
Chicago: Lower Westside Neighborhood Hosp. Ctr., (312) 942-2460
Chicago: Cook County Health Center, (312) 572-4500
Chicago: W. Town Neighborhood Health Center, (312) 744-4310
Chicago: KoMedical Neighborhood Hospital Center, (312) 268-7600
Chicago: Univ. Of Illinois Infectious Disease Clinic, (312) 996-1596
Clinton: Dewitt County Nursing Home Home, (217) 935-3035
Decatur: Fair Haven Christian Nursing Home, (217) 429-2551
Du Quoin: Marshall Browning Hospital, (618) 542-2146
Lacon: St. Josephs Nursing Home, (309) 246-2175
Lincoln: Christian Nursing Home, (217) 732-2189
Rock Island: Rock Island County Pub. Health Ctr., (309) 793-1955
Rockford: Crusaders Clinic, (815) 398-2160
Skokie: Rush North Shore Medical Center, (708) 677-9600
Waterloo: Monroe County Care & Rehab. Nurs. Home, (618) 939-3488

INDIANA
Bloomington: Univ. Speech Hearing Center, (812) 337-4156
Evansville: Rehabilitation Center, (812) 479-1411

IOWA
Carroll: St. Anthony Reg. Hospital Nursing Home, (712) 792-3581
Fort Dodge: Trinity Reg. Hospital, (515) 573-3101
Lake City: Stewart Memorial Community Hospital, (712) 464-3171
Orange City: Orange City Municipal Hospital, (712) 737-4984
Sioux Center: Sioux Center Community Hospital, (712) 722-1271
Sioux City: Siouxland Comm. Health Center, (712) 252-0733
Waterloo: Peoples Comm. Health Center, (319) 272-4300

KANSAS
Concordia: Mt. Joseph Nursing Home, (785) 243-1347
Hanover: Hanover Hospital, (913) 337-2214

KENTUCKY
Clinton: Clinton & Hickman Nursing Home, (570) 653-2461

Fort Mitchell: Redwood School Rehab. Center, (606) 331-0880
Whitesburg: Whitesburg Medical Clinic, (606) 633-4871
Whitesburg: Leatherwood Blackey Medical Ctr., (606) 633-4871

LOUISIANA
Baton Rouge: Earl K. Long Memorial Hospital, (504) 356-3361
Belle Chasse: Metro. Dev. Ctr., Comm. Mntl. Hlth. Ctr.,(504) 394-1200
Ferriday: Concordia Parish Public Health Center, (318) 757-4991
Franklin: Teche Action Clinic, (318) 828-2550
Jonesville: Heartland Health Center, (318) 339-4144
Lake Charles: Bayou Comp Medical Center, (318) 439-9983
Luling: St. Charles Hospital, (504) 785-6242
New Orleans: Med. Center Of LA At New Orleans, (504) 568-2311
New Orleans: Mandeville Deteige Hospital Center, (504) 482-6023
Shreveport: LSU Medical Center, (318) 675-5000

MAINE
Augusta: Harrington Family Hospital Center, (207) 483-4502
Fort Kent: Northern Maine Medical Center, (207) 834-3155

MARYLAND
Baltimore: J. Hopkins Medical Services, (410) 522-9800
Baltimore: Maryland Rehabilitation Center, (410) 554-9385
Cambridge: Dorchester General Hospital, (410) 228-5511
Chestertown: Magnolia Hall Nursing Home 410-778-4550
Crownsville: Fairfield Nursing Home, (410) 923-6820
Denton: Caroline Nursing Home, (410) 479-2130
Leonardtown: St. Mary's County Health Dept., (301) 475-4330
Rockville: Rockville Nursing Home, (301) 279-9000
Salisbury: Wicomico Nursing Home, (410) 742-8896
Snow Hill: Snow Hill Health Center, (410) 632-1100
Westminster: Carroll County Pub. Health Ctr., (410) 857-5000
Westover: Somerset County Health Dept., (410) 651-0822

MASSACHUSETTS
Boston: Boston City Hospital, (617) 424-5000
Boston: Don Orione Nursing Home, (617) 569-2100
Boston: Jewish Memorial Hospital, (617) 442-8760
Boston: Fenway Community Hospital Center, (617) 267-0900
Boston: Boston Health C/Homeless Nursing Hm., (617) 534-4326
Cambridge: Cambridge Hospital, (617) 864-0845
Dorchester: Dorchester Multi. Serv., (617) 288-3230
Dorchester: Uphams Corner Hospital Center, (617) 287-8000
East Boston: E. Boston Neighborhood Hosp. Ctr., (617) 569-5800
Holyoke: Holyoke Geriatric Center Nursing Home, (413) 536-8110
Jamaica Plain: Lemuel Shattuck Hospital, (617) 522-8110
Nantucket: Our Island Home Nursing Home, (508) 228-0462
New Bedford: New Bedford Jewish Conv. Nsg. Hm., (508) 997-9314
Swampscott: Jewish Rehab. Ctr. Aged Nsg. Home, (617) 598-5310
Worcester: Great Brook Valley Hospital Center, (508) 852-1805

MICHIGAN
Adrian: Lenawee County Nursing Home, (517) 263-6794
Baldwin: Baldwin Family Hospital Center, (616) 745-2743
Bay City: Bay County Public Health Center, (517) 895-4001
Charlotte: Eaton County Medical Care Nsg. Hm., (517) 543-2940
Charlotte: Eaton County Public Health Center, (517) 543-2430
Coldwater: Branch County Human Services, (517) 279-9561
Corunna: Shiawassee County Med. Care Nsg. Hm., (517) 743-3491
Crystal Falls: Iron County Med. Care Nsg. Hm., (906) 875-6671
Detroit: Friendship Manor Nursing Home, (313) 833-7600
Detroit: H. Kiefer Health Complex, (313) 876-4000
East Jordan: East Jordan Family Hosp. Ctr., (616) 536-2208
Escanaba: Delta County Public Health Dept., (906) 786-4111
Frankfort: Benzie County Medical Care Nsg. Hm., (616) 352-2751
Gaylord: Otsego County Memorial Hospital, (517) 732-1731
Gladwin: Mid. Michigan Reg. Medical Center, (517) 426-9286
Hancock: Houghton County Med. Care Nsg. Hm., (906) 482-5050
Hillsdale: Hillsdale-St Joseph Dist. Pub. Health Ctr., (517) 437-7395
Hillsdale: Hillsdale Medical Care Fac. Nsg. Home, (616) 439-9341
Jackson: Jackson County Medical Care Nsg. Home, (517) 783-2726
Lapeer: Lapeer County Med. Care Fac. Nursing Home, (313) 664-8571
Manistee: Manistee County Med. Care Nursing Home, (616) 723-2543
Manistique: Schoolcraft Memorial Hospital, (906) 341-2163
Mt Clemens: Martha T. Berry Med. Care Nsg. Home, (810) 469-5265
Mt Pleasant: Isabella County Med. Care Nsg. Home, (517) 772-2957
Muskegon: Brookhaven Med. Care Fac. Nsg. Home, (616) 773-9146
Newberry: Helen Newberry Joy Hospital, (906) 293-5181
Okemos: Ingham County Medical Care Nsg. Home, (517) 349-1050
Ontonagon: Ontonagon Memorial Hospital, (906) 884-4134

Powers: Pinecrest Medical Care Fac. Nsg. Home, (906) 497-5244
Sandusky: Sanilac Medical Care Fac. Nsg. Home, (810) 648-3017
St Johns: Clinton Memorial Hospital, (517) 224-2315
Standish: Standish Community Hospital, (517) 846-4521
Tawas City: Iosco Medical Care Fac. Nsg. Home, (517) 362-4424
Wakefield: Gogebic County Med. Care Nsg. Home, (906) 224-9811

MINNESOTA
Austin: St. Marks Lutheran Home Nursing Home, (507) 437-4594
Breckenridge: St. Francis Nursing Home, (218) 643-7661
Breckenridge: St. Francis Hospital, (218) 643-3000
Hallock: Kittson Memorial Hospital & Nsg. Home, (218) 843-3612

MISSISSIPPI
Charleston: Tallahatchie General Hospital, (601) 647-5535
Corinth: Alcorn County Health Center, (601) 287-6121
Leakesville: Greene Rural Health Center Nsg. Home, (601) 394-2371
Lexington: Univ. Hosp. & Clinic, (662) 834-1321
Morton: Scott Regional Hospital, (601) 732-6301
Philadelphia: Neshoba County Health Center, (601) 656-4371
Poplarville: Pearl River County Hosp. & Nsg. Hm., (601) 795-4543
Port Gibson: Claiborne County Hospital, (601) 437-5141
Smithville: Access Family Health Service, (601) 651-4637
Starkville: Oktibbeha County Health Dept., (601) 323-4565
Whitfield: MS State Mental Hospital, (601) 351-8000

MISSOURI
Kansas City: Truman Medical Center West, (816) 556-3141
Shelbina: Salt River Nursing Home, (314) 588-4175
St Louis: Family Care Health Center, (314) 353-5190

MONTANA
Big Timber: Pioneer Nursing Home, (406) 932-4603
Choteau: Teton Medical Center, (406) 466-5763
Circle: McCone County Nursing Home, (406) 485-3381
Columbus: Stillwater Community Hospital, (406) 322-5316
Ekalaka: Dahl Memorial Nursing Home, (406) 775-8730
Forsyth: Rosebud Healthcare Center, (406) 356-2161
Glendiv:e Glendive Medical Center, (406) 365-3306
Missoula: U./Mont. Speech, Hearing, Language Clinic, (406) 243-2311
Shelby: Toole County Hospital & Nursing Home, (406) 434-5536
Terry: Prairie Community Medical & Nsg. Home, (406) 637-5511
Wibaux: Wibaux County Nursing Home, (406) 795-2429

NEBRASKA
Burwell: Community Memorial Hosp. Nsg. Hm., (308) 346-4440

NEVADA
Las Vegas: Nevada Rehab. Facility, (702) 486-5230

NEW HAMPSHIRE
Berlin: Coos County Nursing Home, (603) 752-2343
Newmarket: Lamprey Health Ctr./New Market, (603) 659-2494

NEW JERSEY
Cedar Grove: Essex County Mental Hospital/Unit, (201) 239-1900
Clifton: Daughters Of Miriam Nursing Home, (201) 772-3700
Green Brook: Greenbrook Comm. Mental Health Ctr., (201) 968-6000
Jersey City: Jersey City Family Hosp. Ctr., (201) 434-4731
Jersey City: Jersey City Medical Center, (201) 451-9800
Lakeland: Camden Cty. Add. Disease Rehab. Facility, (609) 228-4200
Newark: N. Newark Community Health Center, (201) 733-6430
Newark: Dayton Community Health Center, (973) 483-1300
Newark: Spectrum Aids Day Care Nsg. Home, (973) 596-2850
Newark: Broadway House Continuing Care Nsg. Hm., (973) 268-9797
Newfield: Mater Dei Nursing Home, (609) 358-2061
Paterson: Paterson Health Dept., (201) 881-3900
Pomona: B. Bacharach Rehabilitation Hospital, (609) 652-7000
Rahway: Rahway Hospital, (908) 381-4200
Trenton: H.J. Austin Health Center, (609) 989-3599
Westwood: Pascack Valley Hospital, (201) 358-3300

NEW MEXICO
Albuquerque: NW Bernalillo County Hosp. Ctr., (505) 898-9020
Socorro: Socorro County Public Health Ctr., (505) 835-1700
Sunland Park: La Clinica De Familia, (505) 523-0406
Tierra Amarill: La Clinica Del Pueblo, (505) 588-7252

NEW YORK
Argyle: Pleasant Valley Nursing Home, (518) 638-8274

Batavia: Genesee County Nursing Home, (716) 344-0584
Bay Shore: Southside Hospital, (631) 968-3001
Beacon: St. Francis Hospital, (914) 831-3500
Bronx: Calvary Hospital, (212) 863-6900
Bronx: Bronx-Lebanon Nursing Home, (718) 590-1800
Bronx: Highbridge-Woodycrest Nursing Home, (718) 293-3200
Brooklyn: Bushwick Clinic, (718) 260-2968
Brooklyn: Interfaith Medical Center, (718) 935-7000
Brooklyn: Kings County Hospital Center, (718) 630-3101
Brooklyn: Lutheran Medical Center, (718) 630-7000
Brooklyn: Wyckoff Heights Medical Center, (718) 963-7102
Brooklyn: Cath. Medical Center/St. Mary's Hospital, (718) 774-3600
Brooklyn: Sunset Park Family Health Center, (718) 630-7000
Buffalo: Erie County Medical Center, (716) 898-3707
Calicoon: Comm. General Hospital, (845) 887-5530
Cambridge: Mary McClellan Hospital, (518) 677-2611
Canandaigua: Clifton Springs Hospital, (315) 462-9561
Cuba: Cuba Memorial Hospital, (716) 968-2000
Elizabethtown: Horace Nye Nursing Home, (518) 873-3570
Gloversville: Fulton County Nursing Home, (518) 725-8631
Goshen: Orange County Nursing Home, (914) 294-7971
Gowanda: Tri County Memorial Hospital, (716) 532-3377
Groton: Groton Community Health Center, (607) 898-5873
Harris: Community General Hospital Harris Div., (914) 794-3300.
Kingston: Benedictine Hospital, (914) 338-2500
Kingston: Comm. Rehab Center, (845) 336-7235
Machias: Cattaraugus County Nursing Home, (716) 353-8516
Montour Falls: Schuyler Hospital, (607) 535-7121
Mount Vernon: Mount Vernon Hospital, (914) 664-8000
New York: Coler Memorial Hospital, (212) 848-6027
New York: Goldwater Memorial Hosp. Nursing Home, (212) 750-5980
New York: Harlem Hospital Center, (212) 939-1000
New York: Rivington Hosp. Ctr. Facility Nurs. Home, (212) 539-6450
New York: St. Luke's/Roosevelt Hospital, (212) 523-4000
Newark: Via Health Center of Wayne, (315) 332-2022
Norwich: Chenango Memorial Hospital, (607) 337-4152
Olean: Cattaraugus Nursing Home, (716) 373-1910
Ossining: Ossining O. D. Family Hospital Center, (914) 941-1263
Oswego: Nick Sperio Health Center, (315) 349-3267
Peekskill: Hudson River Health Care, (914) 739-8105
Rochester: Highland Hospital, (716) 473-2200
Southampton: Southampton Hospital, (631) 726-8200
Springville: Bertrand Chaffee Hospital, (716) 592-2871
Valhalla: Blythedale Childs Hospital, (914) 592-7555

NORTH CAROLINA
Albemarle: Lutheran Nursing Home, (704) 982-8191
Fayetteville: Cumberland County Health Dept., (910) 483-9046
Salisbury: Lutheran Nursing Home, (704) 637-3784
Snow Hill: Snow Hill Medical Center, (919) 747-8162

NORTH DAKOTA
Harvey: St. Aloisius Hospital, (701) 342-4651
Jamestown: Anne Carlsen School Rehab. Facility, (701) 252-1050

OHIO
Bowling Green: Wood County Nursing Home, (419) 353-8411
Caldwell: Noble County Public Health Center, (614) 732-4958
Cincinnati: Cincinnati Public Health Center, (513) 352-3000
Cleveland: Achievement C. Children, (216) 795-7100
Columbus: Columbus Health Center, (614) 645-6228
Dayton: Bethany Lutheran Village Nsg. Home, (513) 433-2110
Dayton: Mercy Siena Woods Nursing Home, (513) 278-8211
Elyria: Lorain County Public Health Center, (216) 323-5776
Fostoria; Good Shepherd Nursing Home, (419) 435-1801
Fremont: Countryside Continuing Care Nsg. Home, (419) 334-2602
Green Springs: St. Frances Rehab. Hosp. Nurs. Hm., (419) 639-2626
Greenville: Brethrens Nursing Home, (937) 547-8000
Kenton: Hardin Memorial Hospital, (419) 673-0761
Kingsville: Ashtabula County Nursing Home, (440) 224-2161
Lebanon: Otterbein Nursing Home, (513) 932-2020
Mansfield: Rehab Services N. Central Ohio, (419) 756-1133
Millersburg: Holmes County Public Health Center, (216) 674-5035
Monroe: Mt. Pleasant Rtmnt. Vill. Nursing Home, (513) 539-7391
Urbana: Champaign County Nursing Home, (937) 653-5291
Xenia: Greene County Comb Health District, (513) 376-9411

OKLAHOMA
Boise City: Cimarron Memorial Hospital, (405) 544-2501
Konawa: Konawa Comm. Health Center, (580) 925-3286

Lawton: Comanche County Health Dept., (405) 248-5890
Marietta: Love County Health Dept., (405) 276-2531
Norman: Cleveland County Health Dept., (405) 321-4048
Sallisaw: Sequoyah County Public Health Center, (918) 775-6201
Sand Springs: Lloyd E. Rader Diagnostic Center, (918) 245-2541
Tulsa: Tulsa City-County Pub. Health Center, (918) 744-1000

OREGON
Heppner: Pioneer Memorial Hospital, (503) 676-9133
Hood River: Hood River County Public Health Center, (503) 386-1115
Nyssa: Malheur Memorial Hospital Center, (541) 372-2211
Nyssa: Valley Family Health Care, (503) 642-9376
Portland: Doernbecher Childrens Hospital, (503) 418-5195
Salem: West Salem Clinic, (503) 588-5828

PENNSYLVANIA
Altoona: Bon Secours Holy Family, (814) 944-1681
Bradford: Bradford Nursing Pavilion, (814) 368-4143
Brookville: Brookville Hospital, (814) 849-2312
Everett: Memorial Hospital Bedford County, (814) 623-6161
Johnstown: Lee Hospital, (814) 535-7541
Kittanning: Armstrong County Memorial Hospital, (412) 543-8162
Meadville: Meadville Medical Center, (814) 333-5121
Meadville: Wesbury U. Methodist Nursing Home, (814) 724-8000
Meyersdale: Meyersdale Community Hospital, (814) 634-5911
Orbisonia: S. Huntingdon County Medical Center, (814) 447-5556
Philadelphia: Children's Hospital Of Philadelphia, (215) 590-1619
Philadelphia: Tucker House II Nursing Home, (215) 235-1600
Philadelphia: Kensington Hospital, (215) 426-8100
Philadelphia: St. Agnes Medical Center, (215) 339-4100
Philadelphia: St. Ignatius Nursing Home, (215) 349-8800
Philadelphia: Golden Slipper/Uptown Nursing Home, (215) 722-2300
Punxsutawney: Punxsutawney Area Hospital, (814) 938-4500
Renovo: Bucktail Medical Center, (717) 923-1000
Scranton: Community Medical Center, (717) 969-8910
Scranton: Jewish Nursing Home Of East Penn., (717) 344-6177
Somerset: Somerset Medical Center Health, (814) 443-5000
Sunbury: Sunbury Community Hospital, (717) 286-3333
Wellsboro: Soldiers Sailors Memorial, (712) 724-1631

SOUTH CAROLINA
Barnwell: Barnwell County Nursing Home, (803) 259-2898
Clearwater: Margaret J. Weston Hospital Center, (803) 593-9283
Columbia: RichlandComm. Health Care, (803) 799-8407
Greeleyville: Greeleyville Medical Clinic, (843) 426-2180
Greenwood: Wesley Community Nursing Home, (864) 227-7250
Mcclellanville: St. James-Santee Rural H.P., (843) 887-3274
Saluda: Saluda Nursing Center, (864) 445-2146
W Columbia: Comprehensive Rehab. Center, (803) 822-5331
White Rock: Lowman Nursing Home Infirmary, (803) 732-3000

SOUTH DAKOTA
Hoven: Holy Infant Hospital, (605) 948-2262

TENNESSEE
Dyersburg: Methodist Hospital Of Dyersburg, (901) 285-2410
Knoxville: Hillcrest North Nursing Home, (615) 687-1321
Maryville: Blount County Public Health Center, (615) 983-4582
Nashville: Lentz Public Health Center, (615) 327-9313
Pikeville: Bledsoe County Nursing Home, (423) 447-6811
Waverly: Humphreys County Health Dept., (931) 296-2231
Waynesboro: Wayne County Nursing Home, (615) 722-3641

TEXAS
Austin: Brackenridge Hospital, (512) 476-6461
Austin: Austin/Christop Nursing Home, (512) 342-4700
Azle: Harris Methodist Northwest, (817) 444-8600
Beaumont: Schlesinger Geriatric Nursing Home, (409) 842-4550
Clifton: Clifton Lutheran Sunset Nursing Home, (254) 675-8637
Corpus Christi: Memorial Medical Center, (512) 881-4116
El Paso: R.E. Thomason General Hospital, (915) 544-1200
Fort Worth: Tarrant County Hospital, (817) 921-3431
Galveston: Edgewater Methodist Nursing Home, (713) 763-6437
Houston: L.B. Johnson General Hospital, (713) 636-5000
Houston: MD Anderson Cancer Center, (713) 792-2121
Houston: Riverside General Hospital, (713) 526-2441
Houston: Riverside Neighborhood Hospital Center, (713) 284-9600

Houston: Sunnyside Neighborhood Hospital Center, (713) 734-6699
Houston: West End Health Center, (713) 866-4100
Houston: Bering Care Center Dental Clinic, (713) 529-6071
Houston: Thomas St. Clinic/Health Center Hospital, (713) 793-4000
Plainview: S. Plains Health Provider Org., (806) 293-8561
Rockdale: Richards Memorial Hospital, (512) 446-2513
San Antonio: Golden Manor Nursing Home, (210) 736-4544
Sterling City: Sterling County Nurse Home, (915) 378-3201
Tulia: Swisher Memorial Hospital, (806) 995-3581
Uvalde: Uvalde County Clinic, (830) 278-7105
Van Horn: Culberson County Hospital, (915) 283-2760

UTAH
Tremonton: Bear River Valley Care Nursing Home, (435) 257-5356

VERMONT
Greensboro: Greensboro Nursing Home, (802) 533-7051
Londonderry: Mountain Valley Hospital Center, (802) 824-6901
Northfield: Mayo Healthcare Inc. Nursing Home, (802) 485-3161

VIRGINIA
Charlottesville: Charlottesville Albermarle Hosp. Ctr., (804) 295-0161
Fincastle: Botetourt County Public Health Center, (540) 473-8243
Fredericksburg: Fredericksburg Health Center, (540) 899-4142
Newport News: Peninsula Inst. Community Health, (804) 380-8709
Petersburg: Petersburg Public Health Center, (804) 861-6582
Salem: Richfield Nursing Home, (540) 380-4500
Stafford: Stafford County Public Health Center, (703) 659-3101

WASHINGTON
Bellingham: Whatcom County Health Dept., (206) 676-6720
Friday Harbor: Inter-Island Medical Center, (206) 378-2141
Mount Vernon: Skagit County Public Health Center, (206) 336-9380
Newport: Pend Oreille Pines Nursing Home, (509) 447-2464
Seattle: Bailey-Boushay House Nursing Home, (206) 322-5300
Seattle: Rosehedge House II Nursing Home, (206) 365-6806
Spokane: Spokane County Health Dept., (509) 324-1500
Tacoma: Tacoma Pierce County Pub. Health Ctr., (206) 591-6500

WEST VIRGINIA
Charleston: Kanawha Charleston Health Dept., (304) 348-8069
Eglon: Eglon Clinic, (304) 735-3155
Huntington: Marshall U.Medical Center, (304) 691-1600
Institute: West Virginia Rehab. Center, (304) 348-2396
Morgantown: Robert Byrd Health Science, (304) 293-3528
Moundsville: Adena Hills Community Mntl. Hlth. Ctr., (304) 845-3000
Thomas: Cortland Acres Nursing Home, (304) 463-4181
Union: Monroe Health Center, (304) 772-3064
Wheeling: Easter Seal Rehab. Center, (304) 242-1390
Winfield: Putnam County Health Dept., (304) 757-0318

WISCONSIN
Edgerton: Memorial Community Hospital, (608) 884-3441
Friendship: Adams County Memorial Hospital, (608) 339-3331
Green Bay: Curative Workshop, (414) 468-1161
Hayward: Hayward Area Memorial Hospital, (715) 634-8911
Oneida: Anna John Nursing Home, (920) 869-2797
Portage: Divine Savior Hospital & Nursing Home, (608) 742-4131
Spooner: Spooner Community Memorial Hospital, (715) 635-2111
Watertown: Watertown Memorial Hospital, (414) 261-4210
Wauwatosa: Curative Rehab. Center, (414) 259-1414
Wauwatosa: Milwaukee County Mental Hosp./Unit, (414) 257-7483
Whitehall: Tri County Memorial Hospital, (715) 538-4361

Table 1j: ADMINISTRATION ON AGING REGIONAL OFFICES

REGION I
(RI, VT, CT, ME, MA, NH)
DHHS/Administration on Aging
John F. Kennedy Bldg., Rm. 2075
Boston, Massachusetts 02203
(617) 565-1158

REGION II
(DC, DE, MD, NJ, NY, PA, PR,
VA, VI, WV) (Includes the States
formerly in Region III)
DHHS/Administration on Aging
26 Federal Plaza, Room 38-102
New York, New York 10278
(212) 264-2976 or 2977

REGION IV
(AL, FL, MS, SC, TN, NC, KY, GA)
DHHS/Administration on Aging
61 Forsyth Street, SW, Suite 5M69
Atlanta, GA 30303-8909
(404) 562-7600

REGION VI
(AR, LA, OK, NM, TX)
DHHS/Administration on Aging
1301 Young Street, Room 736
Dallas, TX 75201
(214) 767-2971

REGION V
(IL, IN, MI, MN, OH, WI)
DHHS/Administration on Aging
233 N. Michigan Avenue, Suite 790
Chicago, IL 60601-5519
(312) 353-3141

REGION VII
(IA, KS, MO, NE)
DHHS/Administration on Aging
601 East 12th Street, Room 1731
Kansas City, MO 64106
(816) 426-3511

REGION VIII
(CO, MT, UT, WY, ND, SD)
DHHS/Administration on Aging
1961 Stout Street, Room 1022
Denver, Colorado 80294
(303) 844-2943

REGION IX
(CA, NV, AZ, HI, GU, TTPI,
CNMI, AS)
DHHS/Administration on Aging
50 United Nations Plaza, Room 455
San Francisco, California 94102
(415) 437-8780

REGION X
(AK, ID, OR, WA)
DHHS/Administration on Aging
Blanchard Plaza, RX-33; Rm. 1202
2201 Sixth Avenue
Seattle, Washington 98121
(206) 615-2298

Table 1k: U.S. LEGAL SERVICES CORPORATION LINKS TO STATE AND SPECIALIZED AGENCIES

The following organizations provide free legal assistance or make recommendations to other legal assistance agencies for financially eligible clients. Most of the organizations are grantees of the Legal Services Corporation and subject to restrictions on the kinds of cases they may bring and clients they may represent.

Alaska
Alaska Legal Services Corporation
1016 West Sixth Avenue, Suite 200
Anchorage, Alaska 99501
(907) 272-9431; (800) 478-9431

Arizona
Southern Arizona Legal Aid, Inc.
64 East Broadway Blvd.
Tucson, AZ 85701
(602) 623-9465; (800) 234-7252

Arkansas
Center for Arkansas Legal Services
303 West Capitol, Suite 200
Little Rock, AR 72201

(501) 376-3423; (800) 950-5817

California
Bet Tzedek Legal Services (Los Angeles)
145 South Fairfax Ave., Suite 200
Los Angeles, CA 90036
(323) 939-0506

California Rural Legal Assistance
631 Howard Street, Suite 300
San Francisco, CA 94105-3907
(415) 777-2752

Legal Aid Society, Orange County
(800) 834-5001

Legal Aid Soc.of Santa Clara County
W. Robert Morgan Legal Service Ctr.
480 North First St. (at Empire St.)
San Jose, California 95112
(408) 998-5200

Legal Services Prog. for Pasadena
243 E. Mission Blvd.
Pomona, CA 91766
(909)-620-5547

Legal Services of Northern Calif.
517 - 12th Street
Sacramento CA 95814
(916) 551-2150

Florida
Florida Rural Legal Services
963 E. Memorial Blvd
Lakeland, Fl. 33801
(800)-277-7680

Gulf Coast Legal Services
314 South Missouri Ave. Ste. 109
Clearwater, FL 33756
(727) 443-0657

Three Rivers Legal Services
111 SW First Street
Gainseville, FL 32601
(352) 372-0519

Georgia
Atlanta Legal Aid Society, Inc.
Clayton/DeKalb/Gwinnett Office
246 Sycamore Street, Suite 120
Decatur, GA 30030-3434

(404) 377-0701

Indiana
Legal Aid Corp.of Tippacanoe
212 North Fifth Street
Lafayette, IN 47901
(765) 742-1068

Maine
Pine Tree Legal Assistance
88 Federal St., PO Box 547
Portland ME 04112
(207) 774-8211

Maryland
Legal Aid Bureau, Inc.
500 East Lexington Street
Baltimore, MD 21202
(410) 539-5340; (800) 999-8904

Massachusetts
Leg. Srvs. for Cape Cod and the Islands
460 West Main Street
Hyannis, MA. 02601
(508) 775-7020; (800) 742-4107

Mass. Correctional Legal Services
Eight Winter Street, 11th Floor
Boston, MA 02108
(617) 482-2773; (800) 882-1413

Neighborhood Legal Services (Lynn
and Lawrence Mass.)
37 Friend Street
Lynn, MA 01902
(781) 599-7730

Michigan
Michigan Poverty Law Program
611 Church Street, Suite 4A
Ann Arbor, MI 48104-3000
(734) 998-6100

Legal Aid Bureau of S.W. Michigan
201 W. Kalamazoo, #308
Kalamazoo, MI 49007
(616) 344-8113

Wayne County Neighborhood Legal
Services (Detroit)

Minnesota
Southern MN Regional Legal Services
66 East Third Street, PO Box 1266
Winona, MN 55987-7266
(507) 454-6660; (800) 372-8168.

Mississippi
East Mississippi Legal Services
Metro Professional Plaza Bldg.
2305 Fifth Street, 2nd Floor
Meridian, MS 39301

(601) 693-5470; (800) 479-2529

Missouri
Legal Services of Eastern Missouri, Inc.
4232 Forest Park Avenue
St. Louis, Missouri 63108
(314) 534-4200

Meramec Area Legal Services
1412 Highway 72 East, PO Box 135
Rolla, MO 65402-0135
(573) 341-3655

Nebraska
Legal Aid Society (Omaha, Norfolk,
Walthill)
500 South 18th Street, Suite 300
Omaha, Nebraska 68102
(402) 348-1069

New Hampshire
Legal Advice and Referral Center
PO Box 4147
Concord, NH 03302-4147
(603) 224-3333; (800) 639-5290

New Jersey
Legal Services of New Jersey
PO Box 1357
Edison, New Jersey 08818-1357
(888)-576-5529

New York
Legal Aid Society of New York
90 Church Street
New York, New York 10007
(212) 577-3300

Legal Services of Central New York
472 S. Salina Street
Syracuse, New York 13202
(315) 475-3127

Neighborhood Legal Srvs. (Buffalo)
495 Ellicott Square Building
295 Main Street
Buffalo, New York 14203
(716) 847-0650

Ohio
Advocates for Basic Legal Equality
(Northwest Ohio)
740 Spitzer Building
520 Madison Avenue
Toledo, Ohio 43604
(419) 255-0814; (800) 837-0814

Legal Aid Society of Cincinnati
215 E. 9th Street, Suite 200
Cincinnati OH 45202
(513)241-9400

Ohio State Legal Services Assoc.
555 Buttles Ave
Columbus OH 43215
(614) 221-7201; (800) 589-5888

Pennsylvania
Lehigh Valley Legal Services
65 E. Elizabeth Avenue, Suite 903,
Bethlehem, PA 18018.
(610) 317-8757

Neighborhood Legal Services
Association (Pittsburgh)
928 Penn Avenue
Pittsburgh, PA 15222-3799
(412) 255-6700

Northwestern Legal Services
Renaissance Centre
1001 State St, Suite 1200
Erie, Pennsylvania 16501
(814) 452-6949; (800) 753-5704

Southern Alleghenys Legal Aid, Inc.
616 Main Street, Suite 500
Johnstown, PA 15901-2172
(888) 244-7252

Rhode Island
Rhode Island Legal Services, Inc.
56 Pine Street, Fourth Floor
Providence, Rhode Island 02903
(401) 274-2652; (800) 662-5034

South Carolina
Palmetto Legal Services
P.O.Box 2267
Columbia, SC 29202
(803-799-9668)

Tennessee
Knoxville Legal Aid Society
502 South Gay St., Suite 404
Knoxville, Tennessee 37902
(865) 637-0484

Texas
Legal Aid of Central Texas
2201 Post Road #104
Austin, Texas 78704
(512) 447-7707; (800-369-9270)

Legal Services of North Texas
1515 Main St.
Dallas, TX 75201
(214) 748-1234

Texas Legal Services Center (State
Support)
(800) 662-2520

Virginia

Legal Services of Northern Virginia
6400 Arlington Blvd., Suite 600
Falls Church, VA 22042

PRO BONO SITES
ABA Division of Legal Services -
Center for Pro Bono Services
(ABA state by state information on
over 800 Pro Bono Services)
750 N. Lake Shore Dr.,
Chicago, IL 60611
312-988-5769

Community Law Program of St.
Petersburg, Florida - Community
Outreach Center
3420 Eighth Ave. South, Suite 109
St. Petersburg, FL 33711

Atlanta Volunteer Lawyers Foundtn.
225 Peachtree Street NE, Ste. 1105
Atlanta, Georgia 30303
(404) 521-0790

Hawaii Lawyers Care

Illinois Pro Bono Center
116 N. Chestnut, Suite 220,
Champaign, IL 61820
(217) 359-6811

Volunteer Lawyers Project (Maine)
(800) 442-4293

Pro Bono Information and
Resources (NLS, Massachusetts)

Legal Advice and Referral Center
(New Hampshire)
PO Box 4147
Concord, NH 03302-4147
(603) 224-3333; (800) 639-5290

Pro Bono Affairs (New York State
Bar Association)
One Elk Street
Albany, NY 12207
(518) 463-3200

Pro Bono Information - North
Carolina Bar Association
PO Box 3688
Cary, NC 27513-3688

Pro Bono Volunteer Resource
Guide (Utah Bar Association)

Utah Law & Justice Center
645 South 200 East
Salt Lake City, Utah 84111
(801) 297-7027

PUBLIC INTEREST SITES
Public Interest Clearinghouse, Calif.
*This site has an internet directory of
California Legal Aid Services:*
http://www.pic.org/
100 McAllister Street, 2nd Floor
San Francisco, CA 94102-4929
(415) 255-1714

**OTHER ADVOCACY
ORGANIZATIONS**
Legal Serv. for Elderly (in Maine)
72 Winthrop St., PO Box 2723
Augusta, ME 04338-2723
(800) 750-5353

Public Interest Clearinghouse (Calif.)
100 McAllister Street, 2nd Floor
San Francisco, CA 94102-4929
(415) 255-1714

Advocacy Services Inc. (Arkansas
disability advocacy)

Central California Legal Services
2014 Tulare Avenue, Suite 600
Fresno, California 93721
559-570-1200

Legal Aid for Seniors (Central
California Legal Services)

Montana Advocacy Program
PO Box 1680
316 N. Park, Room 2
(406) 444-3889; (800) 245-4743

Whitman - Walker Clinic Legal
Department (HIV related legal
issues in D.C. area)
1701 14th Street NW
Washington DC 20009
(202-939-7627)

Law School Legal Aid Programs
Georgetown University Law Center
111 F Street, NW, Suite 127
Washington, D.C. 20001
(202) 662-9590

Harvard Legal Aid Bureau
1511 Massachusetts Avenue,
Cambridge, MA 02138
(617) 495-4408

Legal Aid Association - University
of North Dakota School of Law
PO Box 9003
Grand Forks, ND 58202
(701) 777-2932; (800) 752-0312.

BACKUP CENTERS (Assistance
with obtaining the names and phone
numbers of agencies in your area
that potentially can help you.)
Center for Law and Social Policy
1616 P Street, NW, Suite 150
Washington, DC 20036
(202) 328-5140

National Center for Youth Law
114 Sansome Street, Suite 900
San Francisco, CA 94104-3820
(415) 543-3307

National Health Law Program
2639 South La Cienega Boulevard
Los Angeles, CA 90034
(310) 204-6010

National Senior Citizens Law Center
1101 14th St., NW, Suite 400
Washington, DC 20005
(202) 289-6976

Native American Rights Fund
1506 Broadway
Boulder, CO 80302
(303) 447-8760

Pennsylvania Health Law Project
801 Arch St., Suite 610 A
Philadelphia, PA 19107
(215) 625-3663

Welfare Law Center
275 Seventh Avenue, Suite 1205
New York, NY 10001-6708
(212)633-6967

Western New York Law Center
295 Main Street, Suite 454,
Buffalo, New York, 14203
(716) 855-02

Table 1I: STATE FOOD STAMP INFORMATION/HOTLINE NUMBERS

Use the following numbers to get information on food stamp questions in the States and areas of States listed. Most are toll-free numbers.

Alabama
(334) 242-1700

Alaska
(907) 465-3360

Arizona
(800) 352-8401
(For out-of-State calls)
(718) 291-1900

Arkansas
(800) 482-8988

California
(800) 952-5253

Colorado
(303) 866-5087**

Connecticut
(800) 842-1508

Delaware
(800) 464-4357

District of Columbia
(202) 724-5506

Florida
(800) 342-9274

Georgia
(800) 869-1150

Guam
447-KEHA

Hawaii
(808) 586-5230

Idaho
(208) 334-5818

Illinois
(800) 252-8635

Indiana
(800) 622-4932*

Iowa
(800)-972-2017

Kansas
(785)-296-3349**

Kentucky
(800) 372-2973

Louisiana
(800) 256-1548

Maine
Augusta Area Only
(800) 762-7107
All But Augusta Area
(800) 452-4643

Maryland
(800) 492-5515

Massachusetts
(800) 645-8333

Michigan
(517) 373-0707

Minnesota
(800) 657-3698*

Mississippi
(800) 948-3050

Missouri
(800) 392-2160

Montana
(800) 332-2272

Nebraska
(800) 430-3244

Nevada
(800) 992-0900
(Ext. 5765)*

New Hampshire
(800) 852-3345
(Ext. 4238)

New Jersey
(800) 792-9773

New Mexico   (888)-473-3676

New York (upstate)
(800) 342-3009
(800) 343-8859

New York City Area Only
(877) 472-8411

North Carolina
(800) 662-7030

North Dakota
(800) 755-2716

Ohio
Canton
(800) 686-1569*
Cincinnati
(800) 686-1571*
Cleveland
(800) 686-1551*
Columbus
(800) 686-1568*

Toledo
(800) 686-1572*

Oklahoma
(405) 521-3444**

Oregon
(503) 945-6092
(503) 945-6105

Pennsylvania
(800) 692-7642

Rhode Island
(800) 221-5689

South Carolina
(800) 768-5700

South Dakota
(877) 999-5612

Tennessee
(800) 342-1784

Texas
(800) 252-9330

Utah
(877) 817-1800

Vermont
(800) 287-0589

Virgin Islands
(340) 774-2399

Virginia
(800) 552-3431

Washington
(800) 865-7801

West Virginia
(800) 642-8589

Wisconsin
(608) 266-2314

Wyoming
(800) 457-3657

* These numbers are for in-State and out-of-State calls. All other 800 numbers are for in-State calls only.
** The State agency will accept collect calls on this number.

Chapter 2
HOW TO COLLECT MONEY TO START A BUSINESS

Small business — comprised of some 20 million firms — is the backbone of the U.S. economy. It creates two out of every three new jobs, produces almost 40 percent of the national product, and invents more than half the country's technological inventions.

Because this sector of the economy is so important, the federal government has many special programs to help small business. Among the federal agencies with such programs are the **Small Business Administration**, the **Department of Commerce**, the **Department of Housing and Urban Development**, and others.

SMALL BUSINESS ADMINISTRATION (SBA)

The U.S. Small Business Administration is the main government agency concerned with small business. It was specifically created by Congress to help America's entrepreneurs start successful small businesses. Today, the SBA aids, counsels, assists, and protects the interests of small business.

It ensures that small business concerns receive a fair proportion of Government purchases, contracts, and subcontracts. It makes loans to State and local development companies, and the victims of floods or other catastrophes, or certain types of economic injury. And perhaps most important of its function, it has a number of SBA financing programs to make money available to small business concerns.

There are three main types of assistance programs you should know about:

1) **Loans**. This is money lent directly by the federal agency for a specific period of time and with an expectation of repayment.

2) **Loan Guarantees**: These are programs in which the federal agency guarantees to pay back a loan made by a private lender.

3) **Grants**. This is money given by the federal agency which does not have to be paid back.

Who Is Eligible For An SBA Loan. Almost most small businesses are eligible. Eligibility is determined by a number of factors.

Types of Business. The vast majority of small businesses are eligible for financial assistance. The business must operate for profit; be engaged in business in the United States or its possessions; have reasonable owner equity to invest; and use alternative financial resources first including personal

52

assets.

Size of Business. In general, a small business is defined as one that is independently owned and operated, and not dominant in its field. Generally for **manufacturers**, average employment should not exceed 500; for **wholesalers**, average employment should not exceed 100; for **retail and services concerns**, revenues should not be over $13.5 million; for **construction firms**, revenues should not be over $17 million; and for **agricultural enterprises**, gross annual sales should not be over $3.5 million. Veterans are eligible for most programs.

Use of Loans. SBA loans can be used for most business purposes. These may include acquiring real estate to house the business; construction, renovation or leasehold improvements; acquiring furniture, fixtures, machinery and equipment; purchase of inventory; working capital.

Important SBA programs are described below. Information is available from all SBA offices (see Table 2a) or by calling SBA's answer desk at (800) 8-ASK-SBA.

Money—for Businesses Owned by Low-Income Owners or in Areas of High Unemployment
SBA Loans For Small Businesses: "Section 7(a) Loans" (59.012)

Description: This program, the 7(a) Loan Guarantee Program, is one of the Small Business Administration's primary lending programs. It provides guaranteed/insured loans to small businesses which are unable to obtain financing in the private credit marketplace, but can demonstrate an ability to repay loans granted. The program operates through private-sector lenders that provide loans which are guaranteed by the SBA.

It is available to low-income business owners or businesses located in areas of high unemployment or owned by handicapped individuals.

Funds are to be used to construct, expand, or convert facilities; to purchase building equipment or materials; for working capital.

Applicant Eligibility:
- Low-income business owners or businesses located in areas of high unemployment which produce goods or services;
- Small businesses being established, acquired or owned by handicapped individuals;

- Small businesses intended to manufacture, design, market, install, or service specific energy measures.

Financial Information: In the latest reported year, 38,974 loans totaling $9 billion were made; $500,000 high, $226,521 average.

Literature: "*SBA Business Loans from the SBA*," OPC-6.

Who To Contact: *Headquarters Office*: Director, Loan Policy and Procedures Branch, Small Business Administration, 409 Third Street, SW., Washington, DC 20416. Telephone: (202) 205-6570. *Regional or Local Office*: Initial contact should be with a district office listed in Table 2a.

MicroLoans: $100-$25,000
MicroLoan Demonstration Program (59.046)

Description: The MicroLoan Program was developed to increase the availability of very small loans to fledgling entrepreneurs, loans ranging from under $500 to $25,000.

Under this program, the SBA makes loans or provides loan guaranties to private, non-profit agencies and quasi-governmental organizations (intermediary lenders) who use the loan funds to make short-term, fixed interest rate microloans to start-up, newly established, and growing small business concerns. There are more than 300 such microenterprise lenders in the U.S.

Microloans are used for working capital, inventory, supplies, furniture, fixtures, machinery, and/or equipment.

Completed applications can usually be processed by the intermediary in less than a week.

Beneficiary Eligibility: Small businesses, minority entrepreneurs, nonprofit entities, business owners, women and low-income, and other individuals possessing the capability to operate successful business concerns.

Financial Information: Loans are generally for five years, at market rates, with the owner providing 10 percent in equity. Borrowers make a regular monthly payment, depending on the cash flow of the business.

Over $44 million is loaned annually by the SBA or intermediaries to microenterprises. The average loan amount is about $10,000. Depending on the type of business, borrowers can take up to six years to repay a microloan.

Who To Contact: *Headquarters Office*: Small Business Administration, Office of Financial Assistance, Microenterprise Development Branch, 409 Third Street SW., Eighth Floor, Washington, DC 20416. Mail Code 7881. Telephone: (202) 205-6490. *Local Microloan Lenders*: Table 2b

Assistance to Economically and Socially Disadvantaged Business Owners

Minority Business Development: "Section 8(A) Program"
(59.006)

Description: This program was set up to support business ownership by individuals who are both socially and economically disadvantaged; and to promote the competitive viability of such firms by providing business development assistance. It provides access to limited competition Federal contract opportunities to help the firms to achieve competitive viability.

Applicant Eligibility: Small businesses that are at least 51 percent owned, control and managed by an American citizen(s) determined by SBA to be socially and economically disadvantaged African

Americans and Hispanic Americans, or by economically disadvantaged Indian Tribes.

Financial Information: Last year, 32,091 contract actions valued at $6.59 billion were awarded to companies participating in the program.

Who To Contact: *Headquarters Office*:: Associate Administrator for Minority Enterprise Development, Small Business Administration, 409 Third Street, SW., Washington, DC 20416. Telephone: (202) 205-6421. *Regional or Local Office*: Initial contact should be made with the field offices listed Table 2a.

Money—from Small Business Investment Companies

Small Business Investment Companies
(59.011)

Description: SBICs (Small Business Investment Companies) are privately organized and managed firms which provide equity capital and long term loan funds to small businesses. SBICs are licensed by the Small Business Administration but set their own policies. SSBICs (Special Small Business Investment Companies) invest specifically in socially and economically disadvantaged entrepreneurs. There are 215 SBICs and 127 SSBICs.

Applicant/Beneficiary Eligibility: Individual businesses (proprietorship, partnership or corporation) which satisfy the established criteria of a small business and are owned and operated by socially or economically disadvantaged persons.

Financial Information: In the latest reported year, $2.2 billion in guarantee loans was made..

Who To Contact: *Headquarters Office*: Associate Administrator for Investment, Investment Division, Small Business Administration, 409 Third Street, SW., Washington, DC 20416. Telephone: (202) 205-6510. *Regional or Local Office*: None.

Business Development Assistance To Small Business

(59.005)

Description: Advisory services and counseling, dissemination of technical information, training, to help present and prospective small business owners improve skills to manage and operate a business.

Applicant Eligibility: Small business persons, veterans, community groups.

Financial Information: During the latest reported year, management counseling and training was given to 275,000 potential and existing small business entrepreneurs.

Literature: *"The Resource Directory for Small Business Management."*

Who to Contact: *Headquarters Office*: Associate Administrator for Business Initiatives, Small Business Administration, 409 3rd Street, SW., Washington, DC 20416. Telephone: (202) 205-6665. *Regional or Local Office*: Initial contact should be made with the field offices (Table 2a).

Money—for Businesses that Suffered Due To a Natural Disaster

Economic Injury Disaster Loans (59.002)

Description: Direct, guaranteed and insured loans to assist small business concerns, agricultural cooperatives, nurseries suffering economic injury as a result of Presidential, Small Business Administration (SBA), and/or Secretary of Agriculture declared disasters. Up to 30 years for repayment. A $1,500,000 limit on amount: the interest rate is not to exceed 4 percent.

Applicant Eligibility: Small business concerns, small agricultural cooperative, nurseries unable to obtain credit elsewhere; and must be located within declared disaster area.

Benefits: During the latest reported year, 3,908 loans were made for $147 million; $76,200 average.

Literature: *"Economic Injury Disaster Loans for Small Business,"* DA-3.

Who To Contact: *Headquarters Office*: Office of Disaster Assistance, Small Business Administration, 409 3rd Street, SW., Washington, DC 20416. Program Contact: Herbert Mitchell. Telephone: (202) 205-6734. *Regional or Local Office*: For reference to the Disaster Area Office, contact any office in Table 2a.

Assistance for Socially And Economically Disadvantaged Businesses

Management And Technical Assistance For Socially And Economically Disadvantaged Businesses—"Section 7(J) Development Assistance Program" (59.007)

Description: This program funds qualified organizations and individuals that provide accounting, marketing, proposal preparation workshops and technical assistance to businesses which are economically and socially disadvantaged; businesses operating in areas of high unemployment or low income; firms owned by low-income persons

Eligibility: Socially and economically disadvantaged persons and businesses owned and operated by participants in the 8(a) program, businesses operating in areas of low-income or high-unemployment, and firms owned by low-income individuals.

Financial Information: Management and technical assistance was provided to about 3,000 eligible clients.

Who To Contact: *Headquarters Office*: Associate Administrator for Minority Enterprise Development, 409 3rd Street, SW., Washington, DC 20416. Telephone: (202) 205-7343 *Regional or Local Office*: SBA District offices listed in Table 2a.

Money—for Victims of Physical Disasters
Physical Disaster Loans (59.008. 7b loans DL)

Description:: Direct loans and guaranteed/insured loans to victims of declared physical-type disasters for uninsured losses. Loans made to homeowners, renters, businesses of all sizes to repair and/or replace damaged and/or destroyed real property and/or personal property to its pre-disaster conditions.

Applicant Eligibility: Individuals, business concerns, and charitable and nonprofit organizations. that have suffered physical property loss as a result of a disaster which occurred in an area declared as eligible for assistance by the President or SBA. Agricultural enterprises are ineligible.

Financial Information: An estimated 53,500 loans totaling $860,000,000 were made in the latest reported year.

Literature: "*Physical Disaster Business Loans,*" DA-2; "*Disaster Loans for Homes and Personal Property,*" DA-1.

Who To Contact: *Headquarters Office*: Office of Disaster Assistance, Small Business Administration, 409 3rd Street, SW., Washington, DC 20416. Program Contact: Herbert Mitchell. Phone: (202) 205-6734. *Regional or Local Office*: For reference to the Disaster Area Office, contact your local field office in Table 2a.

Help for Businesses to Get Government Contracts
Procurement Assistance To Small Businesses (59.009)

Description: This program assists small business in obtaining a "fair" share of contracts and subcontracts for Federal Government purchases of supplies and services, and a "fair" share of property sold by the Government. One of the ways it does this through small business set-asides (restriction of bidding/award to small business only).

Applicant Eligibility: Existing and potential small businesses..

Financial Information: In the latest reported year, $10.4 billion in government prime contracts were set-aside for procurement from small business.

Who To Contact: *Headquarters Office*: Associate Administrator for Government Contracting, Small Business Administration, 409 3rd Street, SW., Washington, DC 20416. Telephone: (202) 205-6460. *Regional or Local Office*: Contact your local field office in Table 2a.

Money—from Local Development Companies
"502 Loans" (59.013)

Description: Provides guaranteed/insured loans from bank and non-bank lenders to local development companies who, in turn, provide long-term loans to small business concerns located in their areas. The loans are available for the purchase of buildings, machinery, and equipment, or for constructing, expanding, or modernizing buildings. Loans are not available to provide small businesses with working capital or for refinancing purposes. Loans may not exceed 25 years.

Program not funded this year.

Financial Information: No data available.

Literature: "*Key Features of SBA's Principal Lending Programs,*" OPI-7. "*Long-Term Financing Through the Secondary Market of the U.S. Small Business Administration,*" SBA-475.

Who To Contact: *Headquarters Office*: Office of Financial Assistance, Small Business Administration, 409 3rd Street, SW,. Washington, DC 20416. Telephone: (202) 205-6490. *Regional or Local Office*: See Table 1a for a listing of the Small Business Administration offices.

Help for Small Contractors to Get Bonded
Bond Guarantees For Surety Companies (59.016)

Description: To guarantee surety bonds issued by commercial surety companies for small contractors unable to obtain a bond without a guarantee. Guarantees cover up to 90 percent of the losses incurred and paid by participating sureties if certain conditions are met.

Beneficiary Eligibility: A small contractor whose gross receipts have been not more than $5 million as averaged for the last 3 fiscal years; a manufacturer whose number of employees does not exceed the small business standards specified in Small Business Size Regulations, under E.O. 12372.

Financial Information: $1,672,000,000 annually. Size range of contracts awarded and bonded, $475 to $1,250,000; average contract: $177,602; average guarantee: $132,741.

Who To Contact: *Headquarters Office*: Associate Administrator, Office of Surety Guarantees, Small Business Administration, 409 3rd Street, SW., Washington, DC 20416. Contact: Robert J. Moffitt. Telephone: (202) 205-6540. *Regional or Local Office*: Applicants must contact a local agent or broker of surety bonds. General program particulars may be obtained from SBA Area Offices listed in Table 2a.

Free Business Counseling
Service Corps Of Retired Executives Association—"Score" (59.026)

Description: SCORE, The Service Corps. Of Retired Executives, helps small businesses through free business counseling and low-cost workshops. It uses the management experience of retired and active business management professionals who volunteer to counsel and train potential and existing small business owners in need of management counseling. There are 12,400 SCORE volunteers in 389 chapters serving in all 50 States and U.S. possessions.

Applicant Eligibility: All existing and potential small business owners are eligible. The business must be independently owned and operated.

Financial Information: Since SCORE was established in 1964, it has responded to over 4.2 million requests for assistance.

Who To Contact: *Headquarters Office*: National SCORE Office, 409 3rd Street, SW., Washington, DC 20024. Telephone: (202) 205-6762 or (800) 634-0245 or Small Business Administration, Office of Business Development, 409 3rd Street, SW., Washington, DC 20416. Telephone: (202) 205-7414. *Regional or Local Office*: The initial contact can be made directly with SCORE offices or with the SBA field offices in Table 2a.

Help in Getting Contracts
Procurement Automated Source System—"PASS"

Description: PASS is a computerized data base with nationwide access by Federal procurement officials and the private sector which lists the profiles and capabilities of potential small business bidders in response to the requests of Government agencies and major corporations. It permits small firms (including minority and women-owned) registered with PASS to have their capabilities made available when specific source requests are made by Federal procurement officers and other buyers.

Applicant Eligibility: Registration is free to any small business which is organized for profit, independently owned and operated and wishes to do business with the Federal Government or major corporations.

Financial Information: Not applicable. 180,000 small firms are registered. 1,100 locations have direct access to the system.

Literature: "*Procurement Automated Source System-Company Profile*" (SBA Form 1167) is obtainable from any SBA office. The form and a fact sheet may also be obtained by calling (800) 231-PASS.

Who To Contact: *Headquarters Office*: Associate Administrator for Government Contracting, Small Business Administration, 409 3rd Street, SW., Washington, DC 20416. Telephone: (800) 231-PASS. *Regional or Local Office*: Call toll free on (800) 231-PASS, or contact the Regional or Local Office listed in Table 2a.

Free Business Counseling and Training
Small Business Development Centers—"SBDC" (59.037)

Description: Provides management counseling, training, and technical assistance to the small business community through Small Business Development Centers (SBDCs).

Eligibility: Current and potential Small business persons.

Financial Information: Since the start of the SBDC Program in 1977, SBDCs have counseled 2,178,049 clients and trained 3,828,540 attendees.

Who To Contact: *Headquarters Office*: Small Business Administration, Office of Small Business Development Center, 409 Third Street, SW., 4th Floor, Washington, DC 20416. Telephone: (202) 205-6766. *Regional or Local Office*: For addresses of the field offices, see Table 2a.

Money—from Certified Development Companies
Certified Development Company Loans—"504 Loans" (59.041)

Description: The **504** program assists small business concerns by providing long-term fixed rate financing for fixed assets through the sale of debentures to private investors (Certified Development Companies). These investors, in turn, make loans to small businesses for the acquisition of land and buildings, construction, expansion, renovation and modernization, machinery and equipment. Loans may have either a 10 or 20 year term.

Beneficiary Eligibility: Small businesses that are independently owned and operated for profit.

Financial Information: 4,847 loans annually totaling $1.77 billion.

Who To Contact: *Headquarters Office*: Office of Financial Assistance, Small Business Administration, 409 3rd Street SW., Washington, DC 20416. Telephone: (202) 205-6490. *Regional or Local Office*: For addresses of the field offices, see Table 2a.

Money—for Women-Owned Businesses from Special Development Organizations
Women's Business Ownership Assistance (59.043)

Description: This program establishes and funds more than sixty nonprofit economic development centers to assist small business concerns owned and controlled by women. Services and assistance provided by these Women's Business Centers include financial, management, procurement, and marketing training and counseling to start-up or established on-going concerns. Many of them supply micro-loans.

Beneficiary Eligibility: Women entrepreneurs starting their own business or expanding their existing business.

Financial Information: At present, training and counseling is being offered at more than 71 different sites across the nation.

Who To Contact: *Headquarters Office*: Small Business Administration, Office of Women's Business Ownership, 409 Third Street, SW., Washington, DC 20416. Telephone: (202) 205-6673. *Regional or Local Office*: Women's Business Ownership representative, Table 2n.

Free Business Assistance For Veterans Who Want to Start a Small Business
Veterans Entrepreneurial Training And Counseling (59.044)

Description: This program provides veterans and their dependents assistance to start and manage their businesses. The assistance may be in the form of intensive training, counseling, and other specialized services.

Beneficiary Eligibility: Veterans starting and managing a business, and their dependents.

Financial Information: No data available.

Who To Contact: *Headquarters Office*: Director, Office of Veteran Affairs, Small Business Administration, Sixth Floor, 409 Third Street, SW., Washington DC 20416. Telephone: (202) 205-6773. *Regional or Local Office*: Table 2a.

DEPARTMENT OF COMMERCE

The Department of Commerce was established to promote American businesses and trade. It's responsibilities include promoting minority entrepreneurship, expanding U.S. exports, developing innovative technologies, gathering and disseminating statistical data, measuring economic growth, granting patents and predicting the weather.

Free Advice on Export Trade Promotion
Export Trade Promotion (11.108)

Description: Promotes exports by advising businesses on export trade promotion and trade finance by: (1) assisting them to identify and assess potential foreign trade contacts and market opportunities; and (2) by facilitating their export efforts through trade events and market research information.

Services include: contact information; matchmaker missions, multi-state/catalog exhibitions, and other specialized promotions; product promotions through catalog-magazine listings; international buyer shows, certified trade fairs and missions; information on trade statistics, trade opportunities, foreign tariffs, customs regulations and procedures; market potential in individual countries; advice and counseling on foreign trade and individual foreign markets; and assistance on sources of export finance available from the U.S. Export Import Bank, U.S. Small Business Administration and U.S. Agency for International Development in U.S. Export Assistance Centers.

Applicant Eligibility: Any U.S. citizen, firm, or organization needing information or assistance in international business matters.

Financial Benefits: Not applicable.

Literature: "*A Basic Guide to Exporting*."

Who To Contact: *Headquarters Office*: Not applicable; contact your regional or local Export Assistance Centers (EAC) run by the International Trade Administration, Department of Commerce (Table 2c).

Free Assistance if You're in Exporting
Export Trade Development (11.110)

Description: The purpose of this program is to foster the competitiveness and growth of U.S. industries and promote their increased participation in international markets. It does this by being the Federal Government source of industry-specific expertise; industry competitiveness analysis and trade promotion assistance; regular statistical reports and economic studies on current policy issues; forecasts of industry/sector output, cost trends, and their general economic condition; advocacy on behalf of U.S. bidders for foreign procurement projects; export promotion events and foreign market information.

Beneficiary Eligibility: Any business, public official, civic organization or private citizen may request information in person, by letter or telephone.

Financial Benefits: Not applicable.

Who To Contact: *Headquarters Office*: International Trade Administration, U.S. Department of Commerce, 14th and Constitution Avenue, NW., Washington, DC 20230. Inquiries should be directed to Advocacy Center, (202) 482-3896; Technology and Aerospace Industries, (202) 482-1872; Basic Industries, (202) 482-0614; Environmental Technologies Exports, (202) 482-5225; Service Industries and Finance, (202) 482-5261; Export Trading Company Affairs, (202) 482-5131; Textiles, Apparel, and Consumer Goods Industries, (202) 482-3737; Tourism Industries, (202) 482-0140; Trade and Economic Analysis, (202) 482-5145; Export Promotion Coordination, (202) 482-4501; and Planning, Coordination and Resource Management, (202) 482-4921. *Regional or Local Office*: Local offices are listed in (Table 2c).

Help for Communities and Businesses Hurt By Military Base Closings or Long Term Economic Deterioration

Special Economic Development and Adjustment Assistance Program—Sudden and Severe Economic Dislocation and Long-Term Economic Deterioration (11.307)

Description: Grants to assist State and local areas hurt by severe economic dislocation such as plant closings, military base closures and defense contract cutbacks, and natural disasters, or from long-term economic deterioration in the area's economy.

Grants may be used for a number of purposes, including: business development and financing.

Eligibility: Must be in a geographic area suffering economic dislocation as described above. The intent of the program is to save or create jobs.

Financial Information: Range and Average of Financial Assistance: No specific minimum or maximum. Total funds available: $115,700,000.

Who to Contact: *Headquarters Office*: David F. Witschi, Director, Economic Adjustment Division, Economic Development Administration, Room H7327, Herbert C. Hoover Building, Department of Commerce, Washington DC 20230. Telephone: (202) 482-2659. *Regional or Local Office*: See Table 2d.

Minority-Owned Business Help Centers

Minority Business Development Centers (11.800)

Description: This program funds Minority Business Development Centers in order to provide business development services to minority firms and individuals interested in entering, expanding or improving their efforts in the marketplace.

Minority Business Development Centers provide advice and counseling in such areas as preparing financial packages, business planning and counseling, business information and management assistance, accounting guidance, marketing, business/industrial site analysis, production, engineering, construction assistance, procurement, and identification of potential

business opportunities. The agency does not have the authority to make loans to minority businesses, but it may be able to help you locate financing sources.

Beneficiary Eligibility: Minority-owned businesses or minorities interested in starting or expanding a business, including: Hispanic Americans, Asian and Pacific Island Americans, Alaska Natives and Native Americans, African Americans and Hasidic Jews.

Who To Contact: *Headquarters Office*: Stephen J. Boykin, Business Development Specialist, Field Coordination Division, Room 5079, Minority Business Development Agency, Department of Commerce, 14th and Constitution Ave., NW., Washington, DC 20230. Phone: (202) 482-6022. *Regional or Local Office*: Contact nearest Minority Business Development Agency Regional Office (Table 2e).

Help for Native Americans to Start Their Own Businesses

Native American Program (11.801)

Description: This program establishes eight Native American Business Development Centers to provide business development service to Native Americans interested in entering, expanding or improving their efforts in the marketplace. These centers provide clients with advice and counseling in such areas as preparing financial packages, business counseling, business information and management, accounting guidance, marketing, business/industrial site analysis, production, engineering, construction assistance, procurement and identification of potential business opportunities.

They don't have the authority to make loans to Native American firms, but may be able to help you locate financing sources.

Applicant Eligibility: Eligible applicants include Native Americans interested in starting, expanding, or maintaining a business.

Financial Information: Not applicable.

Who To Contact: *Headquarters Office*: Stephen J. Boykin, Business Development Specialist, Field Coordination Division, Room 5079, Minority Business Development Agency, Department of

Commerce, 14th and Constitution Ave., NW., Washington, DC 20230. Phone: (202) 482-6022. *Regional or Local Office*: Contact the nearest Minority Business Development Agency Regional Office (Table 2e).

Support to Help Minority-Owned Businesses Expand
Minority Business Resource Development (*11.802*)

Description: To foster new minority business enterprises and maintain and strengthen existing firms by: identifying and developing private markets and capital sources; expanding business information and business services through trade associations; promoting and supporting the mobilization of resources of Federal agencies and State and local governments at the local level; assisting minorities in entering new and growing markets; sponsoring franchise training seminars.

Beneficiary Eligibility: Minority businesses and individuals, professional organizations, trade associations.

Financial Information: Not applicable.

Who To Contact: *Headquarters Office*: Stephen J. Boykin, Business Development Specialist, Field Coordination Division, Room 5079, Minority Business Development Agency, Department of Commerce, 14th and Constitution Ave., NW., Washington, DC 20230. Phone: (202) 482-6022. *Regional or Local Office*: Contact the nearest Minority Business Development Agency Regional Office (Table 2e).

DEPARTMENT OF HOUSING AND URBAN DEVELOPMENT

Money—from Community Development Block Grants
"CDBG" /Entitlement Grants (14.218)

Description: The goal of this program is to develop viable urban communities by providing decent housing and a suitable living environment, and by expanding economic opportunities, principally for persons of low and moderate income. Local governments with more than 50,000 population apply for funding, and then make grants to local beneficiaries, for example, loans and grants to business activities that will benefit low- and moderate-income persons.

Beneficiary Eligibility: The principal beneficiaries of CDBG funds are low- and moderate-income persons. You must certify that at least 70 percent of the grant funds received during a one, two, or three year period are used for activities that will principally benefit low- and moderate-income persons.

Annual Benefits: Over $3 billion.

Who To Contact: *Headquarters Office*: Entitlement Communities Division, Office of Block Grant Assistance, Community Planning and Development, 451 7th Street, S.W., Washington, DC 20410. Telephone: (202) 708-1577. *Regional or Local Office*: Contact appropriate HUD Field Office, Table 2f.

Money—from Community Development Block Grants for New York and Hawaii
CDBG/Small Cities Program (14.219)

Description: This program is similar to **14.218**, but for cities with under 50,000 population and that are not central cities in a metropolitan area. Small Cities develop their own programs and funding priorities, making grants to local beneficiaries. Only the states of New York and Hawaii have opted for this program.

Beneficiary Eligibility: The principal beneficiaries of "Small Cities" funds are low- and moderate-income persons.

Annual Benefits: $376,000 to $740,000.

Who To Contact: *Headquarters Office*: State and Small Cities Division, Office of Block Grant Assistance Community Planning and Development, Department of Housing and Urban Development, 451 7th Street, S.W., Washington, DC 20410. Telephone: (202) 708-1322. *Regional or Local Office*: Contact appropriate HUD Field Office for New York or Hawaii (Table 2f).

Money—from Community Development Block Grants for the Pacific Islands
CDBG Special Purpose Grants/Insular Areas (14.225)

Description: This program is similar to 14.219, but applies only to American Samoa, Guam, the Northern Mariana Islands, and the Virgin Islands.

Beneficiary Eligibility: Low- and moderate-income persons in the above territories.

Financial Information: $7,000,000 total.

Who To Contact: Headquarters Office: Office of Block Grant Assistance, Community Planning and Development, Department of Housing and Urban Development, 451 7th St., S.W., Washington, DC 20410. Telephone: (202) 708-1322. *Regional or Local Office*: Contact the Headquarters office.

Money—from Community Development Block Grants/State's Program
(14.228)

Description: This program is similar to **14.218**, for funding for small cities in the 48 states (other than New York and Hawaii—see **14.219**) and Puerto Rico that have opted to develop and administer their own programs.

Beneficiary Eligibility: The principal beneficiaries are low- and moderate-income persons. For example, business activities that will benefit low- and moderate-income persons.

Financial Information: $1,314,638,000.

Who To Contact: Headquarters Office: State and Small Cities Division, Office of Block Grant Assistance, Community Planning and Development, Department of Housing and Urban Development, 451 7th Street, S.W., Washington, DC 20410. Telephone: (202) 708-1322. *Regional or Local Office*: Contact the appropriate HUD Field Office (Table 2f).

Money—to Become a Landlord

Description: How would you like to be a landlord, collecting rent checks each month? HUD makes it possible with a number of programs that provide funds to would-be landlords. See Chapter 3, beginning on page 105 for details on these HUD programs.

DEPARTMENT OF AGRICULTURE

Money—to Start a New Business In a Rural or Small Town
Intermediary Relending Program (10.767)

Description: This is a rural development program that provides loans for the establishment of new businesses, expansion or exiting businesses, and the creation of employment opportunities in small towns and rural areas. You may be eligible for financial assistance if your small business is a private, for profit, existing commercial, retail, service related, manufacturing or industrial firm; or private, for-profit, new and innovative small business providing services, and/or products to the public.

Eligible uses:
- land acquisition
- building/renovations costs
- machinery and equipment
- pollution control and abatement
- feasibility studies
- working capital
- aquaculture
- transportation services

Participants should, to the maximum extent possible, use labor of low-income persons, farm families, and displaced farm families needing additional income to supplement farming operations.

Loans are made to Intermediary Relending Organizations such as private nonprofit corporations, any state or local government, Indian group, or cooperative which in turn is re-lent by them to ultimate recipients for business purposes. The ultimate recipient must not be able to obtain credit elsewhere.

Beneficiary Eligibility: Businesses, individuals, nonprofit organizations, Indian tribes and organizations. Recipients must not be located within a city with a population of 25,000 or more, and must be unable to obtain the loan at reasonable rates and terms through commercial credit or other Federal, State, or local programs.

Financial Information: No information.

Who To Contact: *Headquarters Office*: Rural Business-Cooperative Service, Room 6867, South Agriculture Building, Washington, DC 20250-3225. Telephone: (202) 690-4100. *Regional or Local Office*: See Rural Development Field Offices, Table 2h.

Money—to Run a Farm or Start a Teenage Farm–Related Business
Farm Operating Loans (10.406)

Description: This program provides direct loans and guaranteed/insured loans to enable operators of not larger than family farms to make efficient use of their land, labor, and other resources, and to establish and maintain financially viable farming and ranching operations. Farm operating loans provide credit to: (1) establish beginning farmers; (2) assist farmers suffering from the price/cost squeeze, which will enable them to remain on the farm and refinance secured and unsecured debts; and (3) expand farming operations.

Loan funds may be used to:

- Purchase livestock, poultry, fur bearing and other farm animals, fish, and bees;
- Purchase farm equipment;
- Provide operating expenses for farm enterprise;
- Meet family subsistence needs and purchase essential home equipment;
- Refinance secured and unsecured debts subject to certain restrictions;
- Pay property taxes;
- Pay insurance premiums on real estate and personal property.

In addition, this program finances businesses started by teenagers. Some common projects include livestock and crop production, lawn and garden services, repair shops, and roadside stands.

Applicant Eligibility: Except for youth loans, individual applicants must:
1) Have the necessary education and/or farm experience or training;
2) Be unable to obtain sufficient credit elsewhere at reasonable rates, and terms;
3) Project the ability to repay the loan;
4) After the loan is closed, be an owner/tenant operator of a family farm.

Limited resource applicants must meet the above requirements, and, in addition, must have a low income and show a need for increased farm income.

Financial Information: *Range and Average of Financial Assistance*: Direct loans up to $200,000; guaranteed loans up to $731,000; Direct **average** loan size approximately $47,365 and guaranteed **average** loan size approximately $157,339. For the latest reported year, direct loans totaled $2 billion and guaranteed loans totaled $1.7 billion.

Literature: "*Farm Operating Loans*"; "*Youth Project Loans*"; "*Loans to Limited-Resource Farmers.*"

Who To Contact: *Headquarters Office*: Department of Agriculture, Farm Service Agency, Director, Loan Making Division, Ag Box 0522, Washington, DC 20250. Telephone: (202) 720-1632. *Regional or Local Office*: Contact the appropriate FSA State Office listed in Table 2g.

Money—to Buy or Operate a Farm
Farm Ownership Loans (10.407)

Description: The Department of Agriculture, through its Farm Service Agency, makes direct loans and guaranteed/insured loans to assist farmers, ranchers, and aquaculture operators, through the extension of credit and supervisory assistance to: become owner-operators of not larger than family farms; make efficient use of the land, labor, and other resources; carry on sound and successful farming operations; and enable farm families to have a reasonable standard of living.

Loan funds may be used to:

1) Enlarge, improve, and buy family farms;
2) Provide necessary water and water facilities;
3) Provide basic soil treatment and land conservation measures;
4) Construct, repair, and improve essential buildings needed in the operation of a family farm;
5) Construct or repair farm dwellings;
6) Provide facilities to produce fish under controlled conditions.

Eligibility Requirements: An applicant must have the necessary education and/or experience, training, and managerial ability to operate a family farm; realistically project the ability to repay the loan; be the owner-operator of a not larger than family farm after the loan is closed.

Financial Information: *Range and Average of Financial Assistance*: Maximum direct $200,000, maximum guaranteed $731,000. Average direct $111,762, guaranteed $250,421. For the latest reported year, direct loans totaled $150 million and guaranteed loans totaled $1.2 billion.

Who To Contact: *Headquarters Office*: Department of Agriculture, Farm Service Agency, Director, Loan Making Division, Ag Box 0522, Washington, DC 20250. Telephone: (202) 720-1632. *Regional or Local Office*: Contact the appropriate FSA State Office listed Table 2g.

Money—to Farmers Who Can't Get Credit
Interest Assistance Program (10.437)

Description: Guaranteed, insured loans with interest assistance to aid family farms in obtaining credit when they are temporarily unable to project a positive cash flow without a reduction in the interest rate.

The types and loan purposes are as follows:

- **Farm Ownership (FO) Loans** — to buy, improve, or enlarge farms, including construction, improvement, or repair of farm homes and service buildings; improvement of on-farm water supplies;

- **Operating Loans (OL)** — to pay for items needed for farm operations, including livestock, farm and home equipment, feed, seed, fertilizer, fuel, crop insurance, family living expenses, water system development, hired labor.

The loan limit is $300,000 for Farm Ownership Loans and $400,000 for Operating Loans.

Eligibility Requirements: Individuals, partnerships, or joint operations, legal resident aliens, corporations and cooperatives that meet the eligibility requirements for a guaranteed loan and are able to project the required cash flow margins with the aid of interest assistance.

Financial Information:

- *Subsidized Guaranteed Operating Loans*, $231 million. Range and Average of Financial Assistance: To $731,000; $158,000 average. 4,646 family sized farmers received assistance in the latest reported year.

- *Farm Ownership Loans*, no funds currently authorized.

Who To Contact: *Headquarters Office*: Department of Agriculture, Farm Service Agency, Director, Loan Making Division, PO Box 0522, Washington, DC 20250. Telephone: (202) 720-1632. *Regional or Local Office*: A guaranteed loan can be obtained by contacting a lender or the Farm Service Agency county office in the county where the proposed farming operation or headquarters will be located. FSA has more than 2,500 county offices serving every rural county in the United States. FSA state offices can inform applicants of county office locations where applicants may apply for this assistance. FSA State Office locations are listed in Table 2g.

Money—to Expand Businesses in Rural Areas
Business and Industrial Loans (10.768)

Description: Direct loans and guaranteed/insured loans to rural manufacturing, retail, wholesale, and service businesses, Indian tribes, or individuals in rural areas for the purpose of improving, developing or financing business, industry.

Financial assistance may be extended for:
- Business and industrial acquisition
- Construction
- Conversion
- Enlargement
- Repair
- Modernization
- Development costs
- And for purchasing and development of land, machinery and supplies.

Maximum loan size is $10,000,000 and maximum time allowable for final maturity is limited to 30 years for land and buildings, the usable life of machinery and equipment purchased with loan funds, not to exceed 15 years, and 7 years for working capital. Guarantees range from 70 percent to 90 percent of loan amount, depending on amount borrowed.

Applicant Eligibility: Corporations, partnerships, trusts, cooperatives or other legal entities organized and operated on a profit or nonprofit basis; an Indian Tribe; or individuals.

Applicants must be located in one of the fifty States, Puerto Rico, Virgin Islands, Guam, American Samoa, or the Northern Mariana Islands, in rural areas other than cities having a population of 50,000 or more that are immediately adjacent to urbanized and urbanizing areas with a population density of more than 100 persons per square mile.

Preference is given to loans in open country, rural communities and towns of 25,000 or less, and, on applications of equal priority, to veterans.

Benefits: Range: $35,000 to $10 million for direct loans, $35,000 to 25 million for guaranteed loans. Average: $559,471 for direct loans; $1,836,853 for guaranteed loans.

Who To Contact: *Headquarters Office*: Administrator, Rural Business-Cooperative Service, Department of Agriculture, Washington, DC 20250-0700. Telephone: (202) 690-4730. *Regional or Local Office*: Consult your State Rural Development Office in Table 2h.

Money—for Small Rural Businesses
Development Grants (10.769)

Description: Rural business enterprise grants (RBEG) to promote the development of small and emerging businesses in rural areas, including the acquisition and development of land and construction, conversion, enlargement, repair or modernization of buildings, plants, machinery, equipment, access streets and roads, parking areas, transportation serving the site, utility extensions, necessary water supply and waste disposal facilities, pollution control and abatement incidental to site development, provide technical assistance, pay fees, and refinancing.

Beneficiary Eligibility: Generally any private business which will employ 50 or less new employees and has less than $1 million in projected gross. Priority is given to projects in areas with a population of 25,000 or less with a large number of low-income persons.

Annual Benefits: 487 grants totaling $40,664,000. Range: $2,000 to $500,000. Average: $83,309.

Who To Contact: *Headquarters Office*: Director, Specialty Lenders Division, Rural Business-Cooperative Service, Dept. of Agriculture, Washington, DC 20250-3222. Telephone: (202) 720-1400. *Regional or Local Office*: Consult your State Rural Development Office in Table 2h..

Money—for Wind Erosion
Emergency Conservation Program (10.054)

Description: This program provides direct payments to enable farmers to perform emergency conservation measures to control wind erosion on farmlands, or to rehabilitate farmlands damaged by wind erosion, floods, hurricanes, or other natural disasters and to carry out emergency water conservation or water enhancing measures during periods of severe drought.

Applicant Eligibility: Any owner, landlord, tenant, or sharecropper on a farm or ranch. This program is also available in Guam, the Commonwealth of the Northern Mariana Islands, Puerto Rico and the Virgin Islands.

The recipient pays a portion of the cost to restore the loss, from 64 percent of the first $62,500 to 20 percent of the cost above $125,000.

Financial Information: $50 to $64,000; $2,681 average .

Who To Contact: *Headquarters Office*: USDA/FSA/CEPD, Stop 0513, 1400 Independence Ave., SW., Washington, DC 20250-0513. Telephone: (202) 720-6221. *Regional or Local Office*: Farmers are advised to contact their county or state FSA office after a natural disaster has occurred to determine whether the program is available in the county and to determine eligibility for emergency cost-share assistance. State FSA offices are listed in Table 2g.

Small Business Innovation Research
(10.212)

Description: Grants to small business firms and women-owned and socially disadvantaged small business firms to stimulate technological research and innovation, increase the use of innovations derived from USDA-supported research and development efforts, and foster and encourage participation, in technological innovation.

Selected areas for research are forests and related resources; plant production and protection; animal production and protection; air, water, and soils; food science and nutrition; rural and community development; aquaculture; industrial applications; and marketing and trade.

Applicant Eligibility: Small businesses.

Financial Information: $10, 063,752 annually, ranging from $46,000 to $250,000; $94,990 average.

Who To Contact: *Headquarters Office*: SBIR Director, Cooperative State Research, Education, and Extension Service, Department of Agriculture, Ag Box 2243, 14th and Independence Ave., SW., Washington, DC 20250-2243. Telephone: (202) 401-4002. *Regional or Local Office*: None.

Money—for Rural Businesses
Rural Economic Development Loans and Grants (10.854)

Description: Direct loans and project loans to promote rural economic development and job creation projects such as establishment or expansion of factories or businesses, medical facilities and other job creation projects.

The loans are made to rural electric and telephone utilities which in turn pass the funds through to rural economic development projects.

Beneficiary Eligibility: Rural/General Public.

Financial Information: From May 1989 to September 30, 2000, 564 loans totaling $120,338,000 and 208 grants totaling $63,486,865 were made. They created 24,498 jobs and were leveraged with $1.02 billion in supplemental capital. Range: $10,000 to $400,000, Average: $202,000.

Who To Contact: *Headquarters Office*: Director, Specialty Lenders Division, Rural Business-Cooperative Service, Department of Agriculture, Washington, DC 20250. Telephone: (202) 720-1400. *Regional or Local Office*: Consult your State Rural Development Office in Table 2h..

DEPARTMENT OF THE INTERIOR

Money—to Native Americans for Business Development
Indian Loans—for Business Development (15.124)

Description: Guaranteed and insured loans to Indian Tribal Governments, Native American Organizations, and individual American Indians to promote business development initiatives on or near Federally Recognized Indian Reservations.

Beneficiary Eligibility: Federally Recognized Indian Tribal Governments, Native American Organizations, and individual American Indians.

Benefits: For individuals and tribal enterprises, from $2,500-$500,000; $125,000 average.

Who To Contact: *Headquarters Office*: Office of Economic Development, Bureau of Indian Affairs, 1849 C Street, NW, MS-4640, Washington, DC 20240. Telephone: (202) 208-4796. Contact: Woodrow Sneed. *Regional or Local Offices*: See Table 2i.

DEPARTMENT OF TRANSPORTATION

Money—for Bus Companies
Public Transportation For Nonurbanized Areas (20.509)

Description: This program helps finance transportation service in nonurbanized areas. For example, it may support rural intercity bus transportation. The program encourages the maximum feasible participation of private operators.

You may use funding for eligible capital expenses, project administration, and operating expenses. Projects in urbanized areas, as defined by the Bureau of the Census, are not eligible.

Beneficiary Eligibility: Private and public providers of public transportation in nonurbanized areas, including nonprofit organizations and Indian tribes.

Financial Information: Assistance provided to over 1,200 providers of rural and small urban transportation.

Who To Contact: *Headquarters Office*: Federal Transit Administration, Office of Program Management, Office of Capital and Formula Assistance, 400 Seventh Street, SW., Washington, DC 20590. Telephone: (202) 366-2053. *Regional or Local Office*: See Table 2j.

Money—for Minority Transportation-Related Businesses
Human Resource Programs (20.511)

Description: To provide financial assistance so that minorities and women can participate fully in public transportation projects and activities.

Beneficiary Eligibility: Small and disadvantaged businesses, independent contractors, and other for-profit businesses

Financial Information: Not available.

Who To Contact: *Headquarters Office*: Director, Office of Civil Rights, Federal Transit Administration, Department of Transportation, 400 Seventh Street, SW., Room 9102, Washington, DC 20590. Telephone: (202) 366-4018. *Regional or Local Office*: Table 2j.

Money—to Provide Transportation Services for the Elderly and the Disabled
Capital Assistance Program for Elderly Persons and Persons with Disabilities (20.513)

Description: Grants to help private firms provide transportation services for elderly persons and persons with disabilities where public transportation services are unavailable, insufficient or inappropriate. Projects must provide for the maximum feasible participation of private-for-profit operators.

Financial Information: $78,851,000 granted annually to purchase vehicles to transport the elderly and disabled.

Who To Contact: *Headquarters Office*: Federal Transit Administration, Office of Program Management, Office of Resource Management and State Programs, 400 7th Street, SW, Washington, DC 20590. Telephone: (202) 366-2053. Sue Masselink, Program Coordinator, (202)366-1630. *Regional or Local Office*: See Table 2j.

Loans—and Assistance to Women- and Minority-Owned Businesses to Help Get Transportation-Related Contracts

Support Mechanisms for Disadvantaged Businesses (20.903)

Description: Loan. assistance and liaison programs to assist small disadvantaged business enterprises to successfully compete on transportation-related contracts.

Beneficiary Eligibility: Small businesses (minority and non-minority), socially and economically disadvantaged persons, and businesses which are owned and operated by women.

Financial Information: Not applicable.

Who To Contact: *Headquarters Office*: Office of Small and Disadvantaged Business Utilization, S-40, Office of the Secretary, 400 Seventh Street, SW., Washington, DC 20590. Telephone: (202) 366-1930. *Regional or Local Office*: Not applicable.

Disadvantaged Businesses— Bonding Assistance Program

(20.904)

Description: Insurance (Guaranteed Surety Bonds) to enable disadvantaged business enterprises to obtain bid, performance and payment bonds for transportation-related contracts emanating from the DOT, its grantees, recipients, their contractors and subcontractors. These include contracts for the maintenance, rehabilitation, restructuring, improvement, or

revitalization of any of the nation's modes of transportation.

Beneficiary Eligibility: The recipient of a bond must be certified by the DOT as a minority-owned or women-owned disadvantaged business enterprises.

Annual Benefits: $17,000,000.

Who To Contact: *Headquarters Office*: Office of Small and Disadvantaged Business Utilization, S-40, Office of the Secretary, Department of Transportation, 400 Seventh Street, SW., Washington, DC 20590. Telephone: (800) 532-1169. *Regional or Local Office*: Not applicable.

Money—for Disadvantaged Businesses

Disadvantaged Business Enterprises—Short Term Lending Program (20.905)

Description: Direct loans to enable disadvantaged business enterprises to obtain accounts receivable financing for the performance of transportation-related contracts emanating from the DOT, its grantees, recipients, their contractors and subcontractors. These include contracts for the maintenance, rehabilitation, restructuring, improvement, or revitalization of any of the nation's modes of transportation.

Beneficiary Eligibility: The recipient of a bond must be certified by the DOT as a minority-owned or women-owned disadvantaged business enterprises.

Financial Information: $8,000,000 annually; the maximum line of credit is $500,000.

Who To Contact: *Headquarters Office*: Office of Small and Disadvantaged Business Utilization, S-40, Office of the Secretary, Department of Transportation, 400 Seventh Street, SW., Washington, DC 20590. Telephone: (202) 366-2852; toll-free (800) 532-1169. *Regional or Local Office*: Not applicable.

GENERAL SERVICES ADMINISTRATION (GSA)

Free Counseling on Doing Business with the Govt.

Business Services: Counseling on Doing Business with the Federal Government (39.001)

Description: This program gives counseling and provides information on government contracting opportunities to small disadvantaged and women-owned businesses. Each year, the General Services Administration (GSA) — the Federal Government's purchasing agent — contracts for over $10 billion worth of goods and services, making the GSA an important market for small businesses.

Applicant Eligibility: Any business concern.

Annual Accomplishments: Business counseling personnel performed 138,620 business and counseling actions, and participated in about 500 business and opportunity meetings.

Literature: *"Doing Business With GSA," "GSA Small Purchases," "Subcontracting Directory,"* and *"Forecast of GSA Contracting Opportunities."* (Available at Small Business Centers listed in Table 2k.)

Who To Contact: *Headquarters Office*: Associate Administrator, Office of Enterprise Development (E), General Services Administration, Washington, DC 20405. Telephone: (202) 501-1021. *Regional or Local Office*: Small Business Centers, Table 2k.

NATIONAL CREDIT UNION ADMINISTRATION

Money—From a Federally-Sponsored Credit Union

Community Development Revolving Loan Program for Credit Unions (44.002)

Description: Direct loans to support low-income credit unions in their efforts to stimulate economic development activities which result in increased income, ownership, and employment opportunities for low-income residents.

Loans up to $300,000 will be made to credit unions to set up revolving loan funds to aid existing businesses and promote establishment of new businesses. Loans made under this program charge interests rate between 1 and 3 percent.

Beneficiary Eligibility: Low-income individuals within the credit union's geographic area, and may include employees who regularly work in the area, businesses located within the area, and the residents of the area.

Financial Information: $3,000,000, total.

Who To Contact: *Headquarters Office*: Mr. Anthony Lacreta, Community Development Revolving Loan Program for Credit Unions, National Credit Union Administration, 1775 Duke Street, Alexandria, VA 22314-3428. Telephone: (703) 518-6610. *Regional or Local Office*: Not applicable.

TENNESSEE VALLEY AUTHORITY

Assistance to Businesses in the Tennessee Valley Region

Tennessee Valley Region, Economic Development (62.004)

Description: This program promotes economic growth in the region through business development services and counseling which increase the produc-

---

Program not funded this year.

---

tion of goods and services and higher incomes.

Financial Information: Not applicable.

Who To Contact: *Headquarters Office*: Betsy L. Child, Senior V.P., Economic Development, Tennessee Valley Authority, 400 W. Summit Hill Drive, Knoxville, TN 37902. Phone: (423) 632-4312. *Regional or Local Office*: Contact Headquarters Office for appropriate regional office.

DEPARTMENT OF VETERANS AFFAIRS

Money—For Disabled Vets to Start a Business
Vocational Rehabilitation for Disabled Veterans (64.116)

Description: Direct payments, direct loans, advisory services and counseling to enable service-disabled veterans and service persons hospitalized or receiving treatment for a service-connected disability pending discharge to achieve maximum independence in daily living and, to the maximum extent feasible, to become employable.

Pays the entire cost of tuition, books, fees, supplies, job-placement and other services, and a monthly subsistence allowance for up to four years. Veterans who meet certain requirements may receive an initial supply of goods and commodities to start a small business.

For a full description of this program see program **64.116**, page 159.

OVERSEAS PRIVATE INVESTMENT CORP.

Money—for Projects Overseas
Foreign Investment Financing (70.002)

Description: Provides guaranteed or direct loans for projects sponsored by eligible U.S. investors in friendly developing countries that contribute to the economic and social development of the host country and have a positive impact on the U.S. economy and will not result in the loss of U.S. jobs. Direct loans are made to private sector projects in which there is significant involvement by a U.S. small business, i.e. non "Fortune 1000" size.

Applicant Eligibility: Citizens of the United States; corporations, partnerships, or other associations created under the laws of the United States, of which more than 50 percent is owned by U.S. citizens; foreign corporations at least 95 percent owned by such entities.

Financial Information: Range and Average of Financial Assistance: $10,000,000 to $75,000,000 for loan guaranties, but can go as high as $200,000,000; average: $60,000,000; $1,000,000 to $30,000,000 for direct loans; average: $8,000,000.

Literature: "*OPIC Program Handbook*," free.

Who To Contact: *Headquarters Office*: Information Officer, Overseas Private Investment Corporation, 1100 New York Ave., N.W., Washington, DC 20527. Telephone: (202) 336-8799. *Regional or Local Office*: None.

Foreign Investment Insurance
(70.003)

Description: Insures investments of eligible U.S. investors in developing countries and emerging markets, against the political risks of inconvertibility, expropriation, and political violence. Investments may be eligible for insurance if they contribute significant benefits to the social and economic development of the host country and do not result in the loss of U.S. jobs.

Applicant Eligibility: Citizens of the United States; corporations, partnerships, or other associations created under the laws of the United States, of which more than 50 percent is owned by U.S. citizens; foreign corporations at least 95 percent owned by such entities.

Financial Information: (Insured amount) $67,500 to $200,000,000.

Who To Contact: Headquarters Office: Information Officer, Overseas Private Investment Corporation, 1100 New York Ave., N.W., Washington, DC 20527. Telephone: (202) 336-8799. *Regional or Local Office*: None.

DEPARTMENT OF ENERGY

Free Rights to Government-Owned Energy Patents
Granting of Patent Licenses (81.003)

Description: Grants nonexclusive licenses on approximately 1,500 DOE owned U.S. patents and 500 DOE owned foreign patents to U.S. citizens and corporations and other responsible applicants with plans for development and/or marketing. Licenses for use or sale in the U.S. may normally be granted only to licensees that agree to manufacture in the U.S.

Applicant Eligibility: Individuals, firms, or corporations with satisfactory plans for development and/or marketing of the invention may apply.

Financial Information: Not applicable. Approximately 12 licenses are granted each year.

Literature: "*U.S. Department of Energy Patents Available for Licensing*" describes the program and is available from the Technical Information Center, Dept. of Energy. Copies of U.S. patents may be obtained from the U.S. Patent and Trademark Office, Department of Commerce, Washington, DC 20231, at $3.00 per copy.

Who To Contact: *Headquarters Office*: Robert J. Marchick, Office of the Assistant General Counsel for Patents, DOE, Washington, DC 20585. Telephone: (202) 586-2802. *Regional or Local Office*: Not applicable.

Money—to Work On Energy-Related Inventions
Energy–Related Inventions (81.036)

Description: Provides project grants, typically for two years; use of property, facilities, and equipment; advisory services and counseling; dissemination of technical information. The purpose is to encourage innovation in developing non-nuclear energy technology by providing assistance to individual and small business companies in the development of promising energy-related inventions.

Applicant Eligibility: Small businesses, individual inventors, entrepreneurs, universities.

Financial Information: Awards average $83,000.

Literature: "*The NIST/DOE Energy-Related Invention Progr*am" brochure available from National Institute of Standards and Technology, Gaithersburg, Maryland 20899.

Who To Contact: *Headquarters Office*: Lisa Barnett, Office of Industrial Technologies, (EE-23), Department of Energy, 1000 Independence Ave., SW., Washington, DC 20585. Phone: (202) 586-2212. *Regional or Local Office*: Not applicable.

Money—to Work On Energy-Related Science
Office of Energy Research Financial Assistance Program (81.049)

Description: Get a project grant for fundamental research, training and related activities in the basic sciences and advanced technology concepts and assessments in fields related to energy.

Support is provided for work in such fields as high energy physics, nuclear physics, materials science, chemical science, engineering, geosciences research, biological, health and environmental research, nuclear medicine, technology assessments, magnetic fusion, applied mathematical sciences, high performance computing and communications, and information infrastructure technologies.

Applicant Eligibility: Industry (particularly small and disadvantaged businesses) and nonprofit institutions and higher education institutions may apply.

Financial Information: Range of Financial Assistance, $10,000 to $2,000,000; Average, $200,000.

Literature: "*Application Guide for the Office of Energy Research Financial Assistance Program.*"

Who To Contact: *Headquarters Office*: William G. Burrier, Grants and Contracts Division, Office of Energy Research, SC-64, DOE, 19901 Germantown Road, Germantown, MD 20874-1290. Telephone: (301) 903-5212. *Regional or Local Office*: Table 2l.

Management and Technical Assistance for Minority Business Enterprises
(81.082)

Description: Advisory services and counseling to promote the participation of minority- and women- owned and operated businesses in DOE energy procurement contracts; to match business opportunities in public and private organizations with minority business firms and educational institutions.

Applicant Eligibility: Minority business enterprises wanting to do business with DOE.

Financial Information: Not applicable.

Who To Contact: *Headquarters Office*: Office of Economic Impact and Diversity, Department of Energy, ED-1, Forrestal Building, Room 5B-110, Washington, DC 20585. Contact: Sterling Nichols. Telephone: (202) 586-8698. *Regional or Local Office*: Not applicable.

DEPARTMENT OF EDUCATION

Money—to Businesses that Employ the Disabled
Projects With Industry (84.234)

Description: Your business can get a grant to create and expand job opportunities for individuals with disabilities. Funds may be used to support projects to prepare persons with disabilities for employment in any industrial, business, or commercial enterprise.

Eligibility Requirements: Private employers, labor unions, profit making and nonprofit organizations, institutions.

Financial Information: In the latest reported year, 99 Projects With Industry were funded, in the amount of $22,071,000. The average award was $190,000. The Federal share may not exceed 80 percent of total project cost.

Who To Contact: *Headquarters Office*: Department of Education, Rehabilitation Services

Administration, 400 Maryland Avenue, SW, Washington, DC 20202. Contact: Sonja Turner and Kerrie Brown. Phone: (202) 205-9396. *Regional or Local Office*: State Vocational Rehabilitation Agencies or the Rehabilitation Services Admin. regional offices (Table 2m).

DEPARTMENT OF HEALTH AND HUMAN SERVICES

Money—for Refugees to Start a Small Business
Refugee and Entrant Assistance—Discretionary Grants (93.576)

Description: This program funds demonstration projects which promote refugee self-sufficiency. State and local governments and private nonprofit organizations are eligible to apply for these funds, which they may then use for micro-financing to refugees engaged in small businesses activities.

Beneficiary Eligibility: Eligibility for individual refugees is determined by the various grantee agencies.

Financial Information: From $5,000.

Who To Contact: *Headquarters Office*: For program information, contact Carmel Clay-Thompson, Office of Refugee Resettlement, Administration for Children, Youth and Families, Department of Health and Human Services, 6th Floor, 370 L'Enfant Promenade, SW., Washington DC 20447. Telephone: (202) 401-4557. *Regional or Local Office*: None.

DEPARTMENT OF DEFENSE

Purchasing Specialists

Description: The U.S. Department of Defense has over 700 small business specialists at various buying offices throughout the United States to help small businesses and businesses owned by women and minorities learn of opportunities to sell their goods and services to the Department of Defense, other Federal agencies, and State and local governments. They also provide marketing and technical assistance.

Some of the areas in which the department is interested in providing small business concerns with opportunities are: environmental, manufacturing, health care, telecommunications and management information systems including simulation.

Beneficiary Eligibility: Small businesses and businesses owned by women and minorities.

Financial Information: Not applicable.

Literature: "*Selling to the Military*," "*Small Business Specialist*," and "*Subcontracting Opportunities With Dept. of Defense Major Prime Contractors*."

Who to Contact: *Headquarters Office*: Defense Logistics Agency, Office of Small and Disadvantaged Business Utilization (DDAS), 8725 John J. Kingman Road, Suite 2533, Fort Belvoir, Va. 22060-6221. Tele(703) 767-1650. **Regional or Local Office**: Contact a local Defense Department facility.

Table 2a: SMALL BUSINESS ADMINISTRATION

REGIONAL OFFICES

Region I
(Connecticut, Maine, Massachusetts, New Hampshire, Rhode Island, Vermont)
10 Causeway Street, Suite 812
Boston, MA 02222
(617) 565-8415

Region II
(New Jersey, New York, Puerto Rico, Virgin Islands)
26 Federal Plaza, Suite 3108
New York, NY 10278
(212) 264-1450

Region III
(Delaware, District of Columbia, Maryland, Pennsylvania, Virginia, West Virginia)
900 Market Street, 5th Floor
Philadelphia, PA 19107
(215) 580-2807

Region IV
(Alabama, Florida, Georgia, Kentucky, Mississippi, North Carolina, South Carolina, Tennessee)
233 Peachtree Rd. NE, Suite 1800
Atlanta, GA 30303
(404) 331-4999

Region V
(Illinois, Indiana, Michigan, Minnesota, Ohio, Wisconsin)
Federal Building
500 West Madison Street
Chicago, IL 60661-2511
(312) 353-4493

Region VI
(Arkansas, Louisiana, New Mexico, Oklahoma, Texas)
4300 Amon Carter Blvd., # 108
Ft. Worth, TX 76155
(817) 684-5581

Region VII
(Iowa, Kansas, Missouri, Nebraska)
323 West 8th Street, Suite 307
Kansas City, MO 64105-1500
(816) 374-6380

Region VIII
(Colorado, Montana, North Dakota, South Dakota, Utah, Wyoming)
721 19th Street, Suite 101
Denver, CO 80202-2599
(303) 844-0503

Region IX
(Arizona, California, Hawaii, Nevada, Pacific Islands)
455 Market Street, Suite 2200
San Francisco, CA 94105
(415) 744-2118

Region X
(Alaska, Idaho, Oregon, Washington)
1200 6th Avenue, Suite 1805
Seattle, WA 98101-1128
(206) 553-5676

DISTRICT OFFICES

Region I
Boston District Office
10 Causeway Street, Room 265
Boston, MA 02222-1093
(617) 565-5590

Springfield Branch Office
1441 Main Street, Suite 410
Springfield, MA 01103
(413) 785-0268

Augusta District Office
Federal Building
40 Western Avenue, Room 512
Augusta, ME 04330
(207) 622-8378

Concord District Office
143 North Main Street, Suite 202
Concord, NH 03301-1257
(603) 225-1400

Hartford District Office
Federal Building
330 Main Street, 2nd Floor
Hartford, CT 06106
(860) 240-4700

Montpelier District Office
Federal Building
87 State Street, Room 205
Montpelier, VT 05602
(802) 828-4422

Providence District Office
380 Westminister Mall, 5th Floor
Providence, RI 02903
(401) 528-4562

Region II
Puerto Rico and Virgin Islands
District Office
Federico Degetau Federal Bldg.
252 Ponce DeLeon Blvd., # 201
Hato Rey, PR 00918
(787) 766-5572

Elmira Branch Office
333 E. Water Street, 4th Floor
Elmira, NY 14901
(607) 734-8130

Rochester Branch Office
100 State Street, Suite 410
Rochester, NY 14614
(716) 263-6700

Melville Branch Office
35 Pinelawn Road, Suite 207W
Melville, NY 11747
(516) 454-0750

New York District Office
26 Federal Plaza, Room 3100
New York, NY 10278
(212) 264-2454

Buffalo District Office
Federal Building
111 West Huron Street, Rm. 1311
Buffalo, NY 14202
(716) 551-4301

Syracuse District Office
401 S. Salina Street, 5th Floor
Syracuse, NY 13202
(315) 471-9393

New Jersey District Office
2 Gateway Center, 15th Floor
Newark, NJ 07102
(973) 645-2434

Region III
Clarksburg District Office
Federal Center, Suite 330
320 West Pike Street
Clarksburg, WV 26301
(304) 623-5631

Harrisburgh Branch Office
100 Chestnut Street, Room 108
Harrisburg, PA 17101
(717) 782-3840

Wilkes-Barre Branch Office
20 N. Pennsylvania Ave. # 2327
Wilkes-Barre, PA 18701
(717) 826-6497

Charleston Branch Office
405 Capitol Street, Suite 412
Charleston, WV 25301

(304) 347-5220

Wilmington Branch Office
824 N. Market Street, Suite 610
Wilmington, DE 19801
(302) 573-6294

Philadelphia District Office
900 Market Street, 5th Floor
Philadelphia, PA 19107
(215) 580-2722

Pittsburgh District Office
1000 Liberty Avenue, Room 1128
Pittsburgh, PA 15222
(412) 395-6560

Richmond District Office
Federal Bldg., Suite 1150
PO Box 10126
Richmond, VA 23240
(804) 771-2400

Washington District Office
1110 Vermont Ave., N.W., # 900
Washington, DC 20005
(202) 606-4000

Baltimore District Office
10 South Howard St., Suite 6220
Baltimore, MD 21201-2565
(410) 962-4392

Region IV
Birmingham District Office
2121 8th Avenue North, Suite 200
Birmingham, AL 35203-2398
(205) 731-1344

Gulfport Branch Office
2909 13th Street, # 203
Gulfport, MS 39501
(228) 863-4449

Atlanta District Office
233 Peachtree Street NE,
Suite 1900
Atlanta, GA 30303
(404) 331-0100

Charlotte District Office
6302 Fairview Road, Suite 300
Charlotte, NC 28210-2227
(704) 344-6563

Columbia District Office
1835 Assembly Street, Room 358
Columbia, SC 29201
(803) 765-5377

Jackson District Office
101 West Capitol St., Suite 400

Jackson, MS 39201
(601) 965-4378

Jacksonville District Office
7825 Baymeadows Way, # 100-B
Jacksonville, FL 32256-7504
(904) 443-1900

Louisville District Office
Federal Building
600 Martin Luther King, Jr. Place,
Room 188
Louisville, KY 40202
(502) 582-5971

Miami District Office
100 S. Biscayne Blvd., 7th Floor
Miami, FL 33131
(305) 536-5521

Nashville District Office
50 Vantage Way, Suite 201
Nashville, TN 37228-1500
(615) 736-5881

Region V
Chicago District Office
500 West Madison St., Rm. 1250
Chicago, IL 60661-2511
(312) 353-4528

Cincinnati Branch Office
550 Main Street
Cincinnati, OH 45202
(513) 684-2814

Marquette Branch Office
501 South Front Street
Marquette, MI 49855
(906) 225-1108

Milwaukee District Office
310 W. Wisconsin Ave., Suite 400
Milwaukee, WI 53203
(414) 297-3941

Springfield Branch Office
511 W. Capitol Avenue, Suite 302
Springfield, IL 62704
(217) 492-4416

Cleveland District Office
1111 Superior Avenue, Suite 630
Cleveland, OH 44114-2507
(216) 522-4180

Columbus District Office
2 Nationwide Plaza, Suite 1400
Columbus, OH 43215-2592
(614) 469-6860
Detroit District Office
477 Michigan Avenue, Room 515
Detroit, MI 48226
(313) 226-6075

Indianapolis District Office
429 North Pennsylvania Street,
Suite 100
Indianapolis, IN 46204-1873
(317) 226-7272

Madison District Office
740 Regent St.
Madison, WI 53715
(608) 441-5263

Minneapolis District Office
100 North 6th Street, Suite 210-C
Minneapolis, MN 55403-1563
(612) 370-2324

Region VI
Albuquerque District Office
625 Silver Ave., S.W., Suite 320
Albuquerque, NM 87102
(505) 346-7909

Corpus Christi Branch Office
606 N. Caranchahua, Suite 1200
Corpus Christi, TX 78476
(361) 888-3331

Houston District Office
9301 Southwest Freeway, # 550
Houston, TX 77074-1591
(713) 773-6500

Little Rock District Office
2120 Riverfront Drive, Suite 100
Little Rock, AR 72202
(501) 324-5278

Lubbock District Office
1205 Texas Ave., Suite 408
Lubbock, TX 79401-2693
(806) 472-7462

Lower Rio Grande Valley District Office
222 East Van Buren St., Rm. 500
Harlingen, TX 78550
(956) 427-8533

New Orleans District Office
365 Canal Street, Suite 2250
New Orleans, LA 70130
(504) 589-6685

Oklahoma City District Office
210 Park Avenue, Suite 1300
Oklahoma City, OK 73102
(405) 231-5521

San Antonio District Office
727 East Durango, Room A-527
San Antonio, TX 78206
(210) 472-5900

Dallas District Office
4300 Amon Center Blvd., Suite 114
Ft. Worth, TX 76155
(817) 885-6581

El Paso District Office
10737 Gateway West, Suite 320
El Paso, TX 79935
(915) 633-7001

Region VII
Des Moines District Office
New Federal Building
210 Walnut Street, Room 749
Des Moines, IA 50309
(515) 284-4422

Springfield Branch Office
620 S. Glenstone St., Suite 110
Springfield, MO 65802
(417) 864-7670

Cedar Rapids District Office
215 4th Avenue, S.E., Suite 200
Cedar Rapids, IA 52401-1806
(319) 362-6405

Omaha District Office
11145 Mill Valley Road
Omaha, NE 68154
(402) 221-4691

St. Louis District Office
815 Olive Street, Room 242
St. Louis, MO 63101
(314) 539-6600

Kansas City District Office
323 West 8th Street, Suite 501
Kansas City, MO 64105
(816) 374-6708

Wichita District Office
271 W. 3rd Street N., Suite 2500
Wichita, KS 67202
(316) 269-6616

Region VIII
Casper District Office
Federal Building
100 East B Street, Room 4001
Casper, WY 82602-2839
(307) 261-6500

Fargo District Office
Federal Building
657 2nd Avenue, North, Rm. 219
Fargo, ND 58108-3086
(701) 239-5131

Helena District Office

Federal Building
10 West 15th Street, Suite 1100
Helena, Montana 59626
(406) 441-1081

Salt Lake City District Office
Federal Building
125 South State St., Room 2229
Salt Lake City, UT 84138-1195
(801) 524-5800

Sioux Falls District Office
110 South Phillips Ave., Suite 200
Sioux Falls, SD 57102-1109
(605) 330-4231

Denver District Office
721 19th Street, Room 400
Denver, CO 80201
(303) 844-3984

Region IX
Honolulu District Office
300 Ala Moana Blvd., Room 2314
Honolulu, HI 96850-4981
(808) 541-2990

Guam Branch Office
400 Route 8, Suite 302
Mongmong, GU 96927
(671) 472-7277

Los Angeles District Office
330 North Brand Blvd., Suite 1200
Glendale, CA 91203-2304
(818) 552-3210

Fresno District Office
2719 North Air Fresno Drive, Suite 200
Fresno, CA 93727-1547
(559) 487-5791

San Francisco District Office
455 Market Street, 6th Floor
San Francisco, CA 94105
(415) 744-6820

Phoenix District Office
2828 North Central Ave., # 800
Phoenix, AZ 85004-1093
(602) 640-2316

Santa Ana District Office
200 West Santa Ana Boulevard,
Suite 700
Santa Ana, CA 92701
(714) 550-7420

San Diego District Office
550 West "C" Street, Suite 550
San Diego, CA 92101-3500
(619) 557-7250

Las Vegas District Office
300 Las Vegas Blvd. S., Suite 1100
Las Vegas, NV 89101
(702) 388-6611

Region X
Anchorage District Office
222 West 8th Avenue, Room A36
Anchorage, AK 99513-7559
(907) 271-4022

Boise District Office
1020 Main Street, Suite 290
Boise, ID 83702-5745
(208) 334-1696

Portland District Office
1515 S.W. Fifth Ave., Suite 1050
Portland, OR 97201-5494

(503) 326-2682

Spokane District Office
801 West Riverside Ave.
Spokane, WA 99201-0901
(509) 353-2800

Seattle District Office
1200 6th Avenue, Suite 1700
Seattle, WA 98101-1128
(206) 553-7310

DISASTER AREA OFFICES
Disaster Area 1 Office (Covers
Regions I and II)
360 Rainbow Blvd. S., 3rd Floor
Niagara Falls, NY 14303-1192
(716) 282-4612

Disaster Area 2 Office (Covers
Regions III, IV and V)
One Baltimore Place, Suite 300
Atlanta, GA 30308
(404) 347-3771

Disaster Area 3 Office (Covers
Regions VI and VII)
4400 Amon Carter Blvd., # 102
Ft. Worth, TX 76155
(817) 885-7600

Disaster Area 4 Office (Covers
Regions VIII, IX and X)
PO Box 13795
Sacramento, CA 95853
(916) 566-7240

Table 2b: **SBA PARTICIPATING MICROLOAN LENDERS**

Alabama
Birmingham Business Resource Ctr.
110 12th Street North
Birmingham, AL 35203
Contact: Rodney E. Evans
(205) 250-6380

Arizona
Chicanos Por La Causa, Inc.
1112 E. Buckeye Road
Phoenix, AZ 85034-4043
Contact: Joe Martinez
(602) 252-0483

PPEP Housing Development Corp.
Micro Industry Credit Rural Org.
901 East 46th Street
Tucson, AZ 85713
Contact: Frank Ballesteros
(520) 806-9513

Self-Employment Loan Fund, Inc.
1601 North 7th St., Suite 340
Phoenix, AZ 85006
Contact: Caroline Newsom
(602) 340-8834

Arizona Council for Economic
Conversion
10 East Broadway, Suite 210
P.O. Box 42108
Tucson, AZ 85701
Contact: Bart T. Murphy
(520) 620-1241

Arkansas
Southern Financial Partners
605 Main Street
Pine Bluff, AR 71923

Contact: William Matthews or
Sandy Linn
(870) 246-9739

Forge-Financing Ozarks Rural
Growth and Economy
208 East Main P.O. Box 1138
Huntsville, AR 72740
Contact: Charlie Stockton
(501) 738-1585

White River Planning & Devel.
Dist., Inc.
1652 White Drive, PO Box 2396
Batesville, AR 72501
Contact: Bill Ray
(870) 793-5233

California
Arcata Economic Develop. Corp.
100 Ericson Court, Suite 100
Arcata, CA 95521
Contact: Arianne Knoeller
(707) 822-4616

California Coastal Rural
Development Corporation
221 Main Street Suite 300
P.O. Box 479
Salinas, CA 93906
Contact: Rey Hidalgo
(831) 424-1099

CDC Small Business Finance Corp.
925 Ft. Stockton Dr.
San Diego, CA 92110
Contact: Alex Robinson
(619) 291-3594

Oakland Business Development
Corporation
519 17th Street Suite 100
Oakland, CA 94612
Contact: Robert Gebauer
(510) 763-4297

PCR Small Business Development
3255 Wilshire Blvd.
Los Angeles, CA 90010
Contact: Mark Robertson, Jr.
(213) 739-2999, ext. 222

Sierra Economic Development
District
560 Wall Street Suite F
Auburn, CA 95603
Contact: Tom Dille
(530) 823-4703

Center for Southeast Asian Refugee
Resettlement
875 O'Farrell Street
San Francisco, CA 94109
Contact: Victor Hsi
(415) 885-2743

Valley Economic Development
Corp.
5121 Van Nuys Blvd. 3rd Floor
Van Nuys, CA 91403
Contact: Rebecca Haas
(818) 907-9977

Valley Rural Development Corp.
3417 W. Shaw, Suite 100
Fresno, CA 93711
Contact: Michael E. Foley
(559) 438-9680

Colorado
Colorado Enterprise Fund
1888 Sherman Street Suite 530
Denver, CO 80203
Contact: Angela Valdez
(303) 860-0242

Region 10 LEAP, Inc.
PO Box 849
Montrose, CO 81401
Contact: Bob Bolt
(970) 249-2436

Connecticut
Community Economic
Development Fund
50-G Weston Street
Hartford, CT 06120
Contact: Thomas Holloway
(860) 249-3800

CT Comm. Investment Corp.
100 Crown St.
New Haven, CT 06510
Contact: Mark Cousineau
(203) 776-6172

Delaware
Wilmington Economic Devel. Corp.
100 W. 10th St. Suite 706
Wilmington, DE 19801
Contact: Constance McCarthy
(302) 571-9088

District of Columbia
ARCH Development Corporation
1227 Good Hope Road SE
Washington, DC 20020
Contact: Duane Gautier
(202) 889-5023

Dist. of Columbia H Street Dev. Corp.
501 H Street NE
Washington, DC 20002
Contact: William J. Barrow
(202) 544-8353

East of the River Community
Development Corporation
3101 Martin Luther King Jr Ave SE
Washington, DC 20032
Contact: W. Retta Gilliam
(202) 561-4974

Florida
Central Florida Community
Development Corporation
P.O. Box 15065
Daytona Beach, FL 32115
Contact: Gerald O. Chester
(368) 258-7520

Clearwater Neighborhood Housing
Services, Inc.
608 North Garden Avenue
Clearwater, FL 33755
Contact: John J. Moloney
(727) 442-4155

Community Equity Investments Inc.
302 North Barcelona Street
Pensacola, FL 32501
Contact: Daniel R. Horvath
(850) 595-6234

Minority/Women Business
Enterprise Alliance, Inc.
625 E. Colonial Drive
Orlando, FL 32803
Contact: Geovanny Sepulveda
(407) 428-5860

Micro-Business, USA
3000 Biscayne Boulevard Suite 102
Miami, FL 33137
Contact: Diane Silverman
(877) 722-4505

Tampa Bay Develop. Corp.
2105 N. Nebraska Avenue 2nd
Floor
Tampa, FL 33602
Contact: George Guida
(813) 274-7969

The Business Loan Fund of the
Palm Beaches, Inc.
1016 North Dixie Highway, 2nd
Floor
West Palm Beach, FL 33401
(561) 838-9027

United Gainesville Community
Development Corporation, Inc.
505 NW 2nd Ave., PO Box 2518
Gainesville, FL 32602
Contact: Appie L. Graham
(352) 376-8891

Georgia
Enterprise Funding Corp/GRASP
Enterprises
241 Peachtree Street, Suite 200
Atlanta, GA 30303
Contact: Tim Scott/Tracy Vaughan
(404) 659-5955

Small Business Assistance Corp.
111 E. Liberty Street, Suite 100
P.O. Box 10750
Savannah, GA 31412-0950
Contact: Tony O'Reilly
(912) 232-4700

Hawaii
Pacific Gateway Center
720 North King Street
Honolulu, HI 96817
Contact: Tin Myaing Thein
(808) 845-3918

Idaho
Sage Community Resources
10624 W. Executive Drive
Boise, ID 83713
Contact: Bob Richards
(208) 322-7033

Panhandle Area Council
11100 Airport Drive
Hayden, ID 83835-9743
Contact: Jim Deffenbaugh
(208) 772-0584

Illinois
Accion Chicago, Inc.
3245 W. 26th
Chicago, IL 60623
Contact: Jonathan Brereton
(773) 376-9004

Neighborhood Inst./Women's Self
Employment Project
11 South LaSalle Street, Suite 1850
Chicago, IL 60603
Contact: Wanda White
(312) 606-8255

Indiana
Bloomington Area Microenterprise
Initiative
216 W. Allen Street
Bloomington, IN 47403
Contact: Charlotte Zietlow
(812) 339-8937

Iowa
Siouxland Economic Devel. Corp.
428 Insurance Center, 507 7th Street
P.O. Box 447
Sioux City, IA 51102
Contact: Kenneth A. Beekley
(712) 279-6286

Kansas
South Central Kansas Economic
Development District, Inc.
209 East William Street, Suite 300
Wichita, KS 67214
Contact: Christie Henry
(316) 262-7035

Growth Opportunity Connection
4747 Troost Avenue
Kansas City, MO 64110
Contact: Rebecca Gubbels
(816) 235-6146

Kentucky
Community Ventures Corporation
1450 North Broadway
Lexington, KY 40505
Contact: Kevin R. Smith
(859) 231-0054

Kentucky Highlands Invest. Corp.
362 Old Whitley Rd., PO Box 1738
London, KY 40743
Contact: Jerry A. Rickett
(606) 864-5175

Louisville Central Develop. Corp.
1407 West Jefferson Street, Ste. 200
Louisville, KY 40203
Contact: Sam Watkins, Jr.
(502) 583-8821

Purchase Area Develop. District
1002 Medical Drive, PO Box 588
Mayfield, KY 42066
Contact: Henry A. Hodges
(270) 247-7171

Louisiana
NewCorp Business Assistance Ctr.
1600 Canal Street, Suite 601
New Orleans, LA 70112
Contact: Romona D. Summers
(504) 539-9340

Maine
Androscoggin Valley Council of
Government
125 Manley Road
Auburn, ME 04210
Contact: Julie Sherman
(207) 783-9186

Coastal Enterprises, Inc.
PO Box 268, Water Street,
Wiscasset, ME 04578
Contact: Ronald L. Phillips
(207) 882-7552

Northern Maine Regional Planning
Commission
302 South Main Street, PO Box 779
Caribou, ME 04736
Contact: Robert P. Clark
(207) 498-8736

Community Concepts, Inc.
19 Market Square, PO Box 278
South Parris, ME 04281
Contact: Charleen M. Chase
(207) 743-7716

Maryland
The Development Credit Fund
2526 N. Charles Stree Suite 200

Baltimore, MD 21218Contact:
Contact: Erik Johnson
(410) 235-8100

Massachusetts
Community Transportation
Association of America
1341 G Street, NW, Suite 600
Washington, DC 20005
Contact: Patrick Kellogg
(202) 661-0210

Economic Dev. Indust. Corp. of Lynn
37 Central Square, 3rd Floor
Lynn, MA 01901
Contact: Peter M. DeVeau
(781) 581-9399

Greater Springfield Entrepreneurial
Fund
1176 Main Street
Springfield, MA 01103
Contact: Jim Krzytofik
(413) 781-6900 ext. 277

Jewish Vocational Service, Inc.
105 Chauncy St., 6th Floor
Boston, MA 02111
Contact: Barbara S. Rosenbaum
(617) 451-8147

Jobs for Fall River, Inc.
One Government Center
Fall River, MA 02722
Contact: Stephen Parr
(508) 324-2620

South Eastern Economic
Development Corp/SEED
80 Dean Street
Taunton, MA 02780
Contact: Janice Johnson Plumer
(508) 822-1020

Western Massachusetts Enterprise
Fund
308 Main Street Suite 2B
Greenfield, MA 01301
Contact: Christopher Sikes
(413) 774-4033

Michigan
Center for Empowerment and
Economic Development (CEED)
2002 Hogback Road Suite 12
Ann Arbor, MI 48105
Contact: Michelle Richards
(734) 677-1400

Community Capital and Devel. Corp.
The Walter Reuther Center

316 West Water St.
Flint, MI 48503
Contact: Bobby J. Wells
(810) 239-5847

Kent Area MicroBusiness Loan
Services
233 East Fulton St., Ste. 101
Grand Rapids, MI 49503
Contact: Edward L. Garner
(616) 771-6880

Northern Initiatives Corporation
228 W. Washington St.
Marquette, MI 49855
Contact: Todd Horton
(906) 226-1662

Rural Michigan Intermediary
Relending Program, Inc.
121 East Front Street Suite 201
Traverse City, MI 49686
Contact: Scott A. Joseph
(231) 941-5858

Saginaw Economic Development
Corporation
301 E. Genesee, 3rd Floor
Saginaw, MI 48607
Contact: Leslie Weaver
(989) 759-1395

Minnesota
Minnesota Minneapolis Consortium
of Community Developers
2308 Central Avenue, N.E.
Minneapolis, MN 55418-3710
Contact: Tamaica Fisher
(612) 789-7337

Southern Minnesota Initiative
Foundation
525 Florence Avenue
P.O. Box 695
Owatonna, MN 55060
Contact: Patrick T. Stallman
(507) 455-3215

Southwest Minnesota Foundation
1390 HWY 15 South
P.O. Box 428
Hutchinson, MN 55350
Contact: Bernadette Berger
(320) 587-4848

Northeast Entrepreneur Fund, Inc.
820 Ninth Street North, Ste. 200
Virginia, MN 55792
Contact: Mary Mathews
(218) 749-4191

Northwest Minnesota Foundation
4225 Technology Drive, NW
Bemidji, MN 56601
Contact: Tim Wang
(218) 759-2057

Women Venture
2324 University Avenue, Suite 200
St. Paul, MN 55114
Contact: Jan Jordet
(651) 646-3808

Mississippi
Delta Foundation
819 Main Street
Greenville, MS 38701
Contact: Harry J. Bowie
(662) 335-5291

Friends of Children of Miss., Inc.
Center for Business Innovations, Inc.
939 North President Street
Jackson, MS 39202
Contact: Brenntta Walker
(601) 353-3264

Missouri
Growth Opportunity Connection
4747 Troost Avenue
Kansas City, MO 64110
Contact: Alan Corbet
(816) 561-8567

Justine Petersen Housing &
Reinvestment Corporation
5031 Northrup Avenue
St. Louis, MO 63110
Contact: Sheri Fanigan-Vazquez
314-664-5051 ext. 117

Rural Missouri, Incorporated
1014 Northeast Drive
Jefferson City, MO 65109
Contact: Zola Finch
(573) 635-0136

Montana
Capital Opportunities/ District IX
Human Resource Develop. Council
321 East Main Street, Suite 300
Bozeman, MT 59715
Contact: Jeffery Rupp
(406) 587-5444

Montana Community Development
Corp.
110 East Broadway, 2nd Floor
Missoula, MT 59802
Contact: Mica Nioleyczik
(406) 728-9234

Nebraska
Rural Enterprise Assistance Project

PO Box 406
Walthill, NE 68067
Contact: Chuck Hassebrook
(402) 846-5428

W. Central Nebraska Devel.
District, Inc.
201 E. 2nd Street, Ste. C, Box 599
Ogailala, NE 69153
Contact: Paul Rausch
(308) 284-6077

Nevada
Nevada Microenterprise Initiative
113 West Plumb Lane
Reno, NV 89509
Contact: Anna Siefert
(702) 734-3555

New Hampshire
Northern Community Investment Corp.
347 Portland Street, PO Box 904
St. Johnsbury, VT 05819
Contact: Carol Walker
(802) 748-5101

New Jersey
Cooperative Business Assistance Corp.
433 Market Street 2nd Floor, Suite
201
Camden, NJ 08102
Contact: R. Michael Diemer
(856) 966-8181

Trenton Business Assistance Corp.
209 E. Front St. P.O. Box 2451
Trenton, NJ 08608
Contact: Russ Haas
(609) 396-8271

Greater Newark Business
Development Consortium
744 Broad St. 26th Floor
Newark, NJ 07102
Contact: David Means
(973) 242-4134

Union County Economic Dev. Corp.
Liberty Hall Corporate Center
1085 Morris Avenue, Suite 531
Union, NJ 07083
Contact: Maureen Tinen
(908) 527-1166

Community Lending and
Investment Corp. of Jersey City
30 Montgomery Street
Jersey City, NJ 07302
Contact: John Rodgers
(201) 333-7797

New Mexico

Women's Economic Self
Sufficiency Team
414 Silver South West
Albuquerque, NM 87102-3239
Contact: Agnes Noonan
(505) 241-4760
New York
Adirondack Economic Devel.Corp.
60 Main St, PO Box 747
Saranac Lake, NY 12983
Contact: Ernest Hohmeyer
(518) 891-5523

Alternative Federal Credit Union
301 W. State Street
Ithaca, NY 14850
Contact: John Halleron
(607) 273-3582

Buffalo Economic Renaissance
Corp. (BERC)
617 Main Street
Buffalo, NY 14203
Contact: Marie F. Curie
(716) 842-6923

Buffalo and Erie County Industrial
Land Development Corp.
275 Oak Street
Buffalo, NY 14203
Contact: David Kerchoff
(716) 856-6525

Columbia Hudson Partnership
444 Warren Street
Hudson, NY 12534-2415
Contact: John Galvin
(518) 828-4718

Community Development
Corporation of Long Island
2100 Middle Country Road Suite
300
Centereach, NY 11720
Contact: Trevor Davis
(631) 471-1215

Manhattan Borough Develop. Corp.
55 John St. 17th Floor
New York, NY 10038
Contact: Marta Gomez
(212) 791-3660

Albany-Colonie Regional Chamber
of Commerce
1 Computer Drive South
Albany, NY 12205
Contact: Walter Burke
(518) 453-5223

NY Assoc. for New Americans, Inc.
17 Battery Place
New York, NY 10004

Contact: Maya Crawford
(212) 425-5051

Renaissance Economic
Development Corporation
1 Pike Street
New York, NY 10002
Contact: Susan Yee
(212) 964-6002

Rural Opportunities, Inc.
400 East Avenue
Rochester, NY 14607
Contact: Joan Dallis
(585) 340-3387

North Carolina
Neuse River Development
Authority, Inc.
233 Middle Street 3rd Floor
New Bern, NC 28563
Contact: Donald T. Stewart
(252) 638-6724 Ext. 3032

Self-Help Ventures Fund
301 W. Main St.
Durham, NC 27701
Contact: Robert Schall
(919) 956-4400

W.A.M.Y. Community Action
PO Box 2688
Boone, North Carolina 28607
Contact: Dave Lindsley
(828) 264-2421

North Dakota
Dakota Certified Develop. Corp.
51 Broadway Suite 500
Fargo, ND 58102
Contact: Wendy Simek
(701) 293-8892

Lake Agassiz Regional Council
417 Main Avenue
Fargo, ND 58103
Contact: Irvin D. Rustad
(701) 235-1197

Ohio
Enterprise Development Corp.
9030 Hocking Hills Drive
The Plains, OH 45780-1209
Contact: Lisa Latham
(740) 797-9646

Community Capital Development
Corporation
900 Michigan Ave
Columbus, OH 43215-1165
Contact: Kendra Krebs-Vincenty
(614) 645-6171

County Corp Development
40 W. Fourth St. Ste. 1600
Dayton, OH 45402
Contact: Tracy Shultz
(937) 225-6328

Hamilton County Develop. Co., Inc.
1776 Mentor Avenue
Norwood, OH 45212
Contact: David K Main
(513) 631-8292

Kent Regional Business Alliance
College of Business #300-A, KSU
Kent, OH 44242
Contact: Linda Yost
(330) 672-1275

Women's Organization for
Mentoring, Entrepreneurship, &
Networking
526 South Main Street Suite 235
Arkon, OH 44311-1058
Contact: Janice Robinson
(330) 379-9280

Working for Empowerment through
Community Organizing (WECO)
2700 E. 79th Street, 4th Street
Cleveland, OH 44104
Contact: Judith W. Miles
(216) 881-9650

Oklahoma
Greenwood Community
Development
133 North Greenwood Ave 2nd
Floor
Tulsa, OK 74120
Contact: Reuben Gant
(918) 585-2084

Little Dixie Community Action
502 West Duke St.
Hugo, OK 74743
Contact: Jerry Pool
(580) 326-3351

Rural Enterprises, Inc.
2912 Enterprise Blvd. P.O. Box
1335
Durant, OK 74702
Contact: Tom Smith
(580) 924-5094

Tulsa Economic Development Corp.
907 S. Detroit, Suite 1001
Tulsa, OK 74120
Contact: Tara Martin
(918) 585-8332

Oregon
Cascades West Financial Services, Inc.

1400 Queen Ave.
Albany, OR 97321
Contact: Diane Searle
(541) 924-8480

Southern Oregon Women's Access
to Credit, Inc.
33 North Central #209
Medford, OR 97501
Contact: Dennis Davis
(541) 779-3992

Oregon Association of Minority
Entrepreneurs Credit Corporation
4134 N. Vancouver Avenue
Portland, OR 97217
Contact: Samuel Brooks
(503) 249-7744

Pennsylvania
Aliquippa Alliance for Unity and
Development
392 Franklin Ave
Aliquippa, PA 15001
Contact: Jonathan Pettis
(724) 378-2884

Community First Fund
44 N Queen Street P. O. Box 524
Lancaster, PA 17608-0524
Contact: Glenda Machia
(866) 822-3863

Community Loan Fund of
Southwestern PA, Inc.
1920 Gulf Towers --- 707 Grant
Street
Pittsburgh, PA 15219
Contact: Laura Swiss
(412) 201-2450

Northeastern Pennsylvania Alliance
(aka: NEPA)
1151 Oak St.
Pittston, PA 18640-3795
Contact: Tom Pellegrini
(570) 655-5581

MetroAction, Inc.
222 Mulberry Street P.O. Box 4731
Scranton, PA 18501-0431
Contact: Kristine French
(570) 342-7711

North Central PA Regional
Planning & Dev. Commission
651 Montmorenci Avenue
Ridgway, PA 15853
Contact: Jill Foys
(814) 773-3162

Northwest Pennsylvania Regional
Planning & Dev. Commission

395 Seneca Street
Oil City, PA 16301
Contact: Dale F. Massie
(814) 677-4800

Philadelphia Commercial
Development Corporation
1315 Walnut Street Suite 600
Philadelphia, PA 19107
Contact: Rick Dean/Linda House
(215) 790-2210

Southern Alleghenies Planning &
Development Commission
541 58th Street
Altoona, PA 16602
Contact: Michael Mignogna
(814) 949-6545

The Ben Franklin Technology
Center of Southeastern Penn.
11 Penn Center 1835 Market Street,
Suite 1100
Philadelphia, PA 19103
Contact: Dieter Littles
(215) 972-6700)

The Washington County Council on
Economic Development
40 S. Main Street – Lower Level
Washington, PA 15301
Contact: Ray Grudi
(724) 228-8223

Puerto Rico
Corp. for the Economic Develop. of
the City of San Juan
1103 Avenida Munoz Rivera P.O.
Box 191791
Rio Piedras, PR 00926
Contact: Giovanna Piovanetti
(787) 756-5080

Rhode Island
Rhode Island Coalition for Minority
Investment
216 Weybosset Street 2nd Floor
Providence, RI 02903
Contact: Henry Reid
(401) 351-2999

South Carolina
Carolina Capital Investment
Corporation
P. O. Box 8327 Columbia, SC
29202
Contact: Elliott E. Franks, III
(803) 461-3800

Charleston Development Corp.
75 Calhoun St., 3rd Floor
Charleston, SC 29403
Contact: Sharon Brennan

(843) 724-3796

Santee Lynches Regional Devel. Corp.
Post Office Drawer 1837
Sumter, SC 29150
Contact: James T. Darby, Jr.
(803) 775-7381

South Dakota
Lakota Fund
PO Box 340
Kyle, SD 57752
Contact: Elsie M. Meeks
(605) 455-2500

Tennessee
Economic Ventures, Inc.
P.O. Box 3550
Knoxville, TN 37927-3550
(865) 594-8762

LeMoyne-Owen College
Community Development Corp.
802 Walker Avenue, Suite 5
Memphis, TN 38126
Contact: Austin Emeagwai
(901) 942-6265

Southeast Community Capital
1020 Commerce Park Drive,
Suite L5
Oak Ridge, TN 37830
Contact: Louanne Horton-White
(865) 220-2025

Woodbine Community Organization
222 Oriel Avenue
Nashville, TN 37210
Contact: Oliver Dent
(615) 833-9580

Texas
ACCION Texas, Inc.
2014 S. Hackberry Street
San Antonio, TX 78210
Contact: Elizabeth Montoya
(210) 226-3664

Business Resource Center Incubator
401 Franklin Ave.
Waco, TX 76701
Contact: John Dosher
254-754-8898

Businesses Invest In Growth
912 Bastrop Hwy., Suite 210
Austin, TX 78741
Contact: Jeannette Peten
(512) 928-8010

Neighborhood Housing Services of
Dimmitt County, Inc.

301 Pena Street
Carrizo Springs, TX 78834
Contact: Manuel Estrada, Jr.
(830) 876-5295

Rural Devel. And Finance Corp.
711 Navarro Street Suite 350
San Antonio, TX 78207
Contact: Lucy Brooks
(210) 212-4552

San Antonio Local Develop. Corp.
215 S. Sansaba St., Suite 107
San Antonio, TX 78207
Contact: Robert Ayala
(210) 207-3932

Southern Dallas Development Corp.
1402 Crinth, Suite 1150
Dallas, TX 75215
Contact: Jim Reid
(214) 428-7332

The Corporation for Economic
Development of Harris Co., Inc.
2223 West Loop South Suite 400
Houston, TX 77027-5926
Contact: Janis Fowler
(713) 840-8804

Vermont
Econ. Development Council of
Northern Vermont, Inc.
155 Lake Street
St. Albans, VT 05478
Contact: Connie Stanley-Little
(802) 524-4546

Northern Community Investments
Corp.
347 Portland Street, P.O. Box 904
St. Johnsbury, VT 05819
Contact: Carol Walker
(802) 748-5101

Vermont Develop. Credit Union
18 Pearl Street
Burlington, VT 05401
Contact: Jeff Smith
(802) 865-3404

Virginia
Business Development Centre, Inc.
147 Mill Ridge Road
Lynchburg, VA 24502
Contact: Rich Stallings
(434) 582-6100

Center for Community
Development
440 High Street Suite 204
Portsmouth, VA 23704
Contact: Monique Harrell
(757) 399-0925

Group Enterprise Development
1038 South Highland Street
Arlington, VA 22204
Contact: Haddish Welday
(703) 685-0510

People, Incorporated of S.W. VA
1173 West Main Street
Abingdon, Virginia 24210
Contact: Robert G. Goldsmith
(276) 619-2239

Richmond Economic Development
Corporation
501 E. Franklin St. Suite 358
Richmond, VA 23219
Contact: Brenda Lewis
(804) 780-3013

Total Action Against Poverty
145 Campbell Avenue, S.W. Suite
303
P.O. Box 2868
Contact: William Skeen
540-345-6781

Virginia Community Development
Loan Fund
1624 Hull Street
Richmond, VA 23224
Contact: Janice Fraites
(804) 233-2014

Washington

Community Capital Development
1437 South Jackson, Suite 201
Seattle, WA 98144
Contact: Art Mickel
(206) 324-4330 ext. 104

Tri-Cities Enterprise Association
2000 Logston Boulevard
Richland, WA 99352
Contact: Katie Fast
(509) 375-3268

Washington CASH
1912 East Madison St.
Seattle, WA 98122
Contact: Kathy Gilman
(206) 352-1945

West Virginia
Lightstone Community
Development Corp.
HC 63, Box 73
Moyers, WV 26815
Contact: Anthony E. Smith
(304) 249-5200

Mountain CAP of West Virginia,
Inc.
105 Jerry Burton Drive
Sutton, WV 26601
Contact: Tara Rexroad
(304) 765-7738

Wisconsin
Advocap, Inc.
19 West First Street, PO Box 1108
Fond du Lac, WI 54935

Contact: Morton Gazerwitz
(920) 922-7760

Impact Seven, Inc.
126 Soo Ave. E.
Alemna, WI 54805-9900
Contact: Inger Sanderud
(715) 357-3334

Lincoln Neighborhood
Redevelopment Corp.
2266 S. 13th St.
Milwaukee, WI 53215
Contact: Matthew Maigatter
(414) 671-5619

Northeast Entrepreneur Fund, Inc.
1225 Town Avenue
Superior, WI 54880
Contact: Robert Voss
(800) 422-0374

Wisconsin Women's Business
Initiative Corporation
2745 N. Martin Luther King Jr. Dr.,
Milwaukee, WI 53212
Contact: Carol N. Maria
(414) 263-5450

Wyoming
Wyoming Women's Business Ctr.
13th and Lewis St., PO Box 3661
Laramie, WY 82071
Contact: Rosemary Bratton
(307) 766-3083

Table 2c: # EXPORT ASSISTANCE CENTERS, DEPT. OF COMMERCE

Alabama
George Norton, Director
Medical Forum Building, 7th Floor
950 22nd Street, North
Birmingham, AL 35203
(205) 731-1331

Alaska
Charles Becker, Director
World Trade Center Alaska
421 W. First Street
Anchorage, AK 99501
(907) 271-6237

Arizona
Frank Woods, Director
2901 N. Central Avenue, Suite 970
Phoenix, AZ 85012

(602) 640-2513

Arkansas
Lon J. Hardin, Director
425 West Capitol Avenue, Suite 700
Little Rock, AR 72201
(501) 324-5794

California
Mary Delmege, U.S. and FCS, Dir.
One World Trade Center, Ste. 1670
Long Beach, CA 90831
(310) 980-4550

Sherwin Chen, Manager
11000 Wilshire Blvd., Room 9200
Los Angeles, CA 90024
(310) 235-7104

Arlene Mayeda, Manager
390-B Fir Avenue
Clovis, CA 93611
(209) 325-1619

Dao Le, Manager
Center for Trade Commercial
Diplomacy
411 Pacific Street, Suite 200
Monterey, CA 93940
(408) 641-9850

Paul Tambakis, Director
Orange County Export Assist. Ctr.
3300 Irvine Avenue, Suite 305
Newport Beach, CA 92660
(714) 660-1688

Elizabeth Krauth, Manager
330 Ignacio Boulevard, Suite 102
Novato, CA 94949
(415) 883-1966

Raj Shea, Manager
530 Water Street, Suite 740
Oakland, CA 94607
(510) 273-7350

Fred Latuperissa, Manager
Inland Empire Export Assist. Ctr.
2940 Indland Empire Blvd, Ste. 121
Ontario, CA 91764
(909) 466-4134

Gerald Vaughn, Manager
300 Esplanade Drive, Suite 2090
Oxnard, CA 93030
(805) 981-8150

Brooks Ohlson, Manager
917 7th Street, 2nd Floor
Sacramento, CA 95814
(916) 498-5155

Matt Andersen, Director
6363 Greenwich Drive, Suite 230
San Diego, CA 92122

(619) 557-5395

Vacant
250 Montgomery Street, 14th Floor
San Francisco, CA 94104
(415) 705-2300

James S. Kennedy, Director
101 Park Center Plaza, Suite 1001
San Jose, CA 95113
(408) 271-7300

James Rigassio, Manager
5201 Great America Pkwy., # 456
Santa Clara, CA 95054
(408) 970-4610

Colorado
Nancy Charles-Parker
1625 Broadway, Suite 680
Denver, CO 80202
(303) 844-6622

Connecticut
Carl Jacobsen, Director
213 Court Street, Suite 903
Middletown, CT 06457-3346
(860) 638-6950

Delaware
(see Philadelphia Export Assistance
Center)

Florida
Karl Koslowski, Acting
Miami, USEAC
5600 NW 36th Street, Suite 617

Miami, FL 33166
(305) 526-7425

George L. Martinez, Manager
1130 Cleveland Street
Clearwater, FL 34615
(813) 461-0011

Philip A. Ouzts, Manager
Eola Park Centre
200 East Robinson St., Suite 1270
Orlando, FL 32801
(407) 648-6235

Michael E. Higgins, Manager
The Capitol, Suite 2001
Tallahassee, FL 32399-0001
(904) 488-6469

Georgia
Barbara H. Prieto, Manager
6001 Chatham Center Dr., Suite 100
Savannah, GA 31405
(912) 652-4204

Georgia
Tapan Banerjee, Director
285 Peachtree Ctr. Ave. NE, # 200
Atlanta, GA 30303-1229
(404) 657-1900

Hawaii
George Dolan, Manager
300 Ala Moana Blvd., Room 4106
Honolulu, HI 96850
(808) 541-1782

Idaho
(Portland, Oregon District)
Steve Thompson, Manager
700 West State Street, 2nd Floor
Boise, ID 83720
(208) 334-3857

Illinois
Robin F. Mugford, Acting
Chicago USEAC, Xerox Center
55 West Monroe Street, Room 2440
Chicago, IL 60603
(312) 353-8045

Robin F. Mugford, Manager
610 Central Avenue, Suite 150
Highland Park, IL 60035
(847) 681-8010

James Mied, Manager
Chicago USEAC
515 North Court Street
Rockford, IL 61110-0247
(815) 987-8123

Roy Dube, Manager
Rockford Export Assistance Center
Chicago USEAC
Illinois Institute of Technology

201 East Loop Road
Wheaton, IL 60187
(312) 353-4332

Indiana
Dan Swart, Manager
Indianapolis Export Assist. Center
11405 N. Pennsylvania St., Ste. 106
Carmel, IN 46032
(317) 582-2300

Iowa
Allen Patch, Director
210 Walnut Street, Room 817
Des Moines, IA 50309
(515) 284-4222

**Kansas (Kansas City, Missouri
District)**
George D. Lavid, Manager
151 North Volutsia
Wichita, KS 67214-4695
(316) 269-6160

Kentucky
John Autin, Director
601 West Broadway, Room 634B
Louisville, KY 40202
(502) 582-5066

Sara Melton, Manager
2292 S. Highway 27, Suite 320
Somerset, KY 42501
(606) 677-6160

Louisiana
David Spann, Director
Delta Export Assistance Center
365 Canal Street, Suite 2150
New Orleans, LA 70130
(504) 589-6546

Norbert O. Gannon, Manager
5210 Hollywood Avenue, Annex
Shreveport, LA 71109
(318) 676-3064

**Maine (Boston, Massachusetts
District)**
Jeffrey Porter, Manager
511 Congress Street
Portland, ME 04101
(207) 541-7400

Maryland
Michael Keaveny, Director
Baltimore USEAC
401 E. Pratt Street, Suite 2432
Baltimore, MD 21202
(410) 962-4539

Massachusetts
Frank J. O'Connor, Director
164 Northern Avenue, Suite 307
Boston, MA 02210-2071
(617) 424-5990

William Davis, Manager
100 Granger Boulevard, Unit 102
Marlborough, MA 01752
(508) 624-6000

Michigan
Neil Hesse, Director
211 W. Fort Street, Suite 2220
Detroit, MI 48226
(313) 226-3650

Thomas J. Maquire, Manager
301 West Fulton Street, Suite 718-S
Grand Rapids, MI 49504
(616) 458-3564

Paul Litton, Manager
425 S. Main Street, Suite 103
Ann Arbor, MI 48104
(313) 741-2430

Richard Corson, Manager
Oakland Pointe Office Building
250 Elizabeth Lake Road
Pontiac, MI 48341
(810) 975-9600

Minnesota
Ronald E. Kramer, Director
Room 108, Federal Building
110 South Fourth Street
Minneapolis, MN 55401
(612) 348-1638

Mississippi
Harrison Ford, Director
201 West Capitol Street, Suite 310
Jackson, MS 39201-2005
(601) 965-4388

Missouri
Randall J. LaBounty, Director
8182 Maryland Avenue, Suite 303
St. Louis, MO 63105
(314) 425-3302

Rick Villalobos, Director
601 East 12th Street, Room 635
Kansas City, MO 64106
(816) 426-3141

Montana
(See Boise, ID Export Assistance
Center)

Nebraska
Vacant
11135 "O" Street
Omaha, NE 68137
(402) 221-3664

Nevada
Jere Dabbs, Manager
1755 East Plumb Lane, Room 152
Reno, NV 89502
(702) 784-5203

New Hampshire
(Boston, Massachusetts District)
Susan Berry, Manager
17 New Hampshire Avenue
Portsmouth, NH 03801-2838
(603) 334-6074

New Jersey
Rod Stuart, Director
3131 Princeton Pike
Building #6, Suite 100
Trenton, NJ 08648
(609) 989-2100

Tom Rosengren, Manager
One Gateway Center
Newark, NJ 07102
(201) 645-4682

New Mexico
(Dallas, Texas District)
Sandy Necessary, Manager
NM Dept. of Economic Develop.
PO Box 20003
Santa Fe, New Mexico 87504-5003
(505) 827-0350

New York
George Buchanan, Director
111 West Huron Street, Room 1304
Buffalo, NY 14202
(716) 551-4191

K.L. Fredericks, Manager
Harlem Export Assistance Center
163 West 125th Street, Suite 904
New York, NY 10027
(212) 860-6200

George Soteros, Manager
Long Island Export Assist. Center
1550 Franklin Avenue, Room 207
Mineola, NY 11501
(516) 739-3310

Joel Barkan, Acting Director
6 World Trade Center, Room 635
New York, NY 10048
(212) 466-5222

William Spitler, Director
Westchester Export Assist. Center
707 West Chester Avenue
White Plains, NY 10604
(914) 682-6218

James C. Mariano, Manager
111 East Avenue, Suite 220
Rochester, NY 14604
(716) 263-6480

North Carolina
Roger Fortner, Director
521 E. Morehead Street, Suite 435
Charlotte, NC 28202

(704) 333-4886

Samuel P. Troy, Director
400 West Market Street, Suite 400
Greensboro, NC 27401
(910) 333-5345

North Dakota
(see Minneapolis, MN EAC)

Ohio
Michael Miller, Director
36 E. 7th Street, Suite 2650
Cincinnati, OH 45202
(513) 684-2944

John McCartney, Director
Bank One Center
600 Superior Ave., East, Suite 700
Cleveland, OH 44114
(216) 522-4750

Mary Beth Double, Manager
37 North High Street, 4th Floor
Columbus, OH 43215
(614) 365-9510

Robert Abrahams, Manager
300 Madison Avenue
Toledo, OH 43604
(419) 241-0683

Oklahoma
Ronald L. Wilson, Director
301 N.W. 63rd Street, Suite 330
Oklahoma City, OK 73116
(405) 231-5302

Thomas Strauss, Manager
700 N. Greenwood Ave., Suite 1400
Tulsa, OK 74106
(918) 581-7650

Oregon
Scott Goddin, Director
121 S.W. Salmon Street, Suite 242
Portland, OR 97204
(503) 326-3001

Pamela Ward, Manager
1445 Willamette Street, Suite 13
Eugene, OR 97401-4003
(541) 465-6575

Pennsylvania
Maria Galindo, Director
615 Chestnut Street, Suite 1501
Philadelphia, PA 19106
(215) 597-6101

Deborah Doherty, Manager
One Commerce Square
417 Walnut Street, 3rd Floor
Harrisburg, PA 17101
(717) 232-0051

Ted Arnn, Manager
1000 Liberty Avenue, Room 2002

Pittsburgh, PA 15222
(412) 395-5050

Henry LaBlanc, Manager
Scranton Export Assistance Center
One Montage Mountain Rd., Ste. B
Moosic, PA 18507
(717) 969-2530

**Puerto Rico
(Hato Rey)**
J. Enrique Vilella, Director
525 F.D. Roosevelt Ave., Suite 905
San Juan, PR 00918
(787) 766-5555

**Rhode Island (Hartford,
Connecticut District)**
Raimond Meerbach, Manager
One West Exchange Street
Providence, RI 02903
(401) 528-5104

South Carolina
Ann Watts, Director
Strom Thurmond Fed. Bldg., #172
1835 Assembly Street
Columbia, SC 29201
(803) 765-5345

David Kuhlmeier, Manager
Charleston Chamber of Commerce
81 Mary Street
Charleston, SC 29403
(803) 727-4051

Denis Csizmedia, Manager
Upstate Export Assistance Center
555 N. Pleasantburg Dr., Suite 109
Greenville, SC 29607
(864) 271-1976

**South Dakota (Des Moines, Iowa
District)**
Harvey Timberlake, Manager
Siouxland Export Assistance Center
Augustana College

2001 S. Summit Ave., Rm. SS-29A
Sioux Falls, SD 57197
(605) 330-4264

Tennessee
Jeanne Ree Russell, Manager
22 North Front Street, Suite 200
Memphis, TN 38103
(901) 544-4137

Thomas McGinty, Manager
301 East Church Avenue
Knoxville, TN 37915
(423) 545-4637

Michael Speck, Director
Parkway Towers, Suite 114
404 James Robertson Parkway
Nashville, TN 37219-1505
(615) 736-5161

Texas
Bill Schrage, Director
2050 N. Stemmons Freeway, #170
Dallas, TX 75207
(214) 767-0542

Karen Parker, Manager
1700 Congress, Ste. 300R, 2nd Floor
Austin, TX 78701
(512) 916-5939

Vavie Sellschopp, Manager
711 Houston Street
Fort Worth, TX 76102
(817) 212-2673

James D. Cook, Director
500 Dallas, Suite 1160
Houston, TX 77002
(713) 718-3062

Mitchell Auerbach, Manager
1222 N. Main, Suite 450
San Antonio, TX 78212
(210) 228-9878

Utah

Stephen Smoot, Director
324 South State Street, Suite 221
Salt Lake City, UT 84111
(801) 524-5116

Vermont
James Cox, Manager
109 State Street, 4th Floor
Montpelier, VT 05609
(802) 828-4508

Virginia
William Davis Coale, Jr.,
704 East Franklin Street, Suite 550
Richmond, VA 23219
(804) 771-2246

Washington
Lisa Kjaer-Schade, Director
2001 6th Avenue, Suite 650
Seattle, WA 98121
(206) 553-5615

James K. Hellwig, Manager
1020 West Riverside
Spokane, WA 99210
(509) 353-2625

West Virginia
Vacant
405 Capitol Street, Suite 807
Charleston, WV 25301
(304) 347-5123
Martha Butwin, Manager
1310 Market Street, 2nd Floor
Wheeling, WV 26003
(304) 233-7472

Wisconsin
Paul D. Churchill, Director
517 East Wisconsin Ave., Rm. 596
Milwaukee, WI 53202
(414) 297-3473

Wyoming
(See Denver, CO)

List 2d: REGIONAL OFFICES, ECONOMIC DEVELOPMENT ADMINISTRATION

Denver Regional Office
**(Colorado, Iowa, Kansas, Missouri, Montana,
Nebraska, North Dakota, South Dakota, Utah,
Wyoming)**
1244 Speer Boulevard, Room 670
Denver, CO 80204

(303) 844-4715

Atlanta Regional Office
**(Alabama, Florida, Georgia, Kentucky, Mississippi,
North Carolina, South Carolina, Tennessee)**
401 West Peachtree Street, N.W., Suite 1820

Atlanta, GA 30308-3510
(404) 730-3002

Chicago Regional Office
(Illinois, Indiana, Michigan, Minnesota, Ohio,
Wisconsin)
111 North Canal Street, Suite 855
Chicago, IL 60606-7204
(312) 353-7706

Philadelphia Regional Office
(Connecticut, Delaware, District of Columbia, Maine,
Maryland, Massachusetts, New Hampshire, New Jersey,
New York, Pennsylvania, Puerto Rico, Rhode Island,
Vermont, Virgin Islands, Virginia, West Virginia)
Curtis Center

Independence Square West, Suite 140 South
Philadelphia, PA 19106
(215) 597-4603

Austin Regional Office
(Arkansas, Louisiana, New Mexico, Oklahoma, Texas)
327 Congress Avenue Suite 200
Austin, TX 78701-4037
(512) 381-8144

Seattle Regional Office
(Alaska, American Samoa, Arizona, California, Guam,
Hawaii, Idaho, Marshall Islands, Micronesia, Nevada,
Northern Mariana Islands, Oregon, Washington)
915 Second Avenue
Jackson Federal Bldg. Ste. 1856
Seattle, WA 98174
(206) 220-7660

List 2e: MINORITY BUSINESS DEVELOPMENT AGENCY, DEPARTMENT OF COMMERCE

REGIONAL OFFICES

California
(Federal Regions IX and X:
Alaska, American Samoa,
Arizona, California, Guam,
Hawaii, Idaho, Nevada, Oregon,
and Washington)
221 Main Street, Room 1280
San Francisco, CA 94105
(415) 744-3001

Georgia
(Federal Region IV: Alabama,
Florida, Georgia, Kentucky,
Georgia, Kentucky, Mississippi,
North Carolina, South Carolina,
and Tennessee)
401 West Peachtree Street, N.W.,
Room 1715
Atlanta, GA 30308-3516
(404) 730-3300

Illinois
(Federal Regions V and VII:
Illinois, Indiana, Iowa, Kansas,

Michigan, Minnesota, Missouri,
Nebraska, Ohio, and Wisconsin)
55 East Monroe Street, Suite 1406
Chicago, IL 60603
(312) 353-0182

New York
(Federal Regions I, II and III:
Connecticut, Delaware, District of
Columbia, Maine, Maryland,
Massachusetts, New Hampshire,
New Jersey, New York,
Pennsylvania, Puerto Rico, Rhode
Island, Vermont, the Virgin
Islands, and West Virginia)
26 Federal Plaza, Room 3720
New York, NY 10278
(212) 264-3262

Texas
(Federal Regions VI and VIII:
Arkansas, Colorado, Louisiana,
Montana, New Mexico, North
Dakota, Oklahoma, South
Dakota, Texas, Utah and
Wyoming)

1100 Commerce St., Rm. 7B23
Dallas, TX 75242
(214) 767-8001

California
9660 Flair Drive, Suite 455
El Monte, CA 91731
(818) 453-8636

Florida
Federal Building, Room 1314
51 S.W. First Ave. Box 25
Miami, FL 33130
(305) 536-5054

Massachusetts
10 Causeway Street, Room 418
Boston, MA 02222-1041
(617) 565-6850

Pennsylvania
Federal Office Building
600 Arch Street, Room 10128
Philadelphia, PA 19106
(215) 597-9236

List 2f: DEPARTMENT OF HOUSING AND URBAN DEVELOPMENT

New England Field Offices
(Connecticut, Maine, Massachusetts, New Hampshire, Rhode Island, Vermont)

Headquarters Office: Connecticut
State Coordinator
One Corporate Center, 19th Floor
Hartford, CT 06103-3220
(860) 240-4800

Maine State Office
Maine State Coordinator
202 Harlow St., Room 101
Bangor, ME 04401
(207) 945-0467

Massachusetts State Office
Secretary's Representative
Thomas P. O'Neill, Jr. Fed. Bldg.
10 Causeway Street, Room 301
Boston, MA 02122
(617) 994-8200

New Hampshire State Office
New Hampshire State Coordinator
Norris Cotton Federal Building
275 Chestnut Street
Manchester, NH 03101-2487
(603) 666-7510

Rhode Island State Office
Rhode Island State Coordinator
10 Weybosset Street, Sixth Floor
Providence, RI 02903-2808
(401) 528-5351

Vermont State Office
Vermont State Coordinator
159 Bank St., 2nd Floor
Burlington, VT 05401
(802) 951-6290

New York/New Jersey Field Offices
(New York, New Jersey)

New York State Office
Secretary's Representative
26 Federal Plaza
New York, NY 10278-0068
(212) 264-6500

Albany Area Office
Albany Area Coordinator
52 Corporate Circle
Albany, NY 12203-5121
(518) 464-4200

Buffalo Area Office
Buffalo Area Coordinator
465 Main Street, Fifth Floor
Buffalo, NY 14203-1780
(716) 551-5755

New Jersey State Office
New Jersey State Coordinator
One Newark Center, 13th Floor
Newark, NJ 07102-5260
(973) 622-7900

Camden Area Office
Camden Area Coordinator
800 Hudson Square, 2nd Floor
Camden, NJ 08102-1156
(856) 757-5081

Mid Atlantic Field Offices
(Delaware, District of Columbia, Maryland, Pennsylvania, Virginia, West Virginia)

Delaware State Office
Delaware State Coordinator
920 King St., Ste. 404
Wilmington, DE 19801
(302) 573-6300

District of Columbia Office
District of Columbia Coordinator
820 First Street, N.E., Suite 450
Washington, DC 20002-4205
(202) 275-9200

Maryland State Office
Maryland State Coordinator
10 S. Howard Street, Fifth Floor
Baltimore, MD 21201-2505
(410) 962-2520

Pennsylvania State Office
Secretary's Representative
100 Penn Square East
Philadelphia, PA 19107-3380
(215) 656-0500

Pittsburgh Area Office
Pittsburgh Area Coordinator
339 Sixth Avenue, Sixth Floor
Pittsburgh, PA 15222
(412) 644-6428

Virginia State Office
Virginia State Coordinator
600 E. Broad Street
Richmond, VA 23219
(800) 842-2610

West Virginia State Office
West Virginia State Coordinator
405 Capitol Street, Suite 708
Charleston, WV 25301-1795
(304) 347-7000

Southeast/Caribbean Field Offices
(Alabama, Florida, Georgia, Kentucky, Mississippi, North Carolina, South Carolina, Tennessee, Caribbean, Panama Canal Zone, Puerto Rico, Virgin Islands)

Alabama State Office
Alabama State Coordinator
Medical Forum Building
22nd Street N., Ste. 900
Birmingham, AL 35203
(205) 731-2617

Florida State Office
Florida State Coordinator
909 SE. First Ave., Room 500
Miami, FL 33131
(305) 536-4456

Jacksonville Area Office
Jacksonville Area Coordinator
301 West Bay Street, Suite 2200
Jacksonville, FL 32202-5121
(904) 232-2627

Orlando Area Office
Orlando Area Coordinator
3751 Maguire Blvd., Suite 270
Orlando, FL 32803-3032
(407) 648-6441

Tampa Area Office
Tampa Area Coordinator
500 E. Zack Street, Ste. 402
Tampa, FL 33602-3945
(813) 228-2026

Georgia State Office
Secretary's Representative
Five Points Plaza Building
40 Marietta St.
Atlanta, GA 30303
(404) 331-5136

Kentucky State Office
Kentucky State Coordinator
601 West Broadway
Louisville, KY 40202
(502) 582-525

Mississippi State Office

Mississippi State Coordinator
Doctor A. H. McCoy Federal Bldg.
100 W. Capitol Street, Room 910
Jackson, MS 39269-1096
(601) 965-4757

North Carolina State Office
North Carolina State Coordinator
2306 West Meadowview Road
Greensboro, NC 27407-3707
(336) 547-4000

South Carolina State Office
South Carolina State Coordinator
Strom Thurmond Federal Building
1835 Assembly Street
Columbia, SC 29201-2480
(803) 253-3292

Tennessee State Office
Tennessee State Coordinator
235 Cumberland Bend Dr.. # 200
Nashville, TN 37228-1803
(615) 736-5600

Knoxville Area Office
Knoxville Area Coordinator
John J. Duncan Federal Building
710 Locust Street, Third Floor
Knoxville, TN 37902-2526
(865) 545-4384

Memphis Area Office
Memphis Area Coordinator
200 Jefferson Avenue, Suite 1200
Memphis, TN 38103-2335
(901) 544-3367

Caribbean Office
Caribbean Coordinator
New San Juan Office Building
171 Carlos E. Chardon Ave, Ste 301
San Juan, PR 00918
(787) 766-5400

Midwest Field Offices
(Illinois, Indiana, Michigan, Minnesota, Ohio, Wisconsin)

Illinois State Office
Secretary's Representative
Ralph H. Metcalfe Federal Bldg.
77 West Jackson Boulevard
Chicago, IL 60604-3507
(312) 353-5680

Indiana State Office
Indiana State Coordinator
151 North Delaware Street
Indianapolis, IN 46204-2526
(317) 226-6303

Michigan State Office
Michigan State Coordinator

477 Michigan Ave.
Detroit, MI 48226-2592
(313) 226-7900

Flint Area Office
Flint Area Coordinator
1101 South Saginaw St., Suite 200
Flint, MI 48502
(810) 766-5112

Grand Rapids Area Office
Grand Rapids Area Coordinator
Trade Center Building
50 Louis Street, N.W., 3rd Floor
Grand Rapids, MI 49503-2648
(616) 456-2100

Minnesota State Office
Minnesota State Coordinator
920 Second Street, South
Minneapolis, MN 55402
(612) 370-3000

Ohio State Office
Ohio State Coordinator
200 North High Street
Columbus, OH 43215-2499
(614) 469-5737

Cincinnati Area Office
Cincinnati Area Coordinator
15 East 7th Street
Cincinnati, OH 45202-3188
(513) 684-6180

Cleveland Area Office
Cleveland Area Coordinator
Renaissance Building
1350 Euclid Avenue, Suite 500
Cleveland, OH 44115-1815
(216) 522-4058

Wisconsin State Office
Wisconsin State Coordinator
Henry S. Reuss Federal Plaza
310 West Wisconsin Ave. # 1380
Milwaukee, WI 53203-2289
(414) 297-3214

Southwest Field Offices
(Arkansas, Louisiana, New Mexico, Oklahoma, Texas)

Arkansas State Office
Arkansas State Coordinator
TCBY Tower
425 West Capitol Ave. Suite 900
Little Rock, AR 72201-3488
(501) 324-5931

Louisiana State Office
State Coordinator

Hale Boggs Federal Building
501 Magazine Street, 9th Floor
New Orleans, LA 70130-3099
(504) 589-7201

Shreveport Area Office
Shreveport Area Coordinator
401 Edwards Street, Suite 1510
Shreveport, LA 7110
(318) 676-3385

New Mexico State Office
New Mexico State Coordinator
625 Silver Ave. SW, Ste. 100
Albuquerque, NM 87102
(505) 262-6463

Oklahoma State Office
Oklahoma State Coordinator
500 West Main Street, Suite 400
Oklahoma City, OK 73102-2233
(405) 553-7500

Texas State Office
Secretary's Representative
801 Cherry Street
Post Office Box 2905
Fort Worth, TX 76102
(817) 978-5595

Dallas Area Office
Dallas Area Coordinator
525 Griffin Street, Room 860
Dallas, TX 75202-5007
(214) 767-8300

Houston Area Office
Houston Area Coordinator
2211 Norfolk, Suite 200
Houston, TX 77098-4096
(713) 313-2274

San Antonio Area Office
San Antonio Area Coordinator
Washington Square
800 Dolorosa Street
San Antonio, TX 78207-4563
(210) 472-6885

Great Plains Field Offices
(Iowa, Kansas, Missouri, Nebraska)

Iowa State Office
Iowa State Coordinator
Federal Building
210 Walnut Street, Room 239
Des Moines, IA 50309-2155
(515) 284-4512

Kansas/Missouri State Office
Secretary's Representative
400 State Avenue
Kansas City, KS 66101-2406

(913) 551-5644

St. Louis Area Office
St. Louis Area Coordinator
Robert A. Young Federal Building
1222 Spruce Street, Third Floor
St. Louis, MO 63103-2836
(314) 539-6583

Nebraska State Office
Nebraska State Coordinator
10909 Mill Valley Road
Omaha, NE 68154-3955
(402) 492-3100

Rocky Mountains Field Offices
**(Colorado, Montana, North
Dakota, South Dakota, Utah,
Wyoming)**

Colorado State Office
Secretary's Representative
First Interstate Tower North
633 17th Street
Denver, CO 80202-3607
(303) 672-5440

Montana State Office
Montana State Coordinator
Power Block Building
7 West 6th Ave.
Helena, MT 59601
(406) 449-5050

North Dakota State Office
North Dakota State Coordinator
Federal Building
657 2nd Avenue
Fargo, ND 58108-2483
(701) 239-5136

South Dakota State Office
South Dakota State Coordinator
2400 West 49th Street, # I-201
Sioux Falls, SD 57105-6558
(605) 330-4223

Utah State Office
Utah State Coordinator
257 Tower Building
257 East - 200 South, Suite 550
Salt Lake City, UT 84111-2048
(801) 524-6070

Wyoming State Office
Wyoming State Coordinator
Federal Office Building

150 East B Street, Room 1010
Casper, WY 82601
(307) 261-6250

Pacific/Hawaii Field Offices
**(Arizona, California, Nevada,
Hawaii)**

Arizona State Office
Arizona State Coordinator
400 North 5th Street, Suite 1600
Phoenix, AZ 85004-2361
(602) 379-4434

Tucson Area Office
Tucson Area Coordinator
Security Pacific Bank Plaza
33 North Stone Avenue, # 700
Tucson, AZ 85701-1467
(602) 670-6237

California State Office
Secretary's Representative
Phillip Burton Federal Building and
U.S. Courthouse
450 Golden Gate Avenue
Post Office Box 36003
San Francisco, CA 94102-3448
(415) 436-6550

Fresno Area Office
Fresno Area Coordinator
2135 Fresno Street, Suite 100
Fresno, CA 93721-1718
(559) 487-5033

Los Angeles Area Office
AT&T Center
611 West 6th Street, Suite 800
Los Angeles, CA 90017-3127
(213) 894-8000

Sacramento Area Office
Sacramento Area Coordinator
925 L Street
Sacramento, CA 95814
(916) 498-5220

San Diego Area Office
San Diego Area Coordinator
Symphony Towers
750 B Street, Suite 1600
San Diego, CA 92101
(619) 557-5305

Santa Ana Area Office

Santa Ana Area Coordinator
1600 North Broadway, Ste. 100
Santa Ana, CA 92706
(888) 827-5605

Nevada State Office
Nevada State Coordinator
Atrium Building
333 North Rancho Drive, # 700
Las Vegas, NV 89106-3714
(702) 388-6500

Reno Area Office
Reno Area Coordinator
3702 South Virginia Street, Ste. G2
Reno, NV 89502
(775) 784-5383

Hawaii State Office
Hawaii State Coordinator
500 Ala Moana Blvd., Ste. 3A
Honolulu, HI 96813-4918
(808) 522-8175

Northwest/Alaska Field Offices
**(Idaho, Oregon, Washington,
Alaska)**

Idaho State Office
Idaho State Coordinator
Plaza IV
800 Park Boulevard, Suite 220
Boise, ID 83712-7743
(208) 334-1990

Oregon State Office
Oregon State Coordinator
400 Southwest Sixth Ave. # 700
Portland, OR 97204-1632
(503) 326-2561

Washington State Office
Secretary's Representative
Seattle Federal Office Building
909 1st Avenue, Suite 200
Seattle, WA 98104-1000
(206) 220-5104

Alaska State Office
Alaska State Coordinator
University Plaza Building
949 East 36th Avenue, Suite 401
Anchorage, AK 99508
(907) 271-4663

Table 2g: FARM SERVICE AGENCY, STATE OFFICES; DEPARTMENT OF AGRICULTURE

Alabama
Danny Crawford
Alabama State FSA Office
4121 Carmichael Road,
Suite 600
Montgomery, AL 36106-2872
(334) 279-3501

Alaska
Chad Padgett
Alaska State FSA Office
800 West Evergreen, Suite 216
Palmer, AK 99645-6389
(907) 761-7700

Arizona
Robert A. Piceno
Arizona State FSA Office
77 East Thomas Road, Suite 240
Phoenix, AZ 85012-3318
(602) 640-5200

Arkansas
Wayne Perryman
Arkansas State FSA Office
700 West Capitol Ave., Rm. 3416
Little Rock, AR 72201-3225
(501) 301-3000

California
John Smythe
California State FSA Office
430 G Street
Davis, CA 95616
(530) 792-5520

Colorado
Lewis Frank
Colorado State FSA Office
655 Parfet St., Rm. E305
Lakewood, CO 80215
(720) 544-2876

Connecticut
John Breakell
Connecticut State FSA Office
344 Merrow Rd Suite B
Tolland, Ct 06084
(860) 871-2944

Delaware
Richard Bergold
Delaware State FSA Office
1201 College Park Drive, Suite 101
Dover, DE 19904-8713
(302) 678-4250

Florida
Kevin Kelley
Florida State FSA Office
4440 N.W. 25th Pl.,
Suite 1
Gainesville, FL 32614-1030
(352) 379-4500

Georgia
Steve Newton
Georgia State FSA Office
355 East Hancock Avenue Stop 100
Athens, GA 30601
(706) 546-2266

Hawaii
JoAnna Nakata
Hawaii State FSA Office
300 Ala Moana Blvd., Room 5-112
Honolulu, HI 96850
(808) 541-2644

Idaho
Wayne Hammon
Idaho State FSA Office
9173 W. Barnes Drive, Suite B
Boise, ID 83709
(208) 378-5650

Illinois
William Graff
Illinois State FSA Office
3500 Wabash Avenue
Springfield, IL 62794-9273
(217) 241-6600

Indiana
Robert Peacock
Indiana State FSA Office
5981 Lakeside Boulevard
Indianapolis, IN 46278
(317) 290-3030, Ext. 200

Iowa
Derryl McLaren
Iowa State FSA Office
10500 Buena Vista Court
Des Moines, IA 50322
(515) 254-1540, Ext. 1600

Kansas
Bill Fuller
Kansas State FSA Office
3600 Anderson Avenue
Manhattan, KS 66503-2511
(785) 539-3531

Kentucky
Hampton (Hoppy) Henton
Kentucky State FSA Office
771 Corporate Drive, Suite 100
Lexington, KY 40503-5478
(859) 224-7601

Louisiana
Willie F. Cooper
Louisiana State FSA Office
3737 Government Street
Alexandria, LA 71302-3395
(318) 473-7721

Maine
Arnold Roach
Maine State FSA Office
967 Illinios Ave.
Bangor, ME 04401
(207) 990-9140

Maryland
Steve Connelly
Maryland State FSA Office
8335 Guilford Road, Suite E
Columbia, MD 21046
(410) 381-4550

Massachusetts
Sandra Adams
Massachusetts State FSA Office
445 West Street
Amherst, MA 01002
(413) 253-4500

Michigan
Chris White
Michigan State FSA Office
3001 Coolidge Road, Suite 100
East Lansing, MI 48823-6321
(517) 324-5110

Minnesota
John Monson
Minnesota State FSA Office
400 Farm Credit Service Building
375 Jackson Street
St. Paul, MN 55101-1852
(612) 602-7700

Mississippi
Mickey Black
Mississippi State FSA Office
6310 I-55 North, Suite W100
Jackson, MS 39211
(601) 965-4184

Missouri
Brad Epperson
Missouri State FSA Office
601 Business Loop 70 West, #225
Columbia, MO 65203
(314) 876-0925

Montana
Randy Johnson
Montana State FSA Office

PO Box 670
Bozeman, MT 59771
(406) 587-6872

Nebraska
Brian Wolford
Nebraska State FSA Office
7131 A Street
Lincoln, NE 68510
(402) 437-5581

Nevada
Roger Van Valkenburg
Nevada State FSA Office
1755 East Plumb Lane, Suite 202
Reno, NV 89502-3207
(775) 784-5411

New Hampshire
Robb Thomson
USDA, NH State FSA Office
22 Bridge Street, 4th Floor
Concord, NH 03301-4987
(603) 224-7941

New Jersey
Paul Hlubik
New Jersey State FSA Office
Mastoris Professional Plaza
163 Route 130, Bldg. 2, Ste. E
Bordentown, NJ 08505-2249
(609) 298-3446

New Mexico
Paul Gutierrez
New Mexico State FSA Office
6200 Jefferson Street, N.E.
Albuquerque, NM 87109
(505) 761-4900

New York
Ron Robbins
New York State FSA Office
441 S. Salina St., Ste. 356, 5th Floor
Syracuse, NY 13202
(315) 477-6300

North Carolina
Keith Weatherly
North Carolina State FSA Office
4407 Bland Road, Suite 175
Raleigh, NC 27609-6296
(919) 875-4800

North Dakota
Gary Nelson
North Dakota State FSA Office
1025 28th Street, SW
Fargo, ND 58103-3046
(701) 239-5224

Ohio

Steve Maurer
Ohio State FSA Office
Federal Building, Rm. 540
200 North High Street
Columbus, OH 43215
(614) 255-2500

Oklahoma
Terry L. Peach
OK State FSA Office, 100 USDA, #102
Farm Road and McFarland Street
Stillwater, OK 74074-2653
(405) 742-1130

Oregon
Larry Frey
Oregon State FSA Office
7620 SW Mohawk
Tualatin, OR 97062-8121
(503) 692-6830

Pennsylvania
William H. Baumgartner
Pennsylvania State FSA Office
One Credit Union Place, Suite 320
Harrisburg, PA 17110-2994
(717) 782-4547

Rhode Island
Paul E. Brule
Rhode Island State FSA Office
West Bay Office Complex
60 Quaker Lane, Room 40
Warwick, RI 02886
(401) 828-8232

South Carolina
Ken Rentiers
South Carolina State FSA Office
1927 Thurmond Mall, Suite 100
Columbia, SC 29201-2375
(803) 806-3080

South Dakota
Kathy Lindquist
South Dakota State FSA Office
200 Fourth Street, S.W., Room 308
Huron, SD 57350-2478
(605) 352-1163

Tennessee
James Hill
Tennessee State FSA Office
U.S. Courthouse, Room 579
801 Broadway
Nashville, TN 37203-3816
(615) 277-2600

Texas
Harold Bob Bennett
Texas State FSA Office

2405 Texas Ave. South., 2nd Floor
College Station, TX 77840
(409) 260-9207

Utah
James L. Humlicek
Utah State FSA Office
125 South State Street, Room 4239
Salt Lake City, UT 84147
(801) 524-5430

Vermont
Stephen Kerr
Vermont State FSA Office
356 Mountain View Drive,
Suite 104
Colchester, VT 05446
(802) 658-2803

Virginia
John Johnson
Virginia State FSA Office
1606 Santa Rosa Road, Suite 138
Richmond, VA 23229
(804) 287-1503

Washington
James Fitzgerald
Washington State FSA Office
316 West Boone Avenue, Suite 568
Spokane, WA 99201-2350
(509) 353-3000

West Virginia
John Rader
West Virginia State FSA Office
75 High Street, Room 239
Morgantown, WV 26507
(304) 284-4800

Wisconsin
Ben Brancel
Wisconsin State FSA Office
6515 Watts Road, Room 100
Madison, WI 53719-2797
(608) 276-8732

Wyoming
Lois Van Mark
Wyoming State FSA Office
951 Werner Court, Suite 145
Casper, WY 82601-1307
(307) 261-5231

Caribbean Area FSA Office
Jaun Ortiz
654 Munoz Rivera Avenue
Suite 829, IBM Building
Hato Rey, PR 00918
Phone: 787-294-1613

List 2h: RURAL DEVELOPMENT FIELD OFFICES, DEPARTMENT OF AGRICULTURE

Alabama
Rural Devel. State Office Director
4121 Carmichael Road Sterling
Center, Suite 601
Montgomery, Al 36106
(334) 279-3400

Alaska
Rural Devel. State Office Director
800 West Evergreen, Suite 201
Palmer, AK 99645-6539
(907) 761-7705

Arizona
Rural Devel. State Office Director
3003 N. Central Avenue Suite 900
Phoenix, AZ 85012
(602) 280-8701

Arkansas
Rural Development Offices
USDA Rural Development
USDA Service Center
Federal Building, Room 3416
700 Capitol Avenue
Little Rock, AR 72201
(501) 301-3200

California
Rural Business-Cooperative Service
430 G St., #4169
Davis, CA 95616
(530) 792-5800

Colorado
Rural Development State Director
655 Parfet Street Room E 100
Lakewood, CO 80215
(720) 544-2903

Connecticut
Rural Development State Office
451 West Street
Amherst, MA 01002
(413) 253-4300

Delaware
Rural Development State Director
5607 South DuPont Highway
Camden, DE 19934
(302) 697-4300

Florida/Virgin Islands
4440 NW 25th Pl.
Gainesville, FL 32606
(352) 338-3402

Georgia
Rural Development State Office
Stephens Federal Building

355 E. Hancock Ave.
Athens, GA 30601
(706) 546-2162

Hawaii
Rural Development State Office
Federal Building, Rm. 311
154 Wainuenue Avenue
Hilo, HI 96720
(808) 933-8380

Idaho
Rural Development Offices
Rural Development State Office
9173 West Barnes Street, Suite A1
Boise, ID 83709
(208) 378-5600

Illinois
USDA, Rural Development
2118 West Park Court, Suite A
Champaign, IL 61821
(217) 403-6202

Indiana
Rural Development
5975 Lakeside Boulevard
Indianapolis, IN 46278
(317) 290-3100

Iowa
Rural Development State Office
210 Walnut Street, Suite 873
Des Moines, IA 50309
(515) 284-4663

Kansas
Rural Development State Office
1303 First American Place
Topeka, KS 66604
(785) 271-2700

Kentucky
Rural Development State Office
771 Corporate Plaza, Suite 200
Lexington, KY 40503
(859) 224-7300

Louisiana
USDA, Rural Development
Louisiana State Office
3727 Government Street
Alexandria, LA 71302
(318) 473-7921

Maine
Rural Development State Office
967 Illinois Ave., Suite 4
Bangor, ME 04402-0405
(207) 990-9160

Maryland
Rural Development State Office
4607 South DuPont Highway
Camden, DE 19934
(302) 697-4300

Massachusetts
Rural Development State Office
451 West Street
Amherst, MA 01002
(413) 253-4300

Michigan
USDA Rural Dev. - State Office
3001 Coolidge Road, Suite 200
East Lansing, MI 48823
(517) 337-6635

Minnesota
Rural Development State Office
410 Farm Credit Service Building
375 Jackson Street
St. Paul, MN 55101-1853
(651) 602-7800

Mississippi
Rural Development State Office
100W Capital SF, Suite 831
Jackson, MS 39269
(601) 965-4318

Missouri
601 Business Loop
70 W. Parkade Ctr. Ste. 235
Columbia, MO 65203
(573) 876-0976

Montana
Rural Development State Office
PO Box 850
Bozeman, MT 59771
(406) 585-2580

Nebraska
100 Centennial Mall N., Rm. 152
Lincoln, NE 68508
(402) 437-5551

Nevada
Rural Development State Office
1390 S. Curry Street
Carson, NV 89703
(775) 887-1222

New Jersey
Rural Development State Office
5th Floor North, Suite 500
8000 Midlantic Drive
Mt. Laurel, NJ 08054
(856) 787-7700

New Mexico
Rural Development State Office
6200 Jefferson St., NE, Rm. 255
Albuquerque, NM 87109
(505) 761-4950

New York
NY Rural Development Office
441 S. Salina Street
Syracuse, NY 13202
(315) 477-6400

North Carolina
4405 Bland Rd., Ste. 260
Raleigh, NC 27609
(919) 873-2000

North Dakota
220 E. Rosser, Rm. 208
Bismarck, ND 58502
(701) 530-2037

Ohio
USDA/Rural Development
200 North High Street, Rm. 507
Columbus, OH 43215
(614) 255-2500

Oklahoma
Rural Development State Office
100 USDA, Suite 108
Stillwater, OK 74074
(405) 742-1000

Oregon
Rural Development State Office
101 SW Main Street, Suite 1410
Portland, OR 97204
(503) 414-3300

Pennsylvania

Rural Development State Office
One Credit Union Place, Suite 330
Harrisburg, PA 17110-9408
(717) 237-2185

Puerto Rico
Rural Development State Office
IBM Building
654 Munoz Rivera Ave., Suite 601
San Juan, PR 00918
(787) 766-5095

Rhode Island
Rural Development State Office
451 West Street
Amherst, MA 01002
(413) 253-4300

South Carolina
Strom Thurman Fed. Bldg., #1007
1835 Assembly St.
Columbia, SC 29201
(803) 765-5163

South Dakota
Rural Development State Office
200 Fourth St, SW, Rm. 210
Huron, SD 57350
(605) 352-1100

Tennessee
Rural Development State Office
3322 West End Avenue, Suite 300
Nashville, TN 37203
(615) 783-1300

Texas
Rural Development State Office
101 South Main, Ste. 102
Temple, TX 76501
(254) 742-9700

Utah
Rural Development State Office
125 S. State St., Rm. 4311
Salt Lake City UT 84137
(801) 524-4321

Vermont
Rural Development State Office
89 Main St. , 3rd Floor
Montpelier, VT 05602
(802) 828-6002

Virginia
Rural Development State Office
1606 Santa Rosa Rd. , Ste. 238
Richmond, VA 23229
(804) 287-1550

Washington
USDA, Rural Development
1835 Black Lake Blvd., SW, Ste. B
Olympia, WA 98501-5715
(360) 704-7740

West Virginia
Rural Development State Office
75 High St.
Morgantown, WV 26505
(304) 284-4860

Wisconsin
Rural Development State Office
4949 Kirschling Court
Stevens Point, WI 54481
(715) 345-7615

Wyoming
Rural Development State Office
100 E. B Street, Room 1005
Casper, WY 82601
(307) 261-6300

Lsit 2i:

BUREAU OF INDIAN AFFAIRS

AREA OFFICES

Deputy Commissioner of Indian
Affairs
1849 C St. N.W., MS-4140 MIB
Washington, DC 20240
(202) 208-5116

Alaska
Juneau Area Office
PO Box 25520
Juneau, AK 99802-5520

(907) 586-7252

Arizona
Phoenix Area Office
PO Box 10
Phoenix, AZ 85001
(602) 379-6600

Navajo Area Office
PO Box #1060
Gallup, NM 87305

(505) 863-8314

California
(See also Arizona (Phoenix)
Sacramento Area Office
Federal Office Building
2800 Cottage Way, Room W-2550
Sacramento, CA 95825-1846
(916) 978-6000

Minnesota
Minneapolis Area Office

One Federal Drive, Rm. 550
Minneapolis, MN 55111
(612) 713-4400

Montana
Billings Area Office
316 North 26th Street
Billings, MT 59101-1397
(406) 247-7943

New Mexico*
(See also Arizona (Navajo)
Albuquerque Area Office
PO Box 26567
Albuquerque, NM 87125-6567
(505) 346-7590

New York*
(See Virginia, Eastern Area Office)

North Carolina*
(See Virginia, Eastern Area Office)

North Dakota*
(See South Dakota)

Oklahoma
Anadarko Area Office
PO Box 368
Anadarko, OK 73005-0368
(405) 247-6673, Ext. 314

Muskogee Area Office
Bureau of Indian Affairs
101 North 5th Street
Muskogee, OK 74401
(918) 678-2296

Oregon*
(See also Arizona (Phoenix)
Portland Area Office
911 N.E. 11th Avenue
Portland, OR 97232-4169
(503) 231-6702

South Dakota
Aberdeen Area Office
Bureau of Indian Affairs
115 4th Avenue S.E.
Aberdeen, SD 57401-4384
(605) 226-7343

Utah*
(see Arizona (Navajo and Phoenix),
and Oregon)

Virginia
Eastern Area Office
711 Stewart Ferry Pike
Nashville, TN 37214
(615) 467-1700

Washington*
(See Oregon)

Wisconsin*
(See Minnesota)

Wyoming*
(See Montana)

* Cross-references denote which
area or offices provide services to
eligible Indians within the State.

FIELD AGENCIES

Alaska
Anchorage Agency
1675 C Street
Anchorage, AK 99501-5198
(907) 271-4088

Fairbanks Agency, 101 12th
Avenue, Room 168
Fairbanks, AK 99701-6270
(907) 456-0222

Arizona
Chinle Agency
PO Box 7H
Chinle, AZ 86503
(520) 674-5201, Ext. 101

Colorado River Agency, Route 1,
Box 9-C
Parker, AZ 85344
(520) 669-7111

Fort Apache Agency
PO Box 560
Whiteriver, AZ 85941
(520) 338-5353

Fort Defiance Agency, PO Box 619
Fort Defiance, AZ 86504
(520) 729-7221

Fort Yuma Agency
PO Box 11000
Yuma, AZ 85364
(619) 572-0248

Hopi Agency
PO Box 158
Keams Canyon, AZ 86034
(520) 738-2228

Papago Agency
PO Box 578
Sells, AZ 85634
(520) 383-3286

Pima Agency
PO Box 8
Sacaton, AZ 85247
(520) 562-3326

Salt River Agency
10000 E. McDowell Road
Scottsdale, AZ 85256
(602) 640-2168

San Carlos Agency
PO Box 209
San Carlos, AZ 85550
(520) 475-2321

Truxton Canon Agency
PO Box 37
Valentine, AZ 86437
(520) 769-2286

Western Navajo Agency
PO Box 127
Tuba City, AZ 86045
(520) 283-2218

California
Central California Agency
1824 Tribute Road, Suite J
Sacramento, CA 95815
(916) 566-7121

Palm Springs Area Field Station
PO Box 2245
555 S. Palm Canyon Drive, Suite A-208
Palm Springs, CA 92263
(760) 322-3086

Southern California Agency
2038 Iowa Avenue, Suite 101
Riverside, CA 92507-0001
(909) 276-6624

Colorado
Southern Ute Agency
PO Box 315
Ignacio, CO 81137
(970) 563-4511

Ute Mountain Ute Agency
General Delivery
Towaoc, CO 81334
(970) 565-8471

Florida
Seminole Agency
6075 Stirling Road
Hollywood, FL 33024
(954) 581-7050

Idaho
Fort Hall Agency
PO Box 220
Fort Hall, ID 83203
(208) 238-2301

Northern Idaho Agency, P.O.
Drawer 277

Lapwai, ID 83540
(208) 843-2300

Kansas
Haskell Indian Nations University
155 Indian Avenue
Lawrence, KS 66046
(913) 749-8404

Horton Agency
PO Box 31
Horton, KS 66439
(913) 486-2161

Minnesota
Minnesota Agency
Route 3, Box 112
Cass Lake, MN 56633
(218) 335-6913

Red Lake Agency
Red Lake, MN 56671
(218) 679-3361

Mississippi
Choctaw Agency
421 Powell Street
Philadelphia, MS 39350
(601) 656-1523

Montana
Blackfeet Agency
PO Box 880
Browning, MT 59417
(406) 338-7544

Crow Agency
Box 69
Crow Agency, MT 59022
(406) 638-2672

Flathead Agency
PO Box A
Pablo, MT 59855-5555
(406) 675-7200

Fort Belknap Agency
RR 1, Box 980
Harlem, MT 59526
(406) 353-2901, Ext. 23

Fort Peck Agency
PO Box 637
Poplar, MT 59255
(406) 768-5312

Northern Cheyenne Agency
PO Box 40
Lame Deer, MT 59043
(406) 477-8242

Rocky Boy's Agency
RR 1, Box 542
Box Elder, MT 59521

(406) 395-4476

Nebraska
Winnebago Agency
PO Box 18
Winnebago, NE 68071
(402) 878-2502

Nevada
Western Nevada Agency
1677 Hotsprings Road
Carson City, NV 89706
(702) 887-3500

Eastern Nevada Agency
1555 Shoshone Circle
Elko, NV 89801
(702) 738-0569

New Mexico
Eastern Navajo Agency
PO Box 328
Crownpoint, NM 87313
(505) 786-6100

Jicarilla Agency
PO Box 167
Dulce, NM 87528
(505) 759-3951

Mescalero Agency
PO Box 189
Mescalero, NM 88340
(505) 671-4423

Northern Pueblos Agency
PO Box 4269
Fairview Station
Espanola, NM 87533
(505) 753-1400

Ramah-Navajo Agency
Route 2, Box 14
Ramah, NM 87321
(505) 775-3235

Shiprock Agency
PO Box 966
Shiprock, NM 87420
(505) 368-4427

Southern Pueblos Agency
PO Box 1667
Albuquerque, NM 87103
(505) 766-3021

Zuni Agency
PO Box 369
Zuni, NM 87327
(505) 782-5591

New York
New York Field Office

100 South Clinton Street, Room 523
Syracuse, NY 13261-7366
(315) 448-0620

North Carolina
Cherokee Agency
Cherokee, NC 28719
(704) 497-9131

North Dakota
Fort Berthold Agency
PO Box 370
New Town, ND 58763
(701) 627-4707

Fort Totten Agency
PO Box 270
Fort Totten, ND 58335
(701) 766-4545

Standing Rock Agency
PO Box E
Fort Yates, ND 58538
(701) 854-3433

Turtle Mountain Agency
PO Box 60
Belcourt, ND 58316
(701) 477-3191

Oklahoma
Anadarko Agency
PO Box 309
Anadarko, OK 73005
(405) 247-6677

Concho Agency
PO Box 68
El Reno, OK 73036-5769
(405) 262-7481

Okmulgee Agency
PO Box 370
Okmulgee, OK 74447
(918) 756-3950

Osage Agency
PO Box 1539
Pawhuska, OK 74056
(918) 287-1032

Miami Agency
PO Box 391
Miami, OK 74355
(918) 542-3396

Pawnee Agency, PO Box 440,
Pawnee, OK 74058-0440
(918) 762-2585

Shawnee Agency
624 West Independence, Suite 114
Shawnee, OK 74801
(405) 273-0317

Talihina Agency, Drawer H
Talihina, OK 74571
(918) 567-2207

Wewoka Agency
PO Box 1060
Wewoka, OK 74884
(405) 257-6259

Oregon
Umatilla Agency
PO Box 520
Pendleton, OR 97801
(541) 278-3786

Warm Springs Agency
PO Box 1239
Warm Springs, OR 97761
(541) 553-2411

South Dakota
Cheyenne River Agency
PO Box 32
Eagle Butte, SD 57625
(605) 964-6611

Crow Creek Agency
PO Box 616
Ft. Thompson, SD 57339
(605) 245-2311

Lower Brule Agency
PO Box 190

Lower Brule, SD 57548
(605) 473-5512

Pine Ridge Agency
PO Box 1203
Pine Ridge, SD 57770
(605) 867-5125

Rosebud Agency
PO Box 550
Rosebud, SD 57570
(605) 747-2224
Sisseton Agency
PO Box 688
Agency Village, SD 57262
(605) 698-7676

Yankton Agency
PO Box 577
Wagner, SD 57380
(605) 384-3651

Utah
Uintah and Ouray Agency
PO Box 130
Fort Duchesne, UT 84026
(801) 722-2406

Southern Paiate
Field Station
PO Box 720
St. George, UT 84771
(801) 674-9720

Washington
Colville Agency
PO Box 111
Nespelem, WA 99155-0111
(509) 634-4901

Spokane Agency
PO Box 389
Wellpinit, WA 99040
(509) 258-4561

Puget Sound Agency
3006 Colby Avenue, Federal
Building
Everett, WA 98201
(425) 258-2651

Yakima Agency
P. O. Box 632
Toppenish, WA 98948
(509) 865-5121

Wisconsin
Great Lakes Agency
615 Main Street, West
Ashland, WI 54806
(715)682-4527

Wyoming
Wind River Agency
PO Box 158
Fort Washakie, WY 82514
(307) 332-7810

List 2j: # FEDERAL TRANSIT ADMINISTRATION

REGIONAL OFFICES

Region I
(Connecticut, Maine,
Massachusetts, New Hampshire,
Rhode Island, Vermont)
Richard Doyle, Regional
Administrator
C/O Volpe National, Transportation
Systems Center
Kendall Square
55 Broadway, Suite 920
Cambridge, MA 02142-1093
(617) 494-2055

Region II
(New Jersey, New York, Virgin
Islands)
Regional Administrator

One Bowling Green, Room 429
New York, NY 10004
(212) 668-2170

Region III
(Delaware, District of Columbia,
Maryland, Pennsylvania,
Virginia, West Virginia)
Regional Administrator
1760 Market St., Suite 500
Philadelphia, PA 19103-4124
(215) 656-7100

Region IV
(Alabama, Florida, Georgia,
Kentucky, Mississippi, North
Carolina, Puerto Rico, South
Carolina, Tennessee)
Regional Administrator

61 Forsyth St., SW, Suite 17T50
Atlanta, GA 30303-8917
(404) 562-3500

Region V
(Illinois, Indiana, Michigan,
Minnesota, Ohio, Wisconsin)
Regional Administrator
200 West Adams St., Rm. 2140
Chicago, IL 60606
(312) 353-2789

Region VI
(Arkansas, Louisiana, New
Mexico, Oklahoma, Texas)
Regional Administrator
819 Taylor Street, Room 8A36
Fort Worth, TX 76102
(817) 978-0550

Region VII
(Iowa, Kansas, Missouri, Nebraska)
Regional Administrator
901 Locust Street, Suite 404
Kansas City, MO 64106
(816) 329-3920

Region VIII
Note grant making activity for Arizona and Nevada falls under Region VIII

(Colorado, Montana, North Dakota, South Dakota, Utah, Wyoming)
Regional Administrator
Columbine Place
216 Sixteenth St., Suite 650
Denver, CO 80202-5120
(303) 844-3242

Region IX
(Arizona, California, Hawaii, Nevada, Guam, American Samoa)
Regional Administrator

201 Mission St., Suite 2210
San Francisco, CA 94105
(415) 744-3133

Region X
(Alaska, Idaho, Oregon, Washington)
Regional Administrator
Jackson Fed. Bldg., Ste. 3142
915 Second Avenue
Seattle, WA 98174-1002
(206) 220-7954

List 2k: BUSINESS SERVICE CENTERS, GENERAL SERVICES ADMINISTRATION

Business Service Center
300 N. Los Angeles St., Rm. 3108
Los Angeles, CA 90012
(213) 894-3210

Office of Enterprise Development
Phillip Burton FOB and Courthouse
450 Golden Gate Ave., # 5-6514
San Francisco, CA 94102
(415) 522-2700

Business Service Center
Denver Federal Center, Building 41,
Room 145
PO Box 25006
Denver, CO 80225-0006
(303) 236-7408

Program Support Division
Seventh & D Streets, S.W.,
Room 1050
Washington, DC 20407
(202) 708-5804

Office of Enterprise Development
401 W. Peachtree St., Rm. 3832
Atlanta, GA 30365-2550
(404) 331-5103

Business Service Center
230 S. Dearborn St. Rm. 3718
Chicago, IL 60604
(312) 353-5383

Business Service Center
Thomas T. O'Neill Federal Office
Building
10 Causeway St., Room 290
Boston, MA 02222
(617) 565-8100

Enterprise Development Staff
1500 E. Bannister Rd., Rm. 1160
Kansas City, MO 64131
(816) 926-7203

Program Service Division
Jacob K. Javits Federal Bldg.

26 Federal Plaza, Rm. 18-130
New York, NY 10278
(212) 264-1234

Program Service Division
Wanamaker Building
100 Penn Square E., Rm. 808
Philadelphia, PA 19107
(215) 656-5525

Business Service Center
819 Taylor St., Room 11A09
Fort Worth, TX 76102
(817) 978-3284

Office of Enterprise Development
General Services Adm. Center,
400 15th St., S.W., Rm. 2413
Auburn, WA 98001
(206) 931-7956

Table 2l: DEPARTMENT OF ENERGY, FIELD OFFICES

California
Department of Energy
Oakland Operations Office
1301 Clay Street
Oakland, CA 94612-5208
(510) 637-1794

Colorado

Department of Energy
Golden Flats Office
1617 Cole Blvd.
Golden, CO 80401
(303) 274-4700

Idaho
Department of Energy
Idaho Operations Office
2050 Energy Drive, MS 1221
Idaho Falls, ID 83401-1536
(208) 526-0111

Illinois
Department of Energy
Chicago Operations Office
9800 South Cass Avenue
Argonne, IL 60439-4899
(630) 252-2001

New Mexico
Department of Energy
Albuquerque Operations Office
PO Box 5400
Albuquerque, NM 87185-5400
(505) 845-0011

Nevada
Department of Energy
Nevada Operations Office
PO Box 98518
Las Vegas, NV 89193-8518
(702) 295-1212

Ohio
Department of Energy
Ohio Field Office
PO Box 3020
Miamisburg, OH 45343-3020
(937) 865-3878

Pennsylvania
Federal Energy Technology Center
PO Box 10940
Pittsburgh, PA 15236-0940
(412) 892-6000

South Carolina
Department of Energy
Savannah River Operations Office
PO Box A
Aiken, SC 29801
(803) 725-6211

Tennessee
Department of Energy

Oak Ridge Operations Office
PO Box 2001
Oak Ridge, TN 37831
(423) 576-5454

Washington
Department of Energy
Richland Operations Office
825 Jadwin Avenue
PO Box 550
Richland, WA 99352
(509) 376-7411

West Virginia
Federal Energy Technology Center
PO Box 880
3610 Collins Ferry Road
Morgantown, WV 26507
(304) 291-476

Table 2m: # REGIONAL COMMISSIONERS FOR REHABILITATIVE SERVICES, DEPARMENT OF EDUCATION

Region I
Mr. John J. Szufnarowski
McCormack P.O. and Courthouse,
Room 232
Boston, MA 02109
(617) 223-4085

Region II
Mr. John Szufarowski
75 Park Place, 12th Floor
New York, NY 10278
(212) 264-4016

Region III
Dr. Ralph Pacinelli
3535 Market St., Rm. 16120
Philadelphia, PA 19104
(215) 596-0317

Region IV
Dr. Ralph Pacinelli

PO Box 1691
Atlanta, GA 30301
(404) 331-2352

Region V
Dr. Douglas L. Burleigh
10220 N. Executive Hills Boulevard
Kansas City, NO 64153-1367
(816) 880-4107

Region VI
Mr. Loerance Deaver
1200 Main Tower Bldg., Rm. 22200
Dallas, TX 75202
(214) 767-2961

Region VII
Douglas Burleigh
10220 N. Executive Hills Blvd., 5th Fl.
Kansas City, MO 64153
(816) 880-4107

Region VIII
Mr. Loerance Deaver
1200 Main Tower Bldg. Rm. 22220
Dallas, TX 752024
(214) 767-2961

Region IX
Mr. Gilbert (Doc) Williams
Federal Office Building
50 United Nations Plaza, Room 215
San Francisco, CA 94102
(415) 437-7840

Region X
Richard Corbridge, Assistant
Regional Commissioner
915 Second Avenue, Room 2848
Seattle, WA 98121
(206) 220-7840

Table 2n: WOMAN'S BUSINESS ASSISTANCE CENTERS (WBAC)

Alabama
Women's Business Assistance Ctr.
Kathryn Cariglino, Director
1301 Azalea Road, Suite 201A
Mobile, AL 36693
(334) 660-2725
(800) 378-7461

Alaska
WOMEN$ Fund, A Program of the
YWCA of Anchorage
Kathryn J. Maieli, Program Director
Sharon Richards, YWCA Executive
245 West Fifth Avenue
Anchorage, AK 99510-2059
(907) 274-1524

Arizona
Self-Employment Loan Fund, Inc.
Jean Rrrosenberg, Director
201 North Central Ave., Suite CC10
Phoenix, AZ 85073-1000
(602) 340-8834

California
Women's Enterprise Develop. Corp.
Phil Borden, Executive Director
100 West Broadway, Suite 500
Long Beach, CA 90802
(562) 983-3747

Women's Initiative for Self
Employment
Barbara Johnson, Exec. Director
450 Mission Street, Suite 402
San Francisco, CA 94105
(415) 247-9473

WEST Company - Ukiah Office
Sheilah Rogers, Executive Director
367 North State Street, Suite 201
Ukiah, CA 95482
(707) 468-3553

WEST Company - Ft. Bragg Office
Cinnamon Sky, Technology Mgr.
Carol Steele, Loan Fund Manager
306 East Redwood Avenue, Suite 2
Fort Bragg, CA 95437
(707) 964-7571

Colorado
Mi Casa Resource Ctr. for Women, Inc.
Barbara DesMarteau, Exec. Director
571 Galapago Street
Denver, CO 80204
(303) 573-1302

Mi Casa Career Development and
Business Center for Women
Agnes Carroll, Dir. of Program Dev.
700 Knox Court

Denver, CO 80204
(303) 573-0333

Connecticut
Women's Business Develop. Center
Fran Pastore, Dir. Training & Programs
400 Main Street, Suite 410
Stamford, CT 06901
(203) 326-7914

District of Columbia
National Women's Business Center
Arlinda Halliburton, Deputy Dir.
Deattra Perkins, Dir. of Training
1250 24th Street, N. W. Suite 350
Washington, DC 20037
(202) 466-0544

Florida
Women's Business Develop. Center
Christine Kurtz-White, Director
10555 West Flagler St., Room 2612
Miami, FL 33174
(305) 348-3951

Georgia
Women's Economic Develop. Agency
Joyce Edwards, Chairperson
675 Ponce de Leon Avenue
Atlanta, GA 30308
(404) 853-7680

Illinois
Women's Business Development Ctr.
Hedy Ratner/C. Dougal, Co-Directors
Linda Darragh, Project Director
8 South Michigan Ave., Suite 400
Chicago, IL 60603
(312) 853-3477

Louisiana
Southeast LA Black Chamber of Com.
Women's Business Center
Laverne Kilgore, Director
2245 Peters Road, Suite 200
Harvey, LA 70058
(504) 365-3866

Women Entrepreneurs for
Economic Development Inc.
Paula Peete, Executive Director
1683 North Claiborne, Ste. 101
New Orleans, L:A 70116
(504) 947-8522

Maine
Coastal Enterprises Inc.
Women's Business Develop. Program
Betsy Tipper, Telecommunications
Business Counselor
7 North Chestnut Street

Augusta, ME 04330
(207) 621-0245

Maine Coastal Enterprises Inc.
Women's Business Develop. Program
Ronald Phillips, President
P. O. Box 268
Wiscasset, ME 04578
(207) 882-7552

Maryland
Women Entrepreneurs of Baltimore Inc.
Amanda Crook Zinn, CEO
28 East Ostend Street
Baltimore, MD 21230
(410) 727-4921

Massachusetts
Mass. Ctr. for Women & Enterprise Inc.
Andrea Silbert, Director
45 Bromfield Street, 6th Floor
Boston, MA 02108
Phone: (617) 423-3001, Ext. 222

Michigan
Women's Initiative for Self-
Employment c/o Center for
Empowerment and Economic Dev.
Michelle Richards, Exec. Director
2002 Hogback Road, Suite 12
Ann Arbor, MI 48105
(313) 677-1400

Grand Rapids Opport. for Women
Inger Giuffrida, Executive Director
25 Sheldon SE, Suite 210
Grand Rapids, MI 49503
(616) 458-3404

Minnesota
Women in New Development
(A Division of Bi-County
Community Action Programs, Inc.)
Susan Hoosier, WIND Coordinator
2715 15th Street NW
Bemidji, MN 56601
(218) 751-4631

Mississippi
Mississippi Women's Economic
Entrepreneurial Project
Jo Thompson, Director
106 West Green Street
Mound Bayou, MS 38762
(601) 741-3342

National Council of Negro Women
Christine Toney, Executive Director
Lucenia Dunn, Dir. of Programs
633 Pennsylvania Avenue, NW
Washington, D. C. 20004
(202) 737-0120

Missouri
National Association of Women's
Business Owners
Irina Bronstein, Executive Director
7165 Delmar, Suite 204
St. Louis, MO 63130
(314) 863-0046

Montana
Montana Women's Capital Fund
Kris Bakula, Executive Director
302 N. Last Chance Gulch, Ste. 400
Helena, MT 59624
(406) 443-3144

MT Community Develop. Corp.
Rosalie S. Cates, Executive Director
127 North Higgins
Missoula, MT 59802
(406) 543-3550

Nevada
Nevada Self-Employment Trust
Virginia Hardman, Project Manager
1600 East Desert Inn Rd., Ste. 209E
Las Vegas, NV 89109
(702) 734-3555

Nevada Self-Employment Trust
Gerry Alcasas, Executive Director
560 Mill Street, Suite 260
Reno, NV 89502
(702) 329-6789

New Hampshire
Women's Business Center, Inc.
Racheal Stuart, Executive Director
150 Greenleaf Avenue, Unit 4
Portsmouth, NH 03801
(603) 430-2892

New Jersey
New Jersey NAWBO Excel
Harriet Scooler, Project Director
225 Hamilton Street
Bound Brook, NJ 08805-2042
(732) 560-9607

New Mexico
NM Women's Economic Self-
Sufficiency Team (WESST Corp.)
Agnes Noonan, Executive Director
414 Silver Southwest
Albuquerque, NM 87102
(505) 241-4760

WESST Corp. - Farmington, NM
Joretta Clement, Regional Manager
500 West Main
Farmington, NM 87401
(505) 325-0678

WESST Corp. - Las Cruces, NM
Jennifer Craig, Regional Manager
691 South Telshor
Las Cruces, NM 88001

(505) 522-3707

WESST Corp. - Roswell, NM
Roberta Ahlness, Regional Manager
200 West First, Suite 324
Roswell, NM 88201
(505) 624-9850

WESST Corp. - Sante Fe, NM
Marisa Del Rio, Regional Manager
418 Cerrillos Road, Suite 26
Sante Fe, NM 87501
(505) 988-5284

WESST Corp. - Taos, NM
Dawn Redpath, Regional Manager
Box 5007 NDCBU
Taos, NM 87571
(505) 758-3099

New York
American Woman's Eco. Dev. Corp.
Suzanne Tufts, President and CEO
71 Vanderbilt Avenue, Suite 320
New York, NY 10169
(212) 692-9100

Women's Venture Fund, Inc.
Maria Semidei-Otero, President
155 East 42nd Street, Suite 316
New York, NY 10017
(212) 972-1146

North Dakota
Women's Business Institute
Penny Retzer, Director
320 North Fifth Street, Suite 203
Fargo, ND 58107-2043
(701) 235-6488

Ohio
Western Reserve Bus. Ctr. for Women
Karen Franks, Director
University of Akron
Community and Technical College
M/185V Polski Building, Room 185
Akron, OH 44325-6002
(330) 972-5592

Women's Org. for Mentoring,
Entrepreneurship & Networking
Carrie Herman, Acting Exec. Dir.
526 South Main Street, Suite 235
Akron, OH 44311-1058
(330) 379-9280

Women's Business Resource
Program of Southeastern Ohio
Debra McBride, Project Director
Ohio University, Technology and
Enterprise Building
20 East Circle Drive, Suite 155
Athens, OH 45701
(614) 593-1797

Micro-Business Assistance
Pyramid Career Services
Mary Ellen Hess, Exec. Dir.
2400 Cleveland Avenue North
Canton, OH 44709
(330) 453-3767

Women Entrepreneurs Inc.
Lyn Marsteller, Director
Sandy Evers, Program Director
36 East 4th Street, Suite 925
Cincinnati, OH 45202
(513) 684-0700

Glenville Development Corporation
Micro-Enterprise Program
Rosalind Brewster, Develop. Officer
10640 St. Clair Ave.
Cleveland, OH 44108
(216) 851-8724

Greater Columbus Women's
Business Development Center
Linda Steward, Program Director
37 North High Street
Columbus, OH 43215-3065
(614) 225-6081

OH Women's Bus. Resource Network
Mary Ann McClure, Director
77 South High Street, 28th Floor
Columbus, OH 43215-1001
(800) 848-1300, Extension 62682

Women's Development Center
Evelyn France, Executive Director
42101 Griswold Road
Elyria, OH 44035
(216) 324-3688

Enterprise Center/Women's
Business Center
Dr. Don McFeeters, Exec. Director
Ohio State University
1864 Shyville Road
Piketon, OH 45661
(614) 289-3727

Northwest Ohio Women's
Entrepreneurial Network
Linda Fayerweather, Director
5555 Airport Highway, Suite 210
Toledo, OH 43615
(419) 381-7555

Oklahoma
Women's Business Center
Working Women's Money Univ.
Lori Smith, Director
234 Quadrum Drive
Oklahoma City, OK 73108
Telephone:(405) 232-8257

Oregon
Southern OR Women's Access to Credit
Mary O'Kief, Director
33 North Central, Suite 209

Medford, OR 97501
(541) 779-3992

ONABEN - A Native American
Business Network
Patrick Borunda, Director
520 Southwest 6th Ave., Suite 930
Portland, OR 97204
(503) 243-5015

Pennsylvania
Women's Business Develop. Center
Geri Swift, President
1315 Walnut Street, Suite 1116
Philadelphia, PA 19107-4711
(215) 790-9232

Puerto Rico
Women's Business Institute
Universidad Del Sagrado Corazon
Joy Vilardi de Camacho, Director
Center for Women's Entrepreneurial
Development
P. O. Box 12383
San Juan, PR 00914-0383
Phone: (787) 728-1515, Ext. 2560

South Carolina
Center for Women Entrepreneurs
Columbia College of South Carolina
Ms. Sam McKee, Director of Grants
1301 Columbia College Drive
Columbia, SC 29203

(803) 786-3582

South Dakota
Watertown Career Learning Center
The Entrepreneur Network for Women
Pat Helgeland, Director
100 South Maple
Watertown, SD 57201-0081
(605) 882-5080

Tennessee
The National Assn. for Women
Busin. Owners - Nashville Chapter
Janice S. Thomas, Exec. Director
P. O. Box 101024
Nashville, TN 37224
(615) 248-3474

Texas
North Texas Women's Business
Development Center Inc.
Branda Williams, Technical
Counseling and Programs
Bill J. Priest Institute for Economic Dev.
1402 Corinth Street, Suite 1536
Dallas, TX 75215-2111
(214) 428-1177

Utah
Women's Business Center, Salt
Lake Area Chamber of Commerce
Ramona Rudert, Director
175 East 400 South, Suite 600

Salt Lake City, UT 84111
(801) 328-5051

Washington
ONABEN - A Native American
Business Network
Sonya Tetnowski, Coordinator
3201 Broadway, Suite C
Everett, WA 98201
(425) 339-6226

West Virginia
Center for Economic Options, Inc.
Pam Curry, Executive Director
601 Delaware Avenue
Charleston, WV 25302
(304) 345-1298

Wisconsin
Wisconsin Women's Business
Initiative Corp. - Madison Office
Marian Walluks, Local Contact
16 North Carroll Street, 7th Floor
Madison, WI 53703
(608) 257-7409

Wisconsin Women's Business
Initiative Corporation
Wendy K. Werkmeister, President
1915 N. Dr. Martin Luther King Jr. Dr.
Milwaukee, WI 53212
(414) 263-5450

Chapter 3
HOW TO COLLECT
MONEY FOR HOUSING

American is a nation of home owners. About 60 percent of us live in our own homes. And for those of us who rent, we look forward to the time when we can own our own home. One of the reasons for this widespread home ownership is that Uncle Sam has many programs in place to make easier for us to buy. And this is in addition to the generous tax deductions Uncle Sam gives us. In addition, many of the States have special programs that subsidize housing costs for low to moderate income families

So if you want to buy a home, fix up the one you're in, need help to pay the rent where you are living now, or even buy a mobile home, here is how government programs can help.

DEPARTMENT OF AGRICULTURE

Money—for Low to Moderate Income Housing in Small Towns
Section 502 Rural Housing Loans (10.410)

Description: You can tap this program to get money to buy, fix up or build a house in a small town or rural area. Under this program, the Dept. of Agriculture offers guaranteed/insured loans and direct loans of up to 30 to 38 years to help lower-income rural families buy, build, rehabilitate, or improve, and to provide the applicant with modest, decent, safe, and sanitary dwellings and related facilities as a permanent residence.

Under the **guaranteed loan program**, the Agency guarantees loans made by conventional agricultural lenders for up to 95 percent of principal.

Applicants unable to qualify for a guaranteed loan may be eligible for a **direct loan** from FSA

If you have a family income below approximately $45,000, you may be eligible for both a direct loan and subsidized interest payments.

Loans may be used for
- Construction
- Repair
- Modernization, such as putting in a modern kitchen and bathroom
- Purchase of housing
- For sewage disposal facilities and/or safe water supply
- For weatherization, putting in central heating
- To buy a minimum adequate site on which to place the dwelling
- And under certain conditions to finance a manufactured home and its site.

Applicant Eligibility: Applicants must be unable to secure the necessary credit from other sources at prevailing terms and conditions for residential type financing and have adequate and dependable available income to meet family living expenses, including taxes, insurance and maintenance, and repayments on debts including the proposed loan.

Financial Information: *Range and Average of Financial Assistance*: $1,000 to $105,000; an average of $65,000 for direct loans, and $74,000 for guaranteed loans.

Literature: 7 CFR Part 3550 *"Direct Singles Family Housing Loans and Grants,"* (cost $5.70). For guaranteed loans, 1980-D *"Subpart D -Rural Housing Loans,"* (cost $8.00).

Who To Contact: *Headquarters Office*: Director, Single Family Housing, Processing Division, Rural Housing Service (RHS), Department of Agriculture, Washington, DC 20250. (202) 720-1474. *Regional or Local Office*: Contact appropriate State office listed in Tables 2g and 2h, Chapter 2.

Money—for the Very Low-Income to Fix Up or Repair a House
Section 504 Rural Housing Loans and Grants (10.417)

Description: Uncle Sam makes direct loans and grants of up to 20 years to assist very low-income single families, located in rural areas, to make home repairs. Grant funds may only be used to make such dwellings safe and sanitary and to remove health and safety hazards. This includes repairs to the foundation, roof, or basic structure as well as water and waste disposal systems, and weatherization.

- **Maximum loan amount** cannot exceed a cumulative total of $20,000 to any eligible person.
- **Maximum lifetime grant assistance** is $7,500 to any eligible person.

Applicant Eligibility: Applicants must own and occupy a home in a rural area.

- **Loan recipients** must have sufficient income to repay the loan.
- **Grant recipients** must be 62 years or older and be unable to repay a loan for that part of the assistance received as a grant.

Applicant's income may not exceed very low-income limits — from $6,300 to $22,650 for a single person household, depending on an area's median income.

Financial Information: The interest rate for these loans is one percent. *Range and Average of Financial Assistance*: Loans to $5,570; Grants to $4,589. In the latest reported year, 10,097 loans and grants were made.

Literature: *"Direct Single Family Housing Loans and Grants,"* (no charge); *"Home Improvement and Repair,"* (no charge).

Who To Contact: *Headquarters Office*: Director, Single-Family Housing Processing Division, Rural Housing Service, Department of Agriculture, Washington, DC 20250. (202) 720-1474. *Regional or Local Office*: Get in touch with the appropriate State office listed in Tables 2g, 2h.

Money—To Fix Up Your Home in the Country
Rural Housing Preservation Grants (10.433)

Description: This program provides loans and grants to agencies and nonprofit organizations so that they can provide assistance to individual homeowners, rental properties or co-ops to pay any part of the cost for repair or rehabilitation of structures. The purpose is to assist very low- and low-income rural homeowners and rental property owners get the necessary assistance to repair or rehabilitate their dwellings. This program is for open country and communities with a population of 10,000 that are rural in character and places with a population of up to 25,000 under certain conditions.

Some of the loans are long term, interest-subsidized loans that lend homeowners the money and "forgiving" 20 percent per year until the loan becomes a grant after five years.

Beneficiary Eligibility: Very low and low-income rural individuals/families who are homeowners and need resources to bring their housing up to code standards, rental property owners.

Financial Information: In the latest year, $8 million was allotted to assist 1,414 units.

Who to Contact: *Headquarters Office*: Multiple Family Housing Processing Division, Rural Housing Service, Department of Agriculture, Washington DC 20250. (202) 720-1660.

Regional or Local Office: Contact the appropriate State office listed in Table 2g and 2h.

Money—for Conserving Water
Water Bank Program (10.062)

Description: Under this program, landowners can receive direct payments to conserve surface waters; preserve and improve the Nation's Wetlands; increase migratory waterfowl habitat in nesting, breeding and feeding areas in the U.S.; and secure environmental benefits for the Nation.

Agreements are for 10 years and may be continued for additional 10 year periods. During the agreement, the participants agree in return for annual payments not to drain, burn, fill, or otherwise destroy the wetland character of such areas and not to use areas for agricultural purposes

Eligibility Requirements: Landowners and operators of specified types of wetlands in designated important migratory waterfowl nesting, breeding and feeding areas.

Financial Information: *Range of Financial Assistance*: $7 to $75 per acre. Ther are currently 4,953 agreements covering 614,648 acres in effect.

Who To Contact: *Headquarters Office*: Natural Resources Conservation Service, Department of Agriculture, PO Box 2890, Washington, DC 20013. (202) 720-1870. *Regional or Local Office*: Get in touch with your State's Natural Resources Conservation Service office listed in Table 3a.

Money—to Build Farm Labor Housing
(10.405)

Description: Get money to build housing for your employees. This program provides project grants and guaranteed/insured loans to provide decent, safe, and sanitary low-rent housing and related facilities for domestic farm laborers and their families. The loans and grants may be used for construction, repair, or purchase of year-round or seasonal housing; acquiring the necessary land

and making improvements on land for housing; and developing related support facilities including central cooking and dining facilities, small infirmaries, laundry facilities, day care centers, other essential equipment and facilities or recreation areas.

Eligibility Requirements: Loans are available to farmers, family farm partnerships, family farm corporations, associations of farmers and federally recognized Indian Tribes.

Financial Information: *Range and Average of Financial Assistance*: Initial grants $135,000 to $2,300,000; $1,104,120 average. Initial loans to individuals $20,000 to $200,000; $34,500 average. Initial loans to organizations $165,000 to $670,000; $292,753 average.

Literature: RD Instruction 1944-D, *"Farm Labor Housing Loan & Grant Policies, Procedures & Authorization."*

Who To Contact: Headquarters Office: Multi-Family Housing Processing Division, Rural Housing Service, Department of Agriculture, Washington, DC 20250. (202) 720-1604. *Regional or Local Office*: Contact the appropriate State office listed in Table 2h.

Money—to Build Rental Housing in Small Towns
Rural Rental Housing Loans Sections 515 and 521 (10.415)

Description: Want money to build rental housing in a small town? This program gives direct loans to provide economically designed and constructed rental and cooperative housing suited for rural residents. Loans can be used to construct, purchase and substantially rehabilitate housing with two or more units, including manufactured housing.

Funds may also be used to provide approved recreational and service facilities appropriate for use in connection with the housing and to buy and improve the land on which the buildings are to be located. Occupants must be very low-, low- or moderate-income families households, elderly, handicapped, or disabled persons.

Eligibility Requirements: Applicants may be individuals, cooperatives, nonprofit organizations,

State or local public agencies, profit corporations, trusts, partnerships, limited partnerships. They must be unable to finance the housing either with their own resources or with credit obtained from private sources. Loans may be made in communities up to 10,000 population (up to 20,000 in some circumstances).

Financial Information: *Range and Average of Financial Assistance*: Loan Limit per application is $1 million.

Literature: RD Instruction 1944-E, "*Rural Rental Housing Loan Policies Procedures, and Authorizations.*"

Who To Contact: *Headquarters Office*: Director, Multi-Family Housing Processing Division, Rural Housing Service, Department of Agriculture, Washington, DC 20250. (202) 720-1604. *Regional or Local Office*: Contact the appropriate State office listed in Table 2h.

DEPARTMENT OF HOUSING AND URBAN DEVELOPMENT

Money—to Buy a Home
Mortgage Insurance—Section 203b (14.117)

Description: You can get a guaranteed/insured loan for up to 30 years in order to undertake home ownership. These loans may be used to finance the purchase of proposed, under construction, or existing one-to four-family housing, as well as to refinance indebtedness on existing housing. This is HUD's most common single family home loan program.

Maximum insurable loans are as follows:
1) One-family, $121,296
2) Two family, $155,232
3) Three-family $187,632
4) Four-family $233,184

These maximum dollar amounts may be increased in designated areas of limited housing opportunities and maximum mortgage amounts.

Eligibility Requirements: Individuals and families intending to occupy the property.

Financial Information: Last year, 921,283 units valued at over $120 billion were insured.

Literature: "*HUD Residential Rehabilitation Program*", no charge; Fact Sheet: "*Rehabilitation Mortgage Insurance,*" no charge.

Who To Contact: *Headquarters Office*: None. *Regional or Local Office*: Persons are encouraged to communicate with the nearest local HUD Office. See Table 2f.

Money—to Buy Fixer-Uppers More Than One Year Old
Rehabilitation Mortgage Insurance—Section 203k (14.108)

Description: The **Section 203K** program complements the **203b** program (above) by providing guaranteed/insured loans of up to 30 years to help families repair or improve, purchase and improve, or refinance and improve existing residential structures more than one year old. These loans may be used to rehabilitate an existing 1 to 4 unit dwelling. Rehabilitation cost must be at least $5,000.

This program is especially valuable to purchasers of foreclosed HUD, Federal Housing Administration, and Veterans Administration-insured homes.

Applicant Eligibility: Individual purchasers or investors are eligible to apply.

Financial Information: The amount you can borrow can be as much as the cost of the rehabilitation plus the "as is" value of the property. Last year 11,000 loans were insured.

Literature: Fact Sheet: "*Rehabilitation Mortgage Insurance,*" no charge.

Who To Contact: *Headquarters Office*: None. *Regional or Local Office*: Persons are encouraged to communicate with the nearest local HUD Office, Table 2f.

Money—to Fix Up Your Home
Property Improvement Loan Insurance (14.142)

Description: This very popular program will help you to spruce up your home. You can get a guaranteed/insured loan of 20-30 years to finance improvements to homes and other existing structures and the building of new nonresidential structures.

Insured loans may be used to:
- Finance improvements, alterations, and repairs of individual homes and apartments buildings;
- The building of new nonresidential structures which substantially protect or improve the utility of the properties.

The maximum loan is $25,000 for improving a single family home or for improving or building a nonresidential structure. For improving a multifamily structure, the maximum loan is $12,000 per family unit, up to a maximum total of $60,000.

Eligibility Requirements: Owners of properties to be improved; lessees having a lease extending at least 6 months beyond maturity of the loan; purchasers of property under a land installment contract.

Financial Information: In the latest reported year, 17,976 loans were insured with a value of $242 million. Since this program started, nearly 35 million loans have been insured with a value of $43 billion.

Literature: *"Fixing Up Your Home,"* HUD-52-H(7), no charge.

Who To Contact: *Headquarters Office*: None. *Regional or Local Office*: Contact HUD Headquarters for program information.

Money—to Buy a Trailer
Title 1 (14.110)

Description: Need money to buy a trailer? This program offers guaranteed/insured loans to finance the purchase of manufactured homes by buyers intending to use them as their principal

places of residence. You must give assurance that the unit will be placed on a site which complies with local zoning and land development requirements. The loan term may extend for up to 20 years and 32 days.

Eligibility Requirements: All persons are eligible to apply

Financial Information: The maximum loan is $48,600, whether single or multiple modules. Last year, 318 loans were insured with a value of $10,747,000.

Literature: *"Financing Manufactured Homes."*

Who To Contact: *Headquarters Office*: Chief, Home Mortgage Division, Department of Housing and Urban Development, 451 7th St., SW, Suite 9272, Washington, DC 20410. (202) 708-2121. *Regional or Local Office*: Contact Headquarters for program information.

Rent Assistance Checks for Low Income Families in Private Housing
Section 8 Rental Certificate Program

Description: This program is becoming the mainstay of the federal government's subsidized housing activities. Instead of building public housing developments, the government assists low and very low income families to obtain decent housing in private rental units by providing housing assistance subsidies that make up the difference between what an eligible family can afford and the fair market rent for a given unit.

Beneficiary Eligibility: Very low income families (whose income does not exceed 50 percent of the median income for the area, with adjustments for smaller and larger families) and, on an exception basis, low income families (whose income does not exceed 80 percent of the median income for the area adjusted for smaller and larger families).

Financial Information: Housing assistance payments are used to make up the difference between the approved rent due to the owner for the apartment and the family's required contribution towards rent.

Assisted families must pay the highest of 30 percent of the monthly adjusted family income, 10 percent of gross monthly family income, or the portion of welfare assistance designated for the monthly housing cost of the family.

As of the latest reported year, 1.4 billion households were bein helped.

(Note that current funding is only for renewals and continued assistance for families in assisted housing. New certificates are for special purposes only.)

Literature: *"Tenant Based Housing Assistance Works" (#6584)*.

Who To Contact: Headquarters Office: Office of the Deputy Assistant Secretary for Public and Assisted Housing Operations, Office of Rental Assistance, Department of Housing and Urban Development, Washington, DC 20410. (202) 708-0477. *Regional or Local Office*: HUD Office listed in Table 2f that has jurisdiction over the area in which the dwellings are located.

Loans—So Disaster Victims Can Buy Homes
Mortgage Insurance Section 203h (14.119)

Description: If you are the victim of a natural disaster, this program provides guaranteed/insured loans of 30-35 years to help finance the purchase or reconstruction of a one-family home.

Eligibility Requirements: Victims of a major disaster as designated by the President.

Financial Information: Last year 512 mortgages were insured with a value of $49,435,346.

Literature: *"Guide To Single Family Home Mortgage Insurance,"* no charge.

Who To Contact: *Headquarters Office*: None. *Regional or Local Office*: Persons are encouraged to communicate with the nearest local HUD Office. See Table 2f.

Money—for Construction or Rehabilitation of Condominium Projects
Mortgage Insurance—Section 234d (14.112)

Description: Guaranteed/insured loans to enable sponsors to develop condominium projects in which individual units will be sold to home buyers. These loans may be used to finance the construction or rehabilitation of multifamily housing structures by a sponsor intending to sell individual units as condominiums. The maximum mortgage term is 40 years, or not in excess of three-quarters of the remaining economic life, whichever is less.

Eligibility Requirements: Private profit-motivated developers, public bodies, and other sponsors who meet FHA requirements for mortgagors.

Financial Information: Cumulatively through the latest reported year, 971 projects with 50,018 units were insured with a value of $529,421,871.

Literature: *"HUD Mortgage Insurance Handbook No. 4580.1 For Condominium Housing Insured under Section 234 (d) of the National Housing Act"*; *"HUD Mortgage Insurance Handbook No. 4265.1, Home Mortgage Insurance-Condominium Units, Section 234(c)."*

Who To Contact: *Headquarters Office*: Chief, Home Mortgage Insurance Division, Room 9272, Department of Housing and Urban Development, Washington, DC 20410. Phone: (202) 708-1212. *Regional or Local Office*: All projects are processed in Regional and Local HUD Offices. Persons are encouraged to communicate with the nearest local HUD Office. (See Table 2f, Chapter 2.)

Get a House at Half Price
"Officer Next Door Program" (14.198)

Description: In order to persuade police officers to live in distressed neighborhoods, this program offers houses at half price to law enforcement personnel who agree to live in them for at least three years. To make the houses even more affordable, when a law enforcement officer chooses to use an FHA-insured mortgage the downpayment is only $100.

The houses, which the Government acquires through foreclosures on HUD-financed mortgages, are scattered in low- and moderate-income neighborhoods that are considered good candidates for improvement.

Applicant Eligibility: Law enforcement officers.

Financial Information: So far, 5,700 officers have bought homes under the program. In addition to getting a house for half-price, 3,000 member banks of the Mortgage Bankers Association of America give such buyers a half-point cut in closing costs or a one-eighth-point cut in mortgage interest rates.

Who To Contact: Asset Management and Disposition Division, 451 7th Street SW, Washington, DC 20410. (202) 708-1672.

Money—for Medical Facilities
Mortgage Insurance Title XI (14.116)

Description: Guaranteed/insured loans to finance the construction or rehabilitation of medical, dental, optometric, osteopathic, or podiatric facilities. These loans may also be used for major movable equipment.

Eligibility Requirements: The owner (mortgagor) of the facility must be organized on a nonprofit basis, but may make it available to a practicing group through a lease.

Financial Information: No mortgages have been insured under this program in many years. Cumulative totals are 27 project mortgages with 848 units insured with a value of $41,501,298.

Literature: HUD Handbook 4630.1-"*Group Medical Practice Facilities*," no charge.

Who To Contact: *Headquarters Office*: Policies and Procedures Division, Office of Insured Multifamily Housing Development, Department of Housing and Urban Development, Washington, DC 20110. (202) 708-0599. *Regional or Local Office*: Persons are encouraged to communicate with the nearest local HUD Field Office, Table 2F.

Money—So Low and Moderate Income Families Hurt By a Disaster or Urban Renewal Can Buy a Home
Section 221d2 (14.120)

Description: Guaranteed/insured loans of 30-40 years to increase homeownership opportunities for low income and moderate income families, and to make homeownership more readily available to families displaced by a natural disaster, urban renewal, or other government actions.

These loans may be used to finance the purchase of proposed or existing low-cost one- to four-family housing or the rehabilitation of such housing.

Maximum insurable loans for an occupant mortgagor are $31,000 for a single family home, or up to $36,000 for a single family home in high cost areas. For a large family (five or more persons) the limits are $36,000 for a single-family home, or up to $42,000 for a single-family home in high cost areas. Higher mortgage limits apply for two- to four-family housing.

Dowpayments can be as small as $200.

Applicant Eligibility: All families are eligible to apply. Displaced families qualify for special terms.

Financial Information: No information.

Literature: Fact Sheet "*Low and Moderate Income Families (Mortgage Insurance)*," no charge.

Who To Contact: *Headquarters Office*: Director, Single Family Development Division, Office of Insured Single Family Housing, Department of Housing and Urban Development, Washington, DC 20410. (202) 708-1112. *Regional or Local Office*: Persons are encouraged to communicate with the nearest local HUD Field Office listed in Table 2f.

Money—To Buy a Home in an Outlying Area
Section 203I (14.121)

Description: How would you like to own a home in the country? This program provides guaranteed/insured loans of 30-35 years to help people purchase homes in outlying areas. Loans may be used to finance the purchase of new or existing one-family nonfarm housing, or new farm housing on two and one-half or more acres adjacent to an all-weather public road.

For most families, the maximum amount of the loan is 97 percent of the first $25,000 of estimated value (including total allowable closing costs) plus 95 percent of the remainder. The downpayment is the difference between the maximum loan and the purchase price of the home.

Eligibility Requirements: All families are eligible to apply.

Financial Information: No information.

Literature: "*Guide To Single Family Home Mortgage Insurance,*" no charge.

Who To Contact: None. *Regional or Local Office*: Persons are encouraged to communicate with the nearest local HUD Field Office listed in Table 2f.

Money—To Buy or Fix Up Homes in Urban Renewal Areas
(14.122)

Description: You can get financing to buy or fix-up a home in an urban renewal area. This program provides guaranteed/insured loans of 30-35 years to help families purchase or rehabilitate homes in such areas. The loans may be used to finance acquisition or rehabilitation of one- to 11-family housing in approved urban renewal or code enforcement areas.

Maximum insurable loans for the occupant mortgagor are the same as prescribed for Program **203(b)**, page 105, plus $9,165 for each family

unit over four. For most families, the maximum amount of the loan is the same as under Section 203(b). The downpayment is the difference between the maximum loan amount and the purchase price of the home, or the estimated value, whichever is less. In addition, the purchaser must pay all items of prepaid expense.

Special terms are available for qualified veterans.

Eligibility Requirements: All families are eligible to apply.

Financial Information: In the last reported year, 45 home mortgage unit were insured for a value of $3,066,904.

Literature: "*Fact Sheet; Urban Renewal Housing (Mortgage Insurance),*" no charge; "*Fact Sheet: Major Home Improvements (Loan Insurance),*" no charge.

Who To Contact: *Headquarters Office*: None. *Regional or Local Office*: Persons are encouraged to communicate with the nearest local HUD Field Office listed in Table 2f, Chapter 2.

Money—to Buy or Rehabilitate Homes in Older Sections of Town
Section 223e (14.123)

Description: This program provides guaranteed/insured loans to finance the purchase, repair, rehabilitation, and construction of housing in older, declining urban areas where conditions are such that certain normal eligibility requirements for mortgage insurance under a particular program cannot be met. The property must be an acceptable risk giving consideration to the need for providing adequate housing for low-and moderate-income families.

Mortgages for housing eligible under this special program may be insured under any one of several HUD programs, but claims are paid from a Special Risk Insurance Fund.

Eligibility Requirements: For single family purposes all purchases are eligible. Multifamily sponsorship is determined by applicable program requirements.

Financial Information: Last year 130 units valued at $4,913,353 were insured. Cumulatively, 201,150 units valued at $3,125,264,125 have been insured.

Literature: HUD Handbook 4260.1, "*Miscellaneous Type Home Mortgage Insurance, Section 223(a), (e), and (d),*" no charge.

Who To Contact: *Headquarters Office*: None. *Regional or Local Office*: All projects are processed in Regional and Local HUD Offices. Persons are encouraged to communicate with the nearest local HUD Field Office listed in Table 2f.

Money—To Buy A Trailer Park

Mortgage Insurance, Manufactured Home Parks (14.127)

Description: Uncle Sam will help you buy a trailer park. This program provides guaranteed/insured loans of up to 40 years to finance the construction or rehabilitation of manufactured home parks with 5 or more spaces. The maximum mortgage limit is $9,000 per space. In areas where cost levels so require, limits may be increased up to 140 percent on a case-by-case basis.

Eligibility Requirements: Investors, builders, developers.

Financial Information: Last year, 4 projects with 913 spaces were insured. Cumulative totals are 394 projects with 67,502 spaces insured with a value of $221,794,420.

Literature: "*Fact Sheet, Manufactured Home Parks*"; "*Mobile Home Parks Financing,*" no charge; "*Mobile Home Park Program,*" no charge.

Who To Contact: *Headquarters Office*: Office of Multifamily Development, Department of Housing and Urban Development, Washington, DC 20410. Phone: (202) 708-1142. *Regional or Local Office*: All projects are processed in Regional and Local HUD Offices. Persons are encouraged to communicate with the nearest local HUD Field Office listed Table 2f.

Money for Homeowners to Buy "Fee-Simple Title" From Lessors

Section 240 (14.130)

Description: Guaranteed/insured loans to help homeowners of one- to four-family houses obtain fee-simple title to the property which they hold under long-term leases and on which their homes are located. The maximum amount insurable is $10,000 ($30,000 if the property is located in Hawaii) per unit.

Eligibility Requirements: All homeowners whose homes are located on property which is held under long-term ground leases are eligible.

Financial Information: Cumulative totals are 362 fee simple title purchases insured with a value of $8,956,250.

literature: "*Fact Sheet: Fee Simple Title,*" free.

Who To Contact: *Headquarters Office*: None. *Regional or Local Office*: Persons should communicate with the nearest local HUD Field Office (Table 2f).

Money—to Finance Rental Housing

Mortgage Insurance Section 207 (14.134)

Description: Our friends in Washington will help you become a landlord. This program will give you a guaranteed/insured loans in order to provide good quality rental housing for middle income families. Insured mortgages may be used to finance the construction or rehabilitation of rental detached, semidetached, row, walk-up, or elevator type structures with 5 or more units.

Eligibility Requirements: Investors, builders, developers others who meet HUD requirements.

Financial Information: Cumulative totals through September 30, 1996 are 2,505 projects with 325,148 units insured with a value of $4,226,482,176.

Literature: "*Fact Sheet: Section 207 Rental Housing,*" no charge; "*Project Mortgage*

Insurance Basic Section 207 Instructions," no charge.

Who To Contact: *Headquarters Office*: Office of Multifamily Development, Department of Housing and Urban Development, Washington, DC 20410. Phone: (202) 708-1142. *Regional or Local Office*: All projects are processed in Regional or Local HUD Offices. Persons are encouraged to communicate with the nearest local HUD Field Office listed in Table 2f.

Money—to Invest in Rental and Cooperative Housing for Moderate Income Families and Elderly

Mortgage Insurance Section 221d-3, 4 (14.135)

Description: Guaranteed/insured loans of up to 40 years to construct or rehabilitate good quality rental or cooperative housing for moderate income families and the elderly and handicapped.

Single Room Occupancy (SRO) may also be insured under this section (see Program **14.184**, page 115). Units may be in detached, semi-detached, row, walkup, or elevator-type housing containing 5 or more units. Project may be designed specifically for the elderly and handicapped.

Eligibility Requirements: Public, profit-motivated sponsors, limited distribution, nonprofit cooperative, builder-seller, investor-sponsor, and general mortgagors are eligible.

Financial Information: Last year, 156 projects with 29,987 units valued at $1.7 billion were insured. Cumulative totals are 11,647 projects with 1,328,803 units valued at $35 billion.

Literature: "*Fact Sheet: Rental Housing for Moderate Income Families*," no charge; HUD Handbook 4560.2, "*Mortgage Insurance for Moderate-Income Housing Projects, Section 221 (d)(4)*," no charge; HUD Handbook 4560.1, Section 221(d)(3), "*Market Interest Rate for Project Mortgage Insurance*," no charge; HUD Handbook 4560.3, "*Mortgage Insurance for Single Room Occupancy Projects*," no charge;

HUD Handbook 4550.3; "*Basic Cooperative Housing Insurance Handbook*," no charge.

Who To Contact: *Headquarters Office*: Office of Multifamily Development, Department of Housing and Urban Development, Washington, DC 20410. Phone: (202) 708-1142. *Regional or Local Office*: All projects are processed in Regional and Local HUD Offices. Persons are encouraged to communicate with the nearest local HUD Office listed in Table 2f.

Mortgages for Home Buyers With Bad Credit

Mortgage Insurance—Special Credit Risks (14.140)

Description: If you have poor credit, this program can make home ownership possible. It provides guaranteed/insured loans to make homeownership possible for low and moderate-income families who cannot meet normal HUD requirements. These loans may be used to purchase or refinance one-to-four family homes or condominiums. The maximum insurable mortgage is $18,000 ($21,000 in high cost areas).

Applicant Eligibility: Only families who do not qualify for homeownership under regular HUD credit standards are eligible. Counseling assistance must be obtained by the applicant from a HUD-approved counseling agency. Information regarding availability of counseling assistance is available through local HUD Field Offices. A limited listing of the names, addresses and telephone numbers of counseling agencies within caller-selected ZIP Code areas is available by calling the toll-free telephone number (800) 569-4278.

Financial Information: A total of 5,255 units have been insured with a value of $81,262,824.

Literature: "*Credit Assistance and Counseling for Low and Moderate Income Home Purchasers (Section 237)*," HUD Handbook FHA 4440.5, no charge.

Who to Contact: *Headquarters Office*: None. *Regional or Local Office*: Contact appropriate local HUD Field Office listed in Table 2f.

Money—To Fix Up Multifamily Rental Housing
Supplemental Loan Insurance (14.151)

Description: Guaranteed/insured loans to finance repairs, additions and improvements and energy conservation improvements to multifamily projects, group practice facilities, hospitals, or nursing homes already insured by HUD or held by HUD. Major movable equipment for health facilities may be covered.

Eligibility Requirements: Owners of multifamily projects or facilities already subject to a mortgage insured by HUD.

Financial Information: Cumulatively, 314 projects with 56,150 units have been insured for a total of $1.4 billion.

Literature: HUD Handbook 4585.1 "*Supplemental Loans for Project Mortgage Insurance, Section 241,*" no charge.

Who To Contact: *Headquarters Office*: Office of Multifamily Development, Department of Housing and Urban Development, Washington, DC 20411. Phone: (202) 708-1142. *Regional or Local Office*: All projects are processed in Regional and Local HUD Offices. Persons are encouraged to communicate with the nearest local HUD Field Office listed in Table 2f.

Money—So You Can Buy a Home With Graduated Mortgage Payments
Section 245 Graduated Payment Mortgage Program (14.159)

Description: This program provides guaranteed/insured loans of up to 30 years to facilitate early home ownership for households that expect their incomes to rise. The program allows homeowners to make smaller monthly payments initially and to increase their size gradually over time.

These mortgage loans may be used by owner-occupant mortgagors to finance the purchase of proposed, under construction, or existing single family housing, and condominiums. Maximum insurable mortgage can be as high as 97 percent of the appraised value and closing costs of the property, minus all the deferred interest under the financing plan—up to $125,000 (more in high-cost areas). The downpayment is the difference between the maximum loan amount and the purchase price of the home.

Eligibility Requirements: All persons intending to occupy the property.

Financial Information: In the latest reported year, 276 units valued at $24,632,803 were insured. Cumulative totals are 522,528 units valued at $29,372,640,373.

Literature: "*Move in...With A Graduated Payment Mortgage,*" no charge; "*Lending and Selling With A Graduated Payment Mortgage*", no charge; *HUD Handbook 4240.2*, no charge.

Who To Contact: *Headquarters Office*: None. *Regional or Local Office*: Persons are encouraged to communicate with their nearest local HUD Field Office (see Table 2f).

Money—to Buy a Trailer and Trailer Lot
Mortgage Insurance Title 1 (14.162)

Description: Want to live in a trailer, fixed in place? This program provides guaranteed/insured loans of up to 90 percent to purchase manufactured homes and lots for buyers intending to use them as their principal places of residence. The maximum term is 20 years for a single-module home and lot; 25 years for a double-module home and lot; and 15 years for a lot only.

Eligibility Requirements: All persons are eligible to apply.

Financial Information: *Range and Average of Financial Assistance*: Up to $64,800 for a manufactured home and a suitably developed lot; $16,200 for a developed lot only. (Maximum loan limits may be increased in designated high-cost areas.)

Literature: "*Financing Manufactured Homes,*" no charge.

Who To Contact: *Headquarters Office*: Chief, Mortgage Insurance Division, Department of Housing and Urban Development, 451 7th Street,

SW., Room 9272, Washington, DC 20410. Phone: (202) 708-2121. *Regional or Local Office*: Contact HUD Headquarters for program information.

Money—to Buy a Home in an Area Hurt by Military Cutbacks
Mortgage Insurance Section 238b (14.165)

Description: Guaranteed/insured loans of 30-35 years to help families undertake home ownership in areas hurt by defense cuts. These loans may be used to finance the purchase of proposed, under construction, or existing one - to four-family housing, as well as to refinance indebtedness on existing housing. The downpayment is the difference between the maximum loan amount and the purchase price of the home.

Eligibility Requirements: All families intending to occupy the property are eligible to apply.

Financial Information: In the latest reported year, 401 units valued at $21,333,986 were insured. Cumulative totals are 3,933 units valued at $176,463,062.

Literature: *"Home Mortgage Insurance,"* no charge; Fact Sheet *"HUD-FHA Program for Home Mortgage Insurance,"* no charge.

Who To Contact: *Headquarters Office*: None. *Regional or Local Office*: Persons are encouraged to communicate with the nearest local HUD field Office listed in Table 2f.

Money—for Members of the Armed Services to Buy Homes
Mortgage Insurance Section 222 (14.166)

Description: If you are in the Armed Forces, you can get a guaranteed/insured loan of 30-35 years to help you purchase a one-family home. These insured loans may be used to finance the purchase of an existing house or to build a new house. (The loan may not be used to refinance a home you already own.) The home may be located any place

in the United States, Puerto Rico, Guam, the Trust Territory of the Pacific Islands, or the Virgin Islands.

Eligibility Requirements: Military personnel on active duty for two or more years in any branch of the United States Armed Forces, the Coast Guard or the National Oceanic and Atmospheric Administration.

Financial Information: In the latest reported year, 19 units were insured, valued at $1,866,512. Cumulative totals are 275,441 units insured, valued at almost $4.5 billion.

Who To Contact: *Headquarters Office*: Director, Single Family Development Division, Office of Insured Single Family Housing, Department of Housing and Urban Development, Washington, DC 20410. (202) 708-2700. *Regional or Local Office*: Persons are encouraged to communicate with their nearest local HUD Field Office (see Table 2f).

Housing—for Persons with AIDS
Housing Opportunities for Persons with Aids
"HOPWA" (14.241)

Description: Persons with AIDS are eligible for housing assistance. Under this program, HUD make grants to States and localities to help meet the housing needs of persons with AIDS or related diseases and their families.

Grants may be used for:
- Tenant-based rental assistance
- Short-term rent, mortgage, and utility payments to prevent the homelessness of the tenant or mortgagor of a dwelling
- Housing information services
- Acquisition and conversion of facilities to provide housing and services
- New construction

Eligibility Requirements: Eligible beneficiaries are low income persons with AIDS or related diseases, including HIV infection, and their families. Regardless of income, persons with AIDS may receive housing information.

Financial Information: Total allotted for the latest reported year, $277,432,000.

113

Who To Contact: *Headquarters Office*: David Vos, Director, Office of HIV/AIDS Housing, Community Planning and Development, Department of Housing and Urban Development, 451 Seventh Street SW, Room 7154, Washington, DC 20410. (202) 708-1934. Information on HOPWA is also available on the HUD home page on the Internet at http://www.hud.gov/home.html. *Regional or Local Office*: Designated Community Planning and Development staff in each HUD Field Office. HUD Field Offices are listed in Table 2f.

Rent Assistance Payments for Low Income Families in Public Housing
Section 8 Rental Voucher Program (14.871)

Description: This program provides rent subsidy payments to public housing agencies on behalf of eligible tenants to provide decent, safe, and sanitary housing for very low income families at rents they can afford.

Beneficiary Eligibility:

- Very low income families (whose income does not exceed 50 percent of the median income for the area with adjustments for smaller and larger families) and, on an exception basis, lower income families (whose income does not exceed 80 percent of the median income for the area, adjusted for smaller and larger families);

- Very low income families including the elderly, handicapped and disabled, large families and those who have been displaced.

Financial Information: Housing assistance payments are used to make up the difference between the local market rent and 30 percent of the family's adjusted income. The family may choose to rent a unit for more or less than the payment standard. However, the family must pay a minimum of 10 percent of its gross income. Assistance is provided for 60 months and can be renewed.

As of the latest reported year, there were approximately 1,636,000 rental vouchers available under this program to assist eligible families.

Who To Contact: *Headquarters Office*: Office of Public and Assisted Housing Delivery, Office of Rental Assistance, Department of Housing and Urban Development, Washington, DC 20410. (202) 708-0477. *Regional or Local Office*: HUD Office listed in Table 2f that has jurisdiction over the area in which the dwellings are located.

Reverse Mortgages to Help Seniors Convert Home Equity into Monthly Income
Home Equity Conversion Mortgages Section 255 (14.183)

Description: Under this program, HUD guarantees loans that enable elderly homeowners to convert the value of their paid-up homes into monthly streams of income or lines of credit by use of "**reverse mortgage**" loans. The amounts that borrowers can receive are determined by using such factors as age of the youngest borrower in the home, the interest rate, and the value of the home.

Eligibility Requirements: Eligible borrowers are persons 62 years of age or older, eligible properties are one unit dwellings (including condominiums).

Financial Information: In the latest reported year, 3,604 units were insured with a value of $368,733,279. Cumulative totals include approximately 16,000 insured loans.

Literature: "*Options for Elderly Homeowners: A Guide to Reserve Mortgages and Their Alternatives*," no charge.

Who To Contact: *Headquarters Office*: Director, Insured Family Development Division, Office of Single Family Housing, Department of Housing and Urban Development, Washington, DC 20410. (202) 708-2700. *Regional or Local Office*: Persons are encouraged to communicate with the nearest local HUD Field Office listed in Table 2f.

Money—to Invest in Single Room Occupancy (SRO) Housing
Mortgage Insurance Section 221d SRO (14.184)

Description: Builders and developers can get guaranteed/insured loans for up to 40 years to finance construction or substantial rehabilitation of projects of 5 or more units comprised primarily of one room residential units (SROs) intended for at those tenants who have a source of income but are priced out of the rental apartment market. No more than 10 percent of the total gross floor space can be dedicated to commercial use (20 percent for substantial rehabilitation projects).

Eligibility Requirements: Profit-motivated entities; nonprofit entities; builder/sellers with a nonprofit purchaser; limited distribution entities; public entities.

Financial Information: Cumulative totals: three projects with 831 units insured for $16,248,700.

Literature: HUD Handbook 4560.3.

Who To Contact: *Headquarters Office*: Office of Multifamily Development, Department of Housing and Urban Development, Washington, DC 20410. Phone: (202) 708-1142. *Regional or Local Office*: All projects are processed in Regional and Local HUD offices. Persons are encouraged to communicate with the nearest local HUD Field Office listed in Table 2f.

Money—from Local Development Organizations for Housing and Business
Community Develop. Block Grants/Entitlement Grants (14.218)

Description: This program provides funds to develop viable urban communities, to furnish decent housing and a suitable living environment, and to expand economic opportunities, principally for persons of low and moderate income.

Local governments with more than 50,000 population apply for funding, and then, acting as intermediaries, make grants to local beneficiaries

for undertakings that will benefit low- and moderate-income persons.

Some of the specific activities that can be carried out with Community Development Block Grant (CDBG) funds include:
- Acquisition of real property
- Relocation and demolition
- Rehabilitation of residential and nonresidential structures
- Assistance to microenterprises or other for-profit entities
- Funds for economic development projects that will expand employment opportunities.

Eligibility Requirements: Central cities in metropolitan areas, other cities over 50,000 in metropolitan areas, and qualified urban counties of at least 200,000 are eligible to receive CDBG entitlement grants. The funds, in turn are granted to support activities—e.g.,, loans and grants to business activities—whose principal beneficiaries are low- and moderate-income persons.

Financial Information: During the latest reported year, 1008 local governmental units were eligible to receive entitlement grants totaling approximately $3 billion, which are then passed down to local beneficiaries.

Who To Contact: *Headquarters Office*: Entitlement Communities Division, Office of Block Grant Assistance, Community Planning and Development, 451 7th Street, S.W., Washington, DC 20410. (202) 708-1577. *Regional or Local Office*: Contact appropriate HUD Field Office listed in Table 2f.

Money—from Local Development Organizations for Projects in New York State and Hawaii
Community Development Block Grants/Small Cities Program (14.219)

Description: Basically the same as **14.218**, for cities under 50,000 populations in New York State and Hawaii.

Financial Information: Funds awarded in latest

reported year, $5,512,000.

Who To Contact: *Headquarters Office*: State and Small Cities Division, Office of Block Grant Assistance Community Planning and Development, Department of Housing and Urban Development, 451 7th Street, S.W., Washington, DC 20410. (202) 708-1322. *Regional or Local Office*: Contact appropriate HUD Field Office for New York or Hawaii listed in Table 2f.

Money—from Local Development Organizations for Projects in American Overseas Possessions
Community Development Block Grants/Special Purpose Grants/Insular Areas (14.225)

Description: Basically the same as **14.218**, for American Samoa, Guam, the Northern Mariana Islands, Palau and the Virgin Islands.

Financial Information: Funds awarded in latest reported year, $6,984,000.

Who To Contact: *Headquarters Office*: Office of Block Grant Assistance, Community Planning and Development, Department of Housing and Urban Development, 451 7th St., S.W., Washington, DC 20410. (202) 708-1322. *Regional or Local Office*: Contact the headquarters office.

Money—from Local Development Organizations for Projects in Small Cities
Community Development Block Grants/State's Program (14.228)

Description: This program is similar to **14.218**, for funding for small cities in the 48 states (other than New York and Hawaii: see **14.219**) and Puerto Rico that have opted to develop and administer their own programs.

Financial Information: Funds awarded in latest reported year, $1,314,638,000.

Who To Contact: *Headquarters Office*: Same as **14.219**. *Regional or Local Office*: Contact appropriate HUD Field Office in Table 2f.

Money—to Invest In Affordable Low-Income Rental Housing
HOME Investment Partnerships Program—"Home Program" (14.239)

Description: This program makes grants to expand the supply of affordable housing, particularly rental housing, for low and very low income Americans.

Funds may be used for:
- Rehabilitation
- New construction of housing
- Acquisition of housing
- Assistance to homebuyers
- Tenant-based rental assistance

States, cities, and urban counties are eligible to receive formula allocations. Acting as inter-mediareis between the Federal government and local borrowers, they can pass these funds down to private developers for projects that will benefit low and very low income families.

Eligibility Requirements: Borrowers who will use funds to benefit homeowners and homebuyers with incomes below 80 percent of the area median.

Financial Information: HOME funds have been committed to assist the acquisition, rehabilitation or construction of 343,072 housing units. An additional 61,944 tenants received rental assistance.

Who To Contact: *Headquarters Office*: Mary Kolesar, Director, Office of Affordable Housing Programs, Community Planning and Development, Department of Housing and Urban Development, 451 7th Street, SW, Washington, DC 20410. (202) 708-2470. *Regional or Local Office*: Contact appropriate HUD Field Office listed in Table 2f.

States Subsidized Housing Programs for Moderate Income Persons

Description: Most States have programs that help make rental apartment, condominiums and condominiums —all in privately owned buildings — affordable for moderate- and lower- income families. Under these programs, the government provides subsidies directly to the owner or builder who then applies those subsidies to the rents he charges moderate- or lower-income tenants.

There are a number of ways the States accomplish this: they pass federal housing credits and block grants on to local developers of affordable housing; they make tax credits and abatements so the buildings pay lower property taxes and can pass the savings to the tenants; they issue mortgage guarantees so builders pay lower interest rates; they make direct subsidies to help pay part of the rent charged to lower-income tenants; and there are a variety of other programs.

In California, for example, the California Housing Finance Agency makes below market interest rate loans to developers and nonprofit sponsors of affordable rental projects. To date 20,912 apartments have been financed.

In New York State, the state's Mitchell-Lama Housing Program encourages the building of private affordable rental and cooperative apartments for moderate income families by making low-interest mortgages and real property exemptions. To date over 115,000 apartments have been built under the program.

In Massachusetts, the Housing Finance Agency provides reduced interest 30-40 year insured loan packages so that affordable private housing can be built.

Eligibility: To be eligible for most programs, your income must be below set maximums for the area.

Who to Contact: If you want to apply for housing in a state-aided privately owned building, the easiest way is to visit or phone the management office for that apartment building and apply. Each development maintains its own waiting list. Get a listing of the privately owned subsidized housing sites in your area by contacting your State's housing agency (see Table 3c, Chapter 3). You can also contact your local U.S. Depart-ment of Housing and Urban Development (HUD) office (see Table 2f, Chapter 2) for a list of privately owned subsidized housing for your area. An Internet site with much helpful information is: http://www.hud.gov\sec8\massachu.html

DEPARTMENT OF ENERGY

Weatherization Assistance for Low–Income Persons
(81.042)

Description: This program provides grants to insulate the dwellings of low-income persons, particularly the elderly and handicapped low-income, in order to conserve needed energy and to aid those persons least able to afford higher utility costs. Up to $1,957 per dwelling unit. Funds may cover improvements such as attic insulation, caulking, weatherstripping and storm windows, furnace efficiency modifications, certain mechanical measures to heating and cooling systems, and replacement furnaces and boilers.

Beneficiary Eligibility: All low-income households are eligible to receive weatherization assistance. A low-income household is one whose combined income falls at or below 125 percent of the poverty level.

Financial Information: Over 5,000,000 homes had been weatherized with DOE funds. Assistance during the latest reported year totals $154,000,000.

Who To Contact:
Headquarters Office: Director, Office of State and Community Programs, Mail Stop EE-44, Office of Energy Efficiency and Renewable Energy, Department of Energy, Forrestal Building, Washington, DC 20585. (202) 586-4074.
Regional or Local offices:
- Boston: Hugh Saussy (617) 565-9710
- Phila.: Brian Conner (215) 656-6954

- Atlanta: Jim Powel, (404) 347-2888
- Chicago: Peter Dreyfuss (312) 886-8575
- Denver: Bill Becker, (303) 275-4801
- Seattle: Kathy M. Vega, (206) 553-1132

FEDERAL EMERGENCY MANAGEMENT AGENCY

Subsidized Flood Insurance for Homeowners
(83.100)

Description: Subsidized property insurance against physical damage or loss of buildings and/ or contents caused by floods, mudslide or flood-related erosion. Maximum coverage available is:

- $250,000 for single-family residential structures
- $250,000 for all other residential structures
- $100,000 for contents per dwelling unit
- $500,000 for non-residential structures
- $500,000 for contents of non-residential structures

Flood insurance must be purchased as a condition of any form of Federal or federally-related financial assistance, including Federal grants, disaster assistance, and mortgage loans from federally regulated lending institutions when the improved real property is located within identified special flood hazard areas where flood insurance is available.

Beneficiary Eligibility: Residents, business, and property owners.

Financial Information: There are 4,262,123 policies in force, worth some $561 billion.

Literature:, *"Answers to Questions About the National Flood Insurance Program," "Mandatory Purchase of Flood Insurance Guidelines," "Repairing Your Flooded Home."*

Who To Contact: *Headquarters Office:* Edward L. Connor, Federal Insurance Administration, FEMA, Washington, DC 20472. (202) 646-3429 *Regional or Local Office:* Contact the appropriate FEMA regional office in Table 3b.

VETERANS ADMINISTRATION

Money—for Veterans to Buy Housing
"VA Home Loans" (64.114)

Description: The Department of Veterans Affairs provides home mortgage loan guarantees to assist veterans, certain service personnel, and certain unremarried surviving spouses of veterans obtain credit for the purchase, construction or improvement of homes on more liberal terms than are generally available to non-veterans.

Generally such loans, because they are guaranteed by the government, are made on more liberal terms than are generally available to non-veterans. Interest rates are lower, there may be no down payment required, and the repayment period may be longer.

Home loans can be used to buy, build or improve a home or condominium; purchase a manufactured home and lot to which the home will be permanently affixed; refinance a mortgage or existing VA loan or other lien on a house owned by the applicant. Applicants must have sufficient present and prospective income to meet loan repayment terms and have a satisfactory credit record. See page 156 for more information.

Money—for Disabled Veterans to Buy a Home
64.118

Description: The VA makes loans or grants of up to $33,000 to certain severely disabled vets for specially adaptive housing with special features or movable facilities made necessary by the nature of their disabilities. See page 157 for details.

Money—for Veterans to Buy Manufactured Mobile Homes
(64.119)

Description: Guaranteed/insured loans (of up to approximately 20 years) to assist veterans, servicepersons, and certain unremarried surviving spouses of veterans purchase a manufactured home on more liberal terms than are available to non-veterans. See page 159 for more information.

Loans—to Native American Veterans to Acquire a Home
VA Native American Veteran Direct Loan Program (64.126)

Description: Direct loans to certain Native American veterans for the purchase, construction, or repair of the veteran's home on trust lands. Also for the purchase of a manufactured home to be permanently affixed to a lot that is already held in lease hold by the applicant. See page 159.

DEPARTMENT OF HEALTH AND HUMAN SERVICES

Low—Income Home Energy Assistance
(93.568)

Description: This program subsidizes heating, air conditioning and home weatherization costs of low-income households. Under the program, Uncle Sam makes grants to States and other jurisdictions, which, in turn, make payments directly to eligible low-income households or, on behalf of such households, to energy suppliers to assist in meeting the cost of home energy.

Beneficiary Eligibility:
- Households whose income doesn't exceed the greater of 150% of the poverty level or 60% of the State median income, or
- Households with recipients getting "welfare," Supplemental Security Insurance (SSI), Food Stamps or certain income-tested veterans' benefits.

Financial Information: $1.2 billion in the latest reported year for heating costs. 4.1 million households receive assistance.

Who To Contact: *Headquarters Office*: Janet M. Fox, Director, Div. of Energy Assistance, Office of Community Services, Administration for Children, Youth and Families, Dept. of Health and Human Services, 370 L'Enfant Promenade, SW., Washington, DC 20447. (202) 401-5661. *Regional or Local Office*: None.

OTHER PROGRAMS

Homesteading Programs

Description: In the past, the Federal Government had a program that gave unused land to people to live on. This program is over, except for a state homesteading program in Alaska and occasionally in some other underpopulated states.

But various States and local governments have an even better program — **Urban Homesteading**. The State and local governments receive title to certain houses in need of repair. They then offer these homes to persons who are willing to fix them up and live in them for a period of time. They generally offer these fixer-upper homes for very little money.

Alaska: Alaska still has a land giveaway program, Alaska's Homestead and Homesite Program. Under this program, Alaskans can acquire state-owned land by:
- building a habitable, permanent dwelling,
- living on the land for a certain period of time,
- paying some of the costs involved, such as surveying.

To qualify you must have resided in the state for at least one year.

Parcels are limited to a minimum of 40 acres for non-agricultural land or up to 160 acres for agricultural land. Homesite parcels range from one-half to five acres.

Who to Contact: Alaska Department of Natural Resources, Public Information Center, Frontier Building, 3601 "C" Street, Suite 200, Anchorage, AK 99503. (907)269-8400. Recorded information is available. Telephone (907) 269-8400 and press 2 for Land Sales/Homesteading.

State and Local Urban Homesteading Programs: These programs give you the opportunity to get a home from the government at very low cost if you promise to fix it up. Many States and cities conduct these programs. You can apply if you do not own a home and if you meet certain income qualifications. Here are some examples.

Minnesota Rural and Urban Homesteading Program: The Minnesota Housing Finance Agency operates this program that makes grants or loans to eligible applicants to acquire and rehabilitate single family homes. ***Who to Contact***: MHFA,400 Sibley Street, #300, St Paul, MN 55101. (651) 296-7608.

Missouri Homesteading: The state has a statute allowing any municipality to establish an urban homesteading program and homesteading agency. ***Who to Contact***: Missouri Housing Development Commission, 3435 Broadway, Kansas City, MO 64111. (816) 759-6600.

Michigan State Housing Development Authority: The MSHDA makes neighborhood housing grants to neighborhood and nonprofit housing organizations for urban homesteading programs. ***Who to Contact***: (517) 373-1974 and (517) 373-6840.

Baltimore Department of Housing and Community Development: This agency administers rehabilitation loans and grants to rehabilitate/rebuild homes. ***Who to Contact***: (410) 528-8457 and (410) 396-3124.

Largo, Florida, Community Development Department: This agency's Urban Homesteading Program is an example of a small city's program. Donated homes, relocated homes, and foreclosed homes purchased by the city are provided to eligible families. ***Who to Contact***: Largo Community Development Department, (813) 587-6749.

For More Information: For information on any particular State's programs contact that state's Housing Finance Agency in Table 3c. To find out about any specific city's programs, contact the city's Department of Community Development as listed in the government pages of the local phone book.

Table 3a: # NATURAL RESOURCES CONSERVATION SERVICE, DEPARTMENT OF AGRICULTURE

Alabama
Natural Resources Conservation Service, Dept. of Agriculture
381 Skyway Drive
Auburn, AL 36830
(334) 887-4500

Alaska
Natural Resources Conservation Service, Dept. of Agriculture
800 W. Evergreen Street, Suite 100
Palmer, Ak. 99645
(907) 761-7700

Arizona
Natural Resources Conservation Service, Dept. of Agriculture
3003 N. Central Ave., Ste. 800
Phoenix, AZ 85012-2945
(602) 280-8801

Arkansas
Natural Resources Conservation Service, Dept. of Agriculture
700 W. Capitol Avenue, RM. 3416
Little Rock, AR 72201-3225

(501) 301-3100

California
Natural Resources Conservation Service, Dept. of Agriculture
430 G Street #4164
Davis, CA 95616
(530) 792-5600

Colorado
Natural Resources Conservation Service, Dept. of Agriculture
655 Parfet Street, Room E200C
Lakewood, CO 80215-5517
(720) 544-2810

Connecticut
Natural Resources Conservation Service, Dept. of Agriculture
344 Merrow Road, Suite A
Tolland, CT 06084-3917
(860) 871-4011

Delaware
Natural Resources Conservation Service, Dept. of Agriculture

1203 College Park Dr., Ste. 101
Dover, DE 19904-8713
(302) 678-4160

Florida
Natural Resources Conservation Service, Dept. of Agriculture
PO Box 141510
Gainesville, FL 32614
(352) 338-9500

Georgia
Natural Resources Conservation Service, Dept. of Agriculture
Federal Building, PO Box 13
355 East Hancock Avenue
Athens, GA 30601-2769
(706) 546-2272

Hawaii
Natural Resources Conservation Service, Dept. of Agriculture
300 Ala Moana Blvd., Rm. 4-118
PO Box 50004
Honolulu, HI 96850-0002
(808) 541-2600

Idaho
Natural Resources Conservation
Service, Dept. of Agriculture
9173 West Barnes Drive, Suite C
Boise, Idaho 83709-1574
(208) 378-5700

Illinois
Natural Resources Conservation
Service, Dept. of Agriculture
2118 W. Park Court
Champaign, IL 61821
(217) 353-6600

Indiana
Natural Resources Conservation
Service, Dept. of Agriculture
6013 Lakeside Boulevard
Indianapolis, IN 46278-2933
(317) 290-3200

Iowa
Natural Resources Conservation
Service, Dept. of Agriculture
Federal Building
210 Walnut Street, Suite 693
Des Moines, IA 50309-2180
(515) 284-4260

Kansas
Natural Resources Conservation
Service, Dept. of Agriculture
760 South Broadway
Salina, KS 67401
(913) 823-4565

Kentucky
Natural Resources Conservation
Service, Dept. of Agriculture
771 Corporate Drive, Suite 110
Lexington, KY 40503-5479
(859) 224-7350

Louisiana
Natural Resources Conservation
Service, Dept. of Agriculture
3737 Government Street
Alexandria, LA 71303
(318) 473-7751

Maine
Natural Resources Conservation
Service, Dept. of Agriculture
967 Illinois Avenue, Suite #3
Bangor, ME 04401
(207) 990-9100, ext. 3

Maryland
Natural Resources Conservation
Service, Dept. of Agriculture
John Hansen Business Ctr., Ste. 301

339 Busch's Frontage Road
Annapolis, MD 21401-5534
(410) 757-0861

Massachusetts
Natural Resources Conservation
Service, Dept. of Agriculture
451 West Street
Amherst, MA 01002-2995
(413) 253-4350

Michigan
Natural Resources Conservation
Service, Dept. of Agriculture
3001 Coolidge Rd., Suite 250
East Lansing, MI 48823-6123
(517) 324-5270

Minnesota
Natural Resources Conservation
Service, Dept. of Agriculture
600 Farm Credit Building
375 Jackson Street
St. Paul, MN 55101-1854
(651) 602-7900

Mississippi
Natural Resources Conservation
Service, Dept. of Agriculture
Suite 1321, Federal Building
100 West Capital Street
Jackson, MS 39269-1399
(601) 965-5196

Missouri
Natural Resources Conservation
Service, Dept. of Agriculture
Parkade Center, Suite 250
601 Business Loop, 70 West
Columbia, MO 65203-2546
(573) 876-0901

Montana
Natural Resources Conservation
Service, Dept. of Agriculture
Federal Building, Room 443
10 East Babcock Street
Bozeman, MT 59715-4704
(406) 587-6813

Nebraska
Natural Resources Conservation
Service, Dept. of Agriculture
Federal Building, Room 152
100 Centennial Mall North
Lincoln, NE 68508-3866
(402) 437-5300

Nevada
Natural Resources Conservation
Service, Dept. of Agriculture
5301 Longley Lane

Building F, Suite 220
Reno, NV 89511-1805
(702) 784-5863

New Hampshire
Natural Resources Conservation
Service, Dept. of Agriculture
Federal Building
2 Madbury Road
Durham, NH 03824
(603) 868-7581

New Jersey
Natural Resources Conservation
Service, Dept. of Agriculture
1370 Hamilton Street
Somerset, NJ 08873
(732) 246-1171

New Mexico
Natural Resources Conservation
Service, Dept. of Agriculture
6200 Jefferson N.E.
Albuquerque, NM 87109-3734
(800) 410-2067

New York
Natural Resources Conservation
Service, Dept. of Agriculture
Suite 354, Room 520
441 South Salina Street
Syracuse, NY 13202-2450
(315) 477-6504

North Carolina
Natural Resources Conservation
Service, Dept. of Agriculture
4405 Bland Road, Suite 205
Raleigh, NC 27609-6293
(919) 873-2100

North Dakota
Natural Resources Conservation
Service, Dept. of Agriculture
Federal Building
220 East Rosser Ave.
Bismarck, ND 58502-1458
(701) 530-2000

Ohio
Natural Resources Conservation
Service, Dept. of Agriculture
Federal Building
200 North High St., Room 522
Columbus, OH 43215-2478
(614) 255-2472

Oklahoma
Natural Resources Conservation
Service, Dept. of Agriculture
100 USDA, Suite 203
Stillwater, OK 74074-2655

(405) 742-1204

Oregon
Natural Resources Conservation
Service, Dept. of Agriculture
101 SW Main Street, Suite 1300
Portland, OR 97204
(503) 414-3200

Pacific Basin Area
Natural Resources Conservation
Service, Dept. of Agriculture
FHB Building, Suite 301
400 Route 8
Mongmong, Guam 96910
(671) 472-7490

Pennsylvania
Natural Resources Conservation
Service, Dept. of Agriculture
One Credit Union Place, Ste. 340
Harrisburg, PA 17110-2993
(717) 237-2100

Puerto Rico
Natural Resources Conservation
Service, Dept. of Agriculture
IBM Building, Suite 604
654 Munoz Rivera Avenue
Hato Rey, PR 00918-4123

Rhode Island
Natural Resources Conservation
Service, Dept. of Agriculture
60 Quaker Lane, Suite 46
Warwick, RI 02886-0111
(401) 828-1300

South Carolina
Natural Resources Conservation
Service, Dept. of Agriculture
Strom Thurmond Federal Bldg.
1835 Assembly Street, Rm. 950
Columbia, SC 29201-2489
(800) 384-8732

South Dakota
Natural Resources Conservation
Service, Dept. of Agriculture
Federal Building
200 4th Street, S.W.
Huron, SD 57350-2475
(605) 352-1200

Tennessee
Natural Resources Conservation
Service, Dept. of Agriculture

801 Broadway, 675 U.S. Courthouse
Nashville, TN 37203-3878
(615) 736-5471

Texas
Natural Resources Conservation
Service, Dept. of Agriculture
W. R. Poage Federal Building
101 South Main Street
Temple, TX 76501-7682
(254) 742 - 9800

Utah
Natural Resources Conservation
Service, Dept. of Agriculture
Wallace F. Bennett Fed. Bldg.
125 South State St.
Salt Lake City, UT 84147
(801) 524-4550

Vermont
Natural Resources Conservation
Service, Dept. of Agriculture
356 Mountain View Dr., Suite 105
Colchester, VT 05446
(802) 951-6795

Virginia
Natural Resources Conservation
Service, Dept. of Agriculture
Culpeper Building
1606 Santa Rosa Rd., Suite 209
Richmond, VA 23229-5014
(804) 287-1691

Washington
Natural Resources Conservation
Service, Dept. of Agriculture
USDA, Natural Resources
Conservation Service
W. 316 Boone Ave., Suite 450
Spokane, WA 99201-2348
(509) 323-2900

West Virginia
Natural Resources Conservation
Service, Dept. of Agriculture
75 High St., Room 301
Morgantown, WV 26505
(304) 284-7540

Wisconsin
Natural Resources Conservation
Service, Dept. of Agriculture
6515 Watts Road, Suite 200
Madison, WI 53719-2726
(608) 276-USDA

Wyoming
Natural Resources Conservation
Service, Dept. of Agriculture
Federal Office Building
100 East B Street, Room 3124
Casper, WY 82601
(307) 261-5201-1911

REGIONAL OFFICES

West Regional Office
Natural Resources Conservation
Service, Dept. of Agriculture
430 G St., Ste. 4165
Davis, CA 95616
(530) 792-5700

Southeast Regional Office
Natural Resources Conservation
Service, Dept. of Agriculture
1720 Peachtree Rd., NW, Ste. 716-N
Atlanta, GA 30367
(404) 347-6105

Northern Plains Regional Office
Natural Resources Conservation
Service, Dept. of Agriculture
100 Centennial Mall N., Rm.152
Lincoln, NE 68508
(402) 437-5315

South Central Regional Office
Natural Resources Conservation
Service, Dept. of Agriculture
501 W. Felix Street, Building 23
PO Box 6459
Ft. Worth, TX 76115
(817) 334-5224, Ext. 3700

East Regional Office
Natural Resources Conservation
Service, Dept. of Agriculture
5601 Sunnyside Ave.,
Mail Stop 5410, Room 1-1290A
Beltsville, MD 20705-5000
(301) 504 2300

Midwest Regional Office
Natural Resources Conservation
Service, Dept. of Agriculture
1 Gifford Pinchot Dr., Rm. 204
Madison, WI 53705-3210
7(608) 264-5281

Table 3b: FEDERAL EMERGENCY MANAGEMENT AGENCY (FEMA) REGIONAL OFFICES

Region I
(Boston)
Regional Director, FEMA
J. W. McCormack
Post Office & Courthouse Building,
Room 442
Boston, MA 02109-4595
(617) 223-9561

Region II
(New York)
Regional Director, FEMA
26 Federal Plaza, Room 1311
New York, NY 10278-0002
(212) 680-3600

Region III
(Philadelphia)
Regional Director, FEMA
One Independence Mall, 6th floor
615 Chestnut St.
Philadelphia, PA 19106-4404
(215) 931-5614

Region IV
(Atlanta)

Kenneth D. Hutchison, FEMA
Regional Director
3003 Chamblee-Tucker Road
Atlanta, GA 30341
(770) 220-5400

Region V
(Chicago)
Regional Director, FEMA
536 S. Clark St., Sixth Floor
Chicago, IL 60605
(312) 408-5532

Region VI
(Dallas)
Regional Director, FEMA
Federal Regional Center
800 North Loop 288
Denton, TX 76201-3698
(940) 898-5127

Region VII
(Kansas City)
Regional Director, FEMA
2323 Grand Blvd., Suite 900
Kansas City, MO 64108-2670

(816) 283-7002

Region VIII
(Denver)
Regional Director, FEMA
Denver Federal Center
Building 710, Box 25267
Denver, CO 80225-0267
(303) 235-4830

Region IX
(San Francisco)
Regional Director, FEMA
Building 105
Presidio of San Francisco
San Francisco, CA 94129-1250
(415) 923-7175

Region X
(Seattle)
Regional Director, FEMA
Federal Regional Center
130-228th Street, S.W.
Bothell, WA 98021-9796
(206) 487-4678

Table 3c: STATE HOUSING FINANCE AGENCIES

NORTHEAST REGION
Connecticut Housing Finance
Authority
999 West Street
Rocky Hill, CT 06067-4005
(860) 721-9501

Delaware State Housing Authority
(302) 577-5001

District of Columbia Housing
Finance Agency
(202) 777-1600

Maine State Housing Authority
353 Water Street
Augusta, Maine 04330
1-800-452-4668

Maryland Department of Housing
and Community Development
100 Community Pl.
Crownsville, MD 21032
(800) 756-0119

Massachusetts Housing Finance
Agency
One Beacon St.
Boston, MA 02108
(617) 854-1000

New Hampshire Housing
Finance Authority
32 Constitution Drive
Bedford, NH 03110
1-800-640-7239

New Jersey Housing and Mortgage
Finance Agency
Single Family Division
637 South Clinton Ave.
Trenton, New Jersey 08650
1-800-NJ-HOUSE

New York City Housing
Development Corporation
(212) 227-5500

New York State Division of

Housing and Community Renewal
25 Beaver St., 6th Floor, New York,
NY 10004
(212) 480-6700

New York State Housing Finance
Agency
641 Lexington Avenue
New York, NY 10022
(212) 688-4000

Pennsylvania Housing Finance
Agency
2101 North Front Street
Harrisburg, PA 17105-8029 (717)
780-3800

Rhode Island Housing and
Mortgage Finance Corporation
44 Washington St.
Providence, RI 02903
(401) 751-5566

Vermont Housing Finance Agency
P.O. Box 408

Burlington, VT 05402-0408
(802) 864-5743

West Virginia Housing
Development Fund
814 Virginia Street, East
Charleston, WV 25301
(800) 933-9843

SOUTHEAST REGION
Alabama Housing Finance
Authority
(334) 244-9200

Arkansas Development Finance
Authority
100 Main Street, Suite 200
Little Rock, AR 72201
(501) 682-5900

Florida Housing Finance Agency
(904) 488-4197

Georgia Housing and Finance
Authority
60 Executive Park South
Atlanta, Georgia 30329
(404) 679-4940

Kentucky Housing Corporation
1231 Louisville Road
Frankfort, KY 40601
(800) 633-8896

Louisiana Housing Finance Agency
(225) 342-1320

Mississippi Home Corporation
PO Box 23369
Jackson, MS, 39225-3369
(601) 718-4642

North Carolina Housing Finance
Agency
3508 Bush Street
Raleigh, NC 27609-7509
(919) 877-5700

Puerto Rico Housing Finance
Corporation
(787) 765-7577

South Carolina State Housing
Finance and Development Authority
919 Bluff Road
Columbia, SC 29201
(803) 734-2000

Tennessee Housing Development
Agency
(615) 741-2400

Virgin Islands Housing Finance
Authority
(809) 772-3180

Virginia Housing Development
Authority
601 S. Belvidere St.
Richmond, Va. 23220
(800) 968-7837

WEST REGION
Alaska Housing Finance
Corporation
P.O. Box 101020
Anchorage, AK 99510
(907) 338-6100 in Anchorage or
(800) 478-AHFC (outside
Anchorage, but within Alaska)

Arizona Department of Commerce
(602) 280-1365

California Housing Finance Agency
(916) 322-3991

Colorado Housing and Finance
Authority
1981 Blake Street
Denver, CO 80202-1272
1-800-877-CHFA

State of Hawaii Housing Finance
and Development Corporation
677 Queen Street, Suite 300
Honolulu, HI 96813
(808) 587-0640

Idaho Housing and Finance
Association
565 West Myrtle
Boise, ID 83707
(208) 331-4882

Montana Board of Housing
Housing Division
(406) 841-2840

Nevada Housing Division
1802 N. Carson St., Suite 154
Carson City, NV 89701
(775) 687-4258

New Mexico Mortgage Finance
Authority
344 4th Street SW
Albuquerque, NM 87102
(800) 444-6880

Oregon Housing and Community
Services Department
PO Box 14508

Salem, OR 97309
(503) 986-2020

Texas Department of Housing
Community Affairs
P.O. Box 13941
Austin, TX 78711
(512) 475-3800

Utah Housing Finance Agency
(801) 521-6950

Washington State Housing
Finance Commission
(206) 464-7139

Wyoming Community
Development Authority
155 N. Beech
Casper, WY 82602
(307) 265-0603

MIDWEST CENTRAL REGION
Illinois Housing Development
Authority
401 N. Michigan Avenue, Suite 900
Chicago, Illinois 60611
(312) 836-5200

Indiana Housing Finance Authority
115 West Washington St.
Suite 1350, South Tower
Indianapolis, IN 46204
(800) 872-0371

Iowa Finance Authority
100 E. Grand, Suite 250
Des Moines, Iowa 50309
(800) 432-7230

Kansas Department of
Commerce & Housing
700 SW Harrison Street, Suite 1300
Topeka, Kansas 66603
(913) 296-5865

Michigan State Housing
Development Authority
401 South Washington Square
Lansing, Michigan 48909
(517) 373-8370

Minnesota Housing Finance Agency
(651) 296-7608

Missouri Housing
Development Commission
(816) 759-6600

Nebraska Investment Finance
Authority
200 Commerce Court,

1230 "O" Street,
Lincoln, NE 68508-1402.
(800) 204-NIFA

North Dakota Housing Finance
Agency
PO Box 1535
Bismarck, ND 58502
(800) 292-8621

Ohio Housing Finance Agency
57 East Main Street
Columbus, OH 43215
(614) 466-7970

Oklahoma Housing Finance
Agency
P. O. Box 26720
Oklahoma City, OK 73126-0720
(800) 256-1489

South Dakota Housing
Development Authority
(605) 773-3181

Wisconsin Housing and Economic
Development Authority
201 West Washington Ave. Ste. 700
Madison, WI 53701
(800) 334-6873

Chapter 4
HOW TO GET MONEY FOR EDUCATION

Many people do not continue with their schooling because of lack of money. They don't realize that Uncle Sam is the largest source of money for students in America. There are so many government grant and loan programs that you don't have to worry about money, whether it's to go to college, vocational school, return to high school, get special training or change your occupation.

The government has various programs to help you pay the cost of education. This help falls into three main categories — grants (scholarships and fellowships), low interest loans, and work-study programs that pay you money while you learn.

DEPARTMENT OF EDUCATION

The U.S. Department of Education has grants, low-interest loans and work-study programs for applicants who can prove financial need.

Money—to Needy Undergrads
Federal Pell Grant Program (84.063)

Description: The Pell Grant is the largest federal education grant program. It provides direct awards to eligible undergraduate students who have demonstrated financial need to help meet educational expenses. These awards do not have to be paid back. The student must have been accepted for enrollment in, or be making satisfactory academic progress at, an eligible institution of higher education (such as colleges, universities, vocational-technical schools, hospital schools of nursing) and for-profit institutions.

Eligibility Requirements: This program is only for undergraduates. Students must be making satisfactory academic progress and meeting financial need criteria.

Financial Information: *Range and Average of Financial Assistance*: From $400 to $3,300; Average award: $2,057. Approximately 3,853,000 students will receive Federal Pell grants this year.

To determine your award, you complete an *"Application for Federal Student Aid"* and submits it to the agency specified on the form. Taken into consideration are your parents' and/or your income and assets (excluding home), your family's household size, and the number of family members attending postsecondary institutions.

Literature: *"The Student Guide; Free Application for Federal Student Aid," "The Expected Family Contribution Formula," "The Student Financial Aid Handbook."*

Who To Contact: *Headquarters Office*: Division of Policy Development, Student Financial Assistance Programs, Office of Postsecondary Education, Department of Education, 400 Maryland Avenue, SW., ROB-3, Washington, DC 20202. Contact: Grants Branch. (202) 708-8242. *Regional or Local Office*: Federal Student Aid

Information Center. (800) 433-3243. Or see the Director of Student Financial Aid at the institution you attend or wish to attend or your high school guidance counselor.

Money—So Needy Undergrads Can Continue in College

Federal Supplemental Educational Opportunity Grants "FSEOG" (84.007)

Description: This grant is available to undergraduate students with exceptional financial need who are also Pell Grant recipients. The program is very similar to the Pell Grant program and supplements it. And it does not have to be paid back.

Grants range from $100 to $4,000 per academic year. For a program of study abroad that has reasonable costs in excess of the home costs, the amount of the grant may exceed the $4,000 maximum by as much as $400. A student is eligible to receive a FSEOG for the period of time needed to complete the first undergraduate baccalaureate course of study being pursued by that student

Beneficiary Eligibility: Needy undergraduate students enrolled or accepted for enrollment as regular students and maintaining satisfactory academic progress in accordance with the standards and practices of the institution.

Financial Information: *Range and Average of Financial Assistance per Student*: $200 to $4,000 per year; $735 average.

Literature: "*Student Guide Fact Sheet*," free; "*Student Financial Aid Handbook*," free.

Who To Contact: *Headquarters Office*: Policy Development Division, Student Financial Assistance Programs, Office of Assistant Secretary for Postsecondary Education, Department of Education, 400 Maryland Avenue, SW., Washington, DC 20202-5446. Contact: Harold McCullough, Chief, Campus-Based Programs Section, Grants Branch. (202) 708-8498. *Regional or Local Office*: You should contact the educational institution you attend or plan to attend.

Student Loans

Federal Family Education Loans, "Federal Stafford Loan Program," "Federal PLUS Loans" (84.032)

Description: These are the Federal Government's major programs of guaranteed/insured loans to vocational, undergraduate, and graduate students who are attending school at least half-time to help pay for educational expenses.

Under this program low-interest loans are made by such lenders as banks, credit unions, savings and loans, and schools, and are insured by a State or private nonprofit guaranty agency and reinsured by the Federal government. Applicants may apply for a loan each year they are in school.

Repayment generally is made over a period of five to ten years. Repayment on Federal Stafford loans begins six months after the student ceases to carry at least one-half the normal full-time academic workload. Repayment of principal and interest on PLUS loans generally begins within 60 days of disbursement of the last installment

Eligibility Requirements: Any U.S. citizen, national, or person in the United States for other than a temporary purpose, who is enrolled or accepted for enrollment in a degree or certificate program on at least a half-time basis as an undergraduate, graduate, or professional student at a participating postsecondary school may apply.

Students enrolled in a program that is required by a State for elementary or secondary teacher certification are also eligible for this program.

Program Details:
Subsidized Federal Stafford Loan Program.
Subsidized Federal Stafford loans are need-based loans for undergraduates and graduate students. Your family's income, assets and expected contribution to your schooling are taken into account in determining how much you may borrow.

The maximum loan may not exceed $2,625 for the first academic year of undergraduate education, $3,500 for the second academic year, and $5,500 for each remaining year of undergraduate education; total undergraduate loans outstanding may not exceed $23,000.

Graduate and professional students may borrow up to $8,500 annually for a maximum outstanding of $65,500 (includes amounts borrowed as an undergraduate student under the Stafford Loan program.

Unsubsidized Stafford Program. This is a non-need based lending program. Graduate or professional students, and independent under-graduate students may apply.

Undergraduate students may borrow up to $4,000 for each of the first two academic years and $5,000 for each remaining year of an undergraduate program, with an aggregate loan maximum of $23,000.

A graduate or professional student may borrow up to $10,000 per academic year, with an aggregate loan maximum of $73,000, including any Unsubsidized Stafford loans borrowed as an undergraduate student;

PLUS Program. This program lets parents borrow for dependent students. Your parents can borrow up to the cost of your education minus other financial aid you are receiving. There is no aggregate loan maximum.

Financial Information: In the latest reported year, 5,563,000 loans were made.

Who To Contact:
Headquarters Office: Office of Student Financial Assistance, Department of Education, Washington, DC 20202. (800) 433-3243.
Regional or Local Office: Applications for the loan are obtained from a participating lender, guaranty agency, or school. The borrower completes his or her portion of the application and submits it to the school.

The school must certify that the student meets the eligibility requirements for the loan and the student's cost of attendance, the estimated financial assistance that the student is expected to receive, and, for a subsidized Stafford Loan, the family's expected contribution as determined by a need analysis formula.

Low-Interest College Loans
Federal Perkins Loan Program—Federal Capital Contributions (84.038)

Description: This loan program makes low interest loans available to both graduate and undergraduate students with demonstrated financial need to help meet educational expenses. Under this program, federal funds are allocated to educational institutions and they in turn award funds to students

Beneficiary Eligibility: Undergraduate, graduate, or professional students enrolled or accepted for enrollment as regular students in an eligible program, are maintaining satisfactory academic progress in accordance with the standards and practices of the institution, have financial need.

Financial Information: In the latest reported year, 677,000 Perkins loans were awarded. The average loan was $1,600.

The maximum annual loan is $6,000 for a graduate or professional student, $4,000 for an undergraduate. The maximum cumulative amount is $40,000 for a graduate or professional student, including loans borrowed as an undergraduate student, $20,000 for an undergraduate.

An eligible student attending an institution participating in the Expanded Lending Option (ELO) is eligible for higher annual and cumulative loans.

For a program of study abroad that has reasonable costs in excess of the home costs, the annual and aggregate limits may be exceeded by 20 percent.

Literature: "*Student Guide,*" no charge; "*Student Financial Aid Handbook,*" no charge.

Who To Contact: ***Headquarters Office***: Policy Development Division, Student Financial Assistance Programs, Department of Education, 400 Maryland Avenue, SW., Washington, DC 20202-5446. Contact: Pamela A. Moran, Chief, Loans Branch. (202) 708-9389. ***Regional or Local Office***: Contact the educational institution you attend or plan to attend.

Work-Study Program to Pay for College
Federal Work-Study Program (84.033)

Description: This program provides financial aid in the form of part-time employment to eligible undergraduate, graduate, or professional students to help meet educational expenses and encourage students receiving program assistance to participate in community service activities. Most jobs are on campus, but you may work off campus in a government or public service job.

The pay is at least current federal minimum wage, but also may be related to the type of position held and experience. Full-time students typically work 15 to 20 hours a week, based around their class schedule.

Beneficiary Eligibility: Postsecondary students enrolled or accepted for enrollment as regular students; are maintaining satisfactory academic progress in accordance with the standards and practices of the institution; have financial need.

Financial Information: In the latest reported year, $1,011,000,000 was paid under this program. The average student payment was $1,228.

Literature: "*Student Guide*," no charge; "*Student Financial Aid Handbook*," no charge.

Who To Contact:
Headquarters Office: Policy Development Division, Office of Student Financial Assistance, Department of Education, 400 Maryland Ave., SW., Washington, DC 20202-5446. Contact: Harold McCollough. Phone: (202) 708-8498.
Regional or Local Office: This program is campus-based. Contact the educational institution you attend or plan to attend.

Money—for Teachers to Attend Overseas Seminars
International: Overseas Seminars Abroad—Bilateral Projects (84.018)

Description: In order to increase mutual understanding and knowledge between the people of the United States and those in other countries, this program offers qualified U.S. educators opportunities to participate in short-term study seminars abroad on topics in the social sciences, the humanities, and foreign languages. Funds provide round-trip economy airfare, room and board, tuition and fees for seminars.

Eligibility Requirements: You must be a U.S. citizen who holds a bachelor's degree, have three years professional experience in U.S. school systems including undergraduate schools, have three years full-time in teaching, administering or supervising in the humanities, the social sciences or social studies, and is currently employed full-time in teaching, administering or supervising in these subjects.

Financial Information: In the latest reported year, approximately 110 participants were enrolled in eight projects.

Literature: Program announcements and related information are available from the Program Officer for International Education, Department of Education.

Who To Contact: *Headquarters Office*: International Studies Branch, International Education Graduate Programs Service, Department of Education, 400 Maryland Ave., SW., Washington, DC 20202-5332. Contact: Rosalie Gendimenico. Phone: (202) 502-7700. *Regional or Local Office*: Not applicable.

Free Adult Basic Education
Adult Education—State Grant Program (84.002)

Description: Uncle Sam finances adult education programs in order to improve educational opportunities for adults, enable adults who so desire to complete secondary school, and enable adults to benefit from job training and retraining programs. Special emphasis is given to programs of instruction in computational skills and in speaking, reading, or writing English.

Beneficiary Eligibility: Out-of-school adults 16 years of age and older or who are beyond the age of compulsory school attendance under their State's law and who lack sufficient mastery of basic educational skills to enable them to function effectively in society or who have not graduated from secondary school.

Financial Information: In the latest reported year, $540,000,000 was granted to over 4,000 local education and literacy providers who provided services at more than 24,000 learning centers. Participant achievements include: over 308,000 passing the GED (high school equivalency) test; more than 340,000 gaining employment or obtaining job advancement; another 34,000 being removed from public assistance registers.

Who To Contact: *Headquarters Office*: Division of Adult Education and Literacy, Office of Vocational and Adult Education, U.S. Department of Education, 400 Maryland Ave., SW., Washington, DC 20202-7240. Contact: Carroll Towey. Phone: (202) 205-9791. *Regional or Local Office*: Not applicable.

Money—for Professors to Do Research Overseas
International: Overseas—Faculty Research Abroad (84.019)

Description: Grants to enable university faculty members to conduct research abroad in order to improve their skills in languages and their knowledge of the cultures on which their academic interests focus. Awards will not be available for projects focusing primarily on Western Europe or on countries where the United States has no diplomatic representation.

The assistance is expected to contribute to the development or improvement of the study of modern foreign languages or area studies in those fields needed for a full understanding of the area, regions, or countries in which the modern foreign languages are commonly used. (Examples of funded projects include Women in Politics in Ecuador; Worker Cooperatives in Japan and Culture of Cooperation.)

Financial provisions include a stipend in lieu of salary; cost of air fare; baggage allowance; project allowance to purchase expendable materials; services and supplies; fees to foreign institutions; and local travel expenditures.

Beneficiary Eligibility: You must be employed by an institution of higher education; have been engaged in teaching relevant to the foreign language or area specialization for the preceding two years; have proposed research relevant to a modern foreign language or area specialization that cannot be conducted in the United States, or for which a foreign country or region provides superior research facilities; not be doing dissertation research for a Ph.D.; and possess adequate language skills.

Financial Information: In the latest reported year, 39 fellowships were awarded. Awards are made for six to 12 months of research. *Range and Average of Financial Assistance*: $6,236 to $71,164; $39,190.

Who To Contact: *Headquarters Office*: Advanced Training and Research Team, International Education and Graduate Programs Service, Office of Postsecondary Education, Department of Education, 400 Maryland Ave., SW., Washington, DC 20202-5331. Contact: Eliza A. Washington. Phone: (202) 502-7700. *Regional or Local Office*: Not applicable.

Money—for Ph.D. Students to Do Research Abroad
International: Overseas—Doctoral Dissertation (84.022)

Description: This program gives grants to doctoral candidates to engage in full-time dissertation research abroad in modern foreign language and area studies. Generally awards will not be available for projects focusing primarily on Western Europe or countries where the United States has no diplomatic representation. The program is designed to develop research knowledge and capability in world areas not widely included in American curricula. (Examples of funded projects include Strategies for Survival:

Women, Power, and HIV Risk in Uganda; Spirit Possession in Northern Brazil.)

Financial provisions include basic stipend; travel costs; dependents allowance; project allowance and expenses, tuition payments to foreign institutions; local travel expenditures; insurance.

Beneficiary Eligibility: Graduate students in good standing at institutions of higher education who, when the fellowship period begins, have been admitted to candidacy in a doctoral degree program in modern foreign languages and area studies at that institution; plan a teaching career in the United States upon graduation; and have appropriate foreign language skills.

Financial Information: In the latest reported year, 88 fellowships were awarded. Awards are made for six to 12 months of research. *Range and Average of Financial Assistance*: $8,583 to $60,274; $23,000 average.

Who To Contact: *Headquarters Office*: Advanced Training and Research Team, International Education and Graduate Programs Service, Office of Postsecondary Education, Department of Education, 400 Maryland Ave., SW., Washington, DC 20202-5331. Contact: Karla Ver Bryck Block. (202) 502-7700. *Regional or Local Office*: Not applicable.

Get Help to Study
TRIO—Student Support Services (84.042)

Description: This is a special program that provides funds to colleges, universities, and community and junior colleges so that they can provide supportive services to disadvantaged college students in order to help them complete the postsecondary education program in which they are enrolled and increase their transfer rates from two-year to four-year institutions.

Services include personal and academic counseling, career guidance, instruction, mentoring and tutoring, and special programs for students of limited English proficiency.

Beneficiary Eligibility: Low-income, first generation college students or disabled students who are enrolled or accepted for enrollment at the institution which is the recipient of the grant and who need academic support to successfully pursue a program of postsecondary education.

Financial Information: In the latest reported year, it is anticipated that about 176,600 students will be served.

Who To Contact: *Headquarters Office*: Department of Education, Office of Postsecondary Education, Federal TRIO Program, 400 Maryland Ave. SW., Washington, DC 20202-5249. Contact: Linda Bird-Johnson. Phone: (202) 502-7600. *Regional or Local Office*: Department of Education's regional offices (see Table 4a, Chapter 4).

Get Help to Go On to College
TRIO—Talent Search (84.044)

Description: Talent Search is a special program to identify low-income, potential first generation college students, to encourage them to complete secondary school and go on to college, and to provide them with information about financial aid.

The program provides funding to sponsoring colleges, public or private agencies or organizations, and in some cases, secondary schools. These, in turn, provide such program services as financial, academic and personal counseling and tutoring.

Beneficiary Eligibility: Individuals residing in the target area or attending a target school who have potential for education at the postsecondary level and who can benefit from one or more of the services provided by the project. Two-thirds must be low-income individuals who are also potential first generation college students. Project participants must be between 11 and 27 years old (exceptions allowed).

Financial Information: In the latest reported year, 320,854 individuals were served.

Who To Contact: *Headquarters Office*: Federal TRIO Program, College and University Preparation and Support Team, Office of Postsecondary Education, Department of Education, 400 Maryland Avenue, SW., Washington, DC 20202-5249. Contact: Peggy Whitehead. Phone: (202) 502-7600. *Regional or Local Office*: Not applicable.

Support for Needy Students
TRIO—Upward Bound (84.047)

Description: Similar to Talent Search **84.044** (above), this program's primary goal is to encourage students to graduate from high school and attend some form of postsecondary education. To accomplish this, Upward Bound makes grants to colleges, universities and other institutions for programs that generate skills and motivation necessary for success in education beyond high school among low-income and potential first-generation college students and veterans so that such persons may successfully pursue postsecondary educational programs.

Funds are to provide academic instructional programs, personal and academic counseling, career guidance and special instruction to prepare project participants for careers in which persons from disadvantaged backgrounds are particularly underrepresented, tutoring, and exposure to cultural events and academic programs not usually available to disadvantaged youths.

Stipends may be paid to students—up to $40 a month during the academic year and $60 a month during the summer.

Beneficiary Eligibility: Low-income individuals and potential first generation college students who have a need for academic support in order to successfully pursue a program of post-secondary education. Except for veterans, who can be served regardless of age, project participants must be between 13 and 19 years old and have completed the eighth grade but have not entered the twelfth grade (exceptions allowed).

Financial Information: Almost 56,600 students were served last year.

Who To Contact: *Headquarters Office*: Federal TRIO Program, College and University Preparation and Support Team, Office of Postsecondary Education, Department of Education, 400 Maryland Avenue, SW., Washington, DC 20202-5249. Contact: Peggy Whitehead. Phone: (202)502-7600. *Regional or Local Office*: Department of Education's regional offices (see Table 4a).

Money—from Your State to Go to College
State Student Incentives Grants (84.069)

Description: This program provides funds to the States to make scholarships and grants of up to $5,000 to eligible postsecondary students with substantial financial need.

Beneficiary Eligibility: Postsecondary education students with real financial need.

Financial Information: In the latest reported year, 90,000 students received grants to attend public, private, and proprietary schools. Maximum grant is $5,000; average grant is $1,000.

Who To Contact: *Headquarters Office*: Policy Development Division, Policy, Training, and Analysis Service, Office of Student Financial Assistance, Department of Education, Grants Branch, 400 Maryland Ave., SW., Washington, DC 20202-5447. Phone: (800) 433-3243. *Regional or Local Office*: Eligible students annually apply to their State of residence for a grant under this program. Program Description and a List of State student scholarship or assistance agencies is available from the Education Department regional offices (Table 4a).

$24,000 a Year—for Eligible Ph.D. Students
Javits Fellowships (84.170)

Description: Fellowships to individuals of superior ability for graduate doctoral study in specified academic fields within the arts, humanities, and social sciences.

Eligibility Requirements: Citizens and nationals of the United States, permanent residents of the United States, and persons in the United States for other than a temporary purpose who intend to become permanent residents. Fellowship applications are evaluated based on scholarly achievements; Graduate Record Examination scores; awards; honors; narratives describing personal goals; and three letters of recommendation.

Financial Information: In the latest reported year, approximately 797 continuing fellowships were awarded. The awards averaged $15,700 plus $10,700 for tuition and fees.

Literature: Javits Fellowship Program, Dept. of Education, Washington, DC 20202-5247. (800) 4 FED AID.

Who To Contact: *Headquarters Office*: International Education and Graduate Programs, Office of Postsecondary Education, Department of Education, Washington, DC 20202-5247. Contact: Carolyn Proctor. Phone: (202) 502-7567. *Regional or Local Office*: Not applicable.

$1,500 a Year—to Eligible Undergrads
Byrd Honors Scholarships (84.185)

Description: In order to recognize and promote student excellence and achievement, $1,500 annual scholarships are awarded to outstanding high school seniors who show promise of continued academic achievement.

The awards are for up to four years of study at any eligible institution of higher education.

Beneficiary Eligibility: You must meet residency and citizenship requirements, be a graduate of a public or private secondary school or have been accepted for enrollment at an institution of higher education, have demonstrated outstanding academic achievement, and show promise of continued academic achievement to be eligible to receive a scholarship.

Financial Information: Annual grants are provided to the State educational agencies to make scholarships to qualifying students. Students apply to their State of legal residence for a scholarship under this program. Last year, approximately $41 million was allotted to 26,572 students who each received a $1,500 scholarship.

Literature: Fact sheet, program description, and *"Directory of State Agency Official Contacts,"* available from the headquarters office below.

Who To Contact: *Headquarters Office*: Department of Education, Office of Postsecondary Education, Division of Higher Education Incentive Programs, 400 Maryland Avenue, SW, Washington, DC 20024-5251. Contact: Argelia

Velez-Rodriguez. Phone: (202) 502-7582. *Regional or Local Office*: Not applicable.

Fellowships—for Study in Areas of National Need
Graduate Assistance in Areas of National Need (84.200)

Description: To provide fellowships through graduate academic departments to graduate students of superior ability who demonstrate financial need for the purpose of sustaining and enhancing their capacity for teaching and research in academic areas of national need.

Beneficiary Eligibility: Graduate students must demonstrate financial need, have excellent academic records, plan teaching or research careers, plan to pursue the highest degree in the field.

Financial Information: In the latest reported year, 221 grants were made. The average grant was for $140,000.

Who To Contact: *Headquarters Office*: International Education and Graduate Programs Service, Office of Postsecondary Education, Department of Education, 400 Maryland Ave., SW., Washington, DC 20202-5247. Contact: Cosette Ryan. (202) 502-7700. *Regional or Local Office*: Not applicable.

Money—for Undergrads Who Want a Career in Public Service
Harry S Truman Scholarship Foundation (85.001)

Description: College scholarships of $3,000-$13,500 annually for 4 years to persons who demonstrate outstanding potential for and who are preparing to pursue a career in public service.

Eligibility Requirements: Undergraduates in their junior year at four year colleges and universities who are properly nominated by accredited colleges or universities recognized by the Department of Education. Applicants must rank in the upper quarter of her or his class and their selected field of study should permit admission to a graduate or professional program allowing better preparation for a career in public service.

Financial Information: Since 1977, the year of the program's inception, 2,016 (of a total of approximately 20,000 nominees) college students studying for careers in public service have received Scholarship assistance. *Range and Average of Financial Assistance*: Up to $13,500 a year; $6,510 average.

Who To Contact: *Headquarters Office*: Louis Blair, Executive Secretary, 712 Jackson Place, NW., Washington, DC 20006. (202) 395-4831. *Regional or Local Office*: Not applicable.

$6,200 a Year—for Undergrads Interested in Studying Math, Science and Engineering
Barry M. Goldwater Scholarship and Excellence in Education Foundation (85.200)

Description: This program honors former Senator Barry Goldwater through the operation of an education scholarship program. Financed by a permanent trust fund endowment, it is designed to encourage outstanding students to pursue careers in mathematics, the natural sciences and engineering.

Eligibility Requirements: Undergraduate sophomore and junior level students at two and four year colleges and universities who are properly nominated by accredited institutions and recognized by the U.S. Department of Education may apply.

Students should rank in the upper fourth of their class, and have selected a field of study that will permit admission to a graduate or professional program in preparation for a career in mathematics, the natural sciences or engineering.

Financial Information: Since the program began operating in 1988, a total of 3,021 Goldwater Scholars have been selected. *Range and Average of Financial Assistance*: To $7,500 a year; $6,650 average.

Who To Contact: *Headquarters Office*: Gerald J. Smith, President, Barry M. Goldwater Scholarship and Excellence In Education Foundation, 6225 Brandon Avenue, Suite 315, Springfield, VA 22150-2519. (703) 756-6012. *Regional or Local Office*: Not applicable.

Money—for Environmental and Native American Scholars
The Morris K. Udall Scholarship and Excellence in National Environmental Policy Foundation (85.400 - 85.402)

Description: Scholarships, internships, and fellowships to develop increased opportunities for Americans to prepare for and pursue careers related to the environment; and for Native Americans and Alaska Natives to pursue careers in health care and tribal public policy. Assistance is intended for the use of scholars only.

Eligibility Requirements:

- College sophomores or juniors in the current academic year having outstanding potential and intending to pursue careers in environmental public policy.

- Native American and Alaska Native students who are college sophomores or juniors in the current academic year and have outstanding potential and intend to pursue careers in health care or tribal public policy may apply.

Students must have at least a "B" average and be in the upper fourth of their class.

Financial Information: In the most recent reported year, 80 scholarships were awarded. *Range of Financial Assistance*: $5,000 a year. **Literature**: Informational bulletins available upon request.

Who To Contact: *Headquarters Office*: Contact: Christopher L. Helms, Executive Director, 110 South Church, Ste. 3350, Tucson, AZ 85701. Phone: (520) 670-5608. *Regional or Local Office*: American College Testing (ACT), 2201 North Dodge, Post Office Box 168, Iowa City, IA 52243. Contact: Jo Ann Hubble. Phone: (319) 337-1707.

Fellowships—to American History Teachers

James Madison Memorial Fellowship Foundation (85.500)

Description: Fellowships are awarded to future and current secondary school teachers (grades seven through twelve) of American history, American government, or social studies. The purpose is to strengthen secondary school teaching of the principles, framing, and development of the U.S. Constitution, to contribute to a deeper understanding of American government, and to foster in both teachers and students the spirit of civic participation that inspired the Nation's founders.

Eligibility Requirements: College seniors and college graduates without teaching experience (*Junior Fellows*) and experienced secondary school teachers of grades seven through twelve (*Senior Fellows*) may apply.

Financial Information: Since 1992, the year of the Madison Foundation's inaugural national competition, more than 494 Fellowship Awards have been made to prospective and existing secondary school teachers. The maximum annual award is $24,000.

Who To Contact:. *Headquarters Office*: James Madison Memorial Fellowship Foundation. Contact: Mr. Steve Weiss, Director of Administration and Finance, 2000 K Street, NW., Suite 303, Washington, DC 20006. 202-653-8700. FAX (202) 653-6045. *Regional or Local Office*: None.

DEPARTMENT OF AGRICULTURE

Fellowships—to Study Food and Agriculture

Food and Agricultural Sciences National Needs Graduate Fellowship Grants (10.210)

Description: This program awards a number of fellowships to graduate students in the fields of food and agricultural sciences. Funds are awarded to selected U.S. universities who then distribute the fellowships so selected graduate students can obtain either a master's or doctoral degree in one of the targeted specializations of the food and agricultural sciences. Funds are allocated to provide support for doctoral fellows for 36 months and for masters fellows for 24 months.

Since 1985, this program has helped Fellows in six areas of the food/agricultural sciences deemed critical to agricultural research and teaching:
- animal biotechnology
- food science and human nutrition
- management and marketing (agribusiness, food, and forest products)
- plant biotechnology
- engineering (food, forest, biological and agricultural)
- water science.

Beneficiary Eligibility: Individuals selected initially by the institution must enroll in a program leading to a graduate, master's or doctoral degree in one of the targeted national needs areas of the food and agricultural sciences.

Financial Information: In addition to domestic study, current fellows are eligible to receive supplemental grants of $3,000 to cover travel and living expenses for special international study or thesis/dissertation research.

The total amount allocated for the program in the latest reported year is $2,880,000.

Literature: Application Kit for the Food and Agricultural Sciences National Needs Graduate Fellowships Grants.

Who to Contact: *Headquarters Office*: Grant

Programs Manager, Higher Education Programs, CSREES, Department of Agriculture, Room 3912, South Building, Washington, DC 20250-2251. (202)720-7854. *Regional or Local Office*: None. Contact the Headquarters Office for a list of participating institutions; then apply directly to them. Here are the current participating institutions (by state):

- CA: University of California, Davis
- CA: University of California, Riverside
- CO: Colorado State University
- FL: University of Florida
- IA: Iowa State University
- IL: University of Illinois
- MA: Worcester Polytechnic Institute
- MI: Michigan State University
- MN: University of Minnesota
- NC: North Carolina State University
- NE: University of Nebraska
- NJ: Rutgers University
- NY: Cornell University
- OK: Oklahoma State University
- OR: Oregon State University
- PA: Pennsylvania State University
- TX: Texas A&M University
- WI: University of Wisconsin

DEPARTMENT OF DEFENSE

Money—to Study Mathematics
Mathematical Sciences Grants Program (12.901)

Description: Concerned about the declining percentage of Americans taking degrees in areas of mathematics most strongly identified with cryptology, the Defense Department makes grants to math researchers and graduate students in order to stimulate developments in the field of cryptography and make careers in these fields of mathematics more attractive to Americans and to make the National Security Agency (NSA) known as a possible employer of such mathematicians.

Fields of mathematics the NSA is interested in include algebra, number theory, discrete mathematics, statistics and probability.

NSA has the authority for the final approval and passes the funds to a college or university. The college or university distributes the funds to the principal investigator, students, postdoctoral students, etc.

Beneficiary Eligibility:
1. Researchers in the mathematical science that are at least permanent residents and employed by a U.S. college or university;
2. Graduate students who are permanent residents of the U.S. and intending to apply for U.S. citizenship.

Financial Information: The grants are usually for two years study, and cover travel, publishing costs, graduate student support, postdoctoral support, and conference support. *Range and Average of Financial Assistance*: $5,000 to $60,000; $15,000 average.

Literature: NSA provides a free brochure describing how to apply for a grant.

Who to Contact: *Headquarters Office*: Dr. Charles F. Osgood, Department of Defense, National Security Agency, ATTN: R51A, Fort George G. Meade, MD 20755-6000. (301) 688-0400. *Regional or Local Office*: Not applicable.

DEPARTMENT OF HEALTH AND HUMAN SERVICES

$14,700—to Become a Nurse Anesthetist Nurse
Anesthetist Traineeships (93.124)

Description: Traineeship grants to support registered nurses to become nurse anesthetists, for up to a maximum of 18 months of full-time study.

Beneficiary Eligibility: Trainees selected by participating institutions. A candidate must be enrolled full time in a participating nurse anesthetist education program, and have successfully completed 12 months of the nurse anesthetist training program, and demonstrate financial need, as determined by the institution.

Financial Information: In the latest reported

year, 1,000 students received aid — from $1,346 to $60,314; $14,706 average.

Literature: *"Fact Sheet for Grants for Nurse Anesthetist Traineeships."*

Who To Contact:
Headquarters Office Program Contact : Ms. Marcia Starbecker, Division of Nursing, Bureau of Health Professions, Health Resources and Services Administration, Public Health Service, Parklawn Building, Room 9-36, 5600 Fishers Lane, Rockville, MD 20857. (301) 443-6195.
Grants Management Contact: Ms. Wilma Johnson, Grants Management Officer, Bureau of Health Professions, Health Resources and Services Administration, Department of Health and Human Services, Parklawn Bldg., Room 8C-26, 5600 Fishers Lane, Rockville, MD 20857. (301) 443-6880.
Regional or Local Office: Not applicable.

$18,000—for Disadvantaged Medical and Dental Students
Financial Assistance for Disadvantaged Health Professions Students (93.139)

Description: This program provides scholarships to disadvantaged students of exceptional financial need, so they can obtain a degree in medicine or dentistry. Scholarships are awarded with a service obligation or with penalties for failure to serve.

Beneficiary Eligibility: To be eligible, a student must be a citizen, national or lawful permanent resident of the United States or its territories.

Financial Information: The average award per student is estimated to be $18,942. Currently no new applications are being accepted.

Literature: *"Financial Assistance for Disadvantaged Health Professions Fact Sheet."*

Who To Contact: *Headquarters Office*: Bruce Baggett, Division of Student Assistance, Bureau of Health Professions, Health Resources and Services Administration, Public Health Service, Parklawn Building, Room 8-34, 5600 Fishers Lane, Rockville, MD 20857. (301) 443-4776.
Regional or Local Office: Not applicable.

Federal Money—for Health Professionals to Repay Educational Loans
National Health Service Corps Loan Repayment Program (93.162)

Description: In order to help assure an adequate supply of trained health professionals for the National Health Service Corps (NHSC), this program provides for the repayment of educational loans for participants who agree to serve an applicable period of time in an approved loan repayment program service site located in a health professional shortage area.

It provides payments of up to $25,000 a year plus tax assistance payment during the first two years of practice at a selected NHSC Loan Repayment Service Site; up to $35,000 plus tax assistance payment in the third and following years.

Priority is given to primary care physicians, dentists, certified nurse midwives and nurse practitioners, physicians assistants, clinical psychologists and social workers, psychiatric nurse specialists, marriage and family therapists, dental hygienists.

Eligibility Requirements: Individuals are eligible to apply if they have a health professions degree or are in professional practice. They must hold an unrestricted health professions license in the State for which they will be working; and be eligible for selection for a Federal civil service appointment.

Financial Information: 337 awards were made in the latest reported year. Range and Average of Financial Assistance: Physician Awards, $10,000 to $69,500; $62,223 average.

Who To Contact: *Headquarters Office*: Division of Scholarships and Loan Repayments, Bureau of Primary Health Care, Health Resources and Services Adm., Public Health Service, Dept. of Health and Human Services, 10th Floor, 4350 East-West Hwy., Bethesda, MD 20814. (301) 594-4400 or (800) 435-6464. *Regional or Local Office*: None.

State Money—for Health Professionals to Repay Educational Loans

Grants for State Loan Repayment—"State Loan Repayment Program" (93.165)

Description: This program is similar to **93.162** and helps fund State programs that repay educational loans of health professionals in return for their practice in "health professional shortage areas" where there are a shortage of primary care professionals.

Eligibility Requirements: Health professionals and graduate students.

Financial Information: $8,000,000 awarded in latest reported year.

Who To Contact:
Headquarters Office: Director, Division of Scholarships and Loan Repayments, Bureau of Primary Health Care, Health Resources and Services Administration, Public Health Service, Department of Health and Human Services, 10th Floor, 4350 East-West Highway, Bethesda, MD 20814. (301) 594-4400.
Grants Management Contact: Office of Grants Management, Bureau of Primary Health Care, Health Resources and Services Administration, Public Health Service, Department of Health and Human Services, 4350 East-West Highway, Bethesda, MD 20814. (301) 594-4235.
Regional or Local Office: None.

Scholarships—to Disadvantaged Undergrads if They Agree to Work for the National Institutes of Health

Undergraduate Scholarship Program for Individuals from Disadvantaged Backgrounds—"NIH Undergraduate Scholarship Program" (93.187)

Description: Scholarships to applicants who are enrolled or accepted for enrollment as full-time undergraduate students and who are from disadvantaged backgrounds.

Each scholarship recipient must agree to serve as a National Institutes of Health employee full-time for not less than 10 consecutive weeks of each year during which the individual is attending the undergraduate institution; and, after graduating, serving as a full-time NIH employee for one year for each year of scholarship support.

Eligibility Requirements: Undergraduate students from disadvantaged backgrounds pursuing academic programs supporting professions needed by the NIH.

Financial Information: 15 awards were made in latest reported year, averaging about $36,000.

Who To Contact: *Headquarters Office*: Program and Business Contact: Marc S. Horowitz, J.D., Office of Loan Repayment and Scholarship, National Institutes of Health, 2 Center Drive, Room 2E30, Bethesda, MD 20892-0230. Phone: (800) 528-7689. FAX: (301) 480-5481. *Regional or Local Office*: Not applicable.

Scholarships—to Health Services Students Who Agree to Work for the National Health Service Corps

National Health Service Corps (NHSC) Scholarship Program (93.288)

Description: Service-obligated scholarships to health professions students to assure an adequate supply of physicians, certified nurse midwives, certified family nurse practitioners, and physician assistants in federally-designated Health Professional Shortage Areas of the U.S.A.; and, if needed by the National Health Service Corps, an adequate supply of other health professionals.

Each year of support incurs one year of service, with a minimum of two years. Service may be as a Federal or salaried nonfederal employee providing full-time primary health services in a service site in the U.S., territories, or possessions.

Eligibility Requirements: You must be a U.S. citizen or national enrolled or accepted for enrollment full-time in an accredited school. Students of "Exceptional Financial Need" or "Disadvantaged Background" are given priority.

Financial Information: The scholarship pays your school for tuition and required annual fees, pays you an $1,028 monthly stipend, and pays a single annual payment to cover costs of all other reasonable educational expenses (books, supplies, equipment, uniforms, clinical travel, etc.).

Literature: "*Information Bulletin*," published annually, and "*Program Fact Sheets*," available at no charge.

Who To Contact: *Headquarters Office*: Chief, Scholarship Program Branch, Division of Scholarships and Loan Repayments, Bureau of Primary Health Care, Health Resources and Services Administration, Public Health Service, 4350 East-West Highway, 10th Floor, Bethesda MD 20814. Public Information Phone: (301) 594-4410; toll-free from outside MD: (800) 638-0824. *Regional or Local Office*: Not applicable.

Health Professions Student Loans

Health Professions Student Loans (HPSL), Including Primary Care Loans/Loans for Disadvantaged Students (LDS) (93.342)

Description: This program provides Direct Health Professions Student Loans (HPSL) to schools for them to provide long-term, low-interest loans to eligible students in need of financial assistance to pursue a course of study in specified health professions. It also provides Loans for Disadvantaged Students (LDS) for students who meet the HPSL criteria and are from a disadvantaged background including members of ethnic groups.

The maximum amount you may borrow is the cost of tuition plus $2,500 for any one academic year. Third and fourth year medical students may be eligible for additional funding to repay earlier educational loans.

Beneficiary Eligibility: You must be enrolled or accepted for enrollment in a school of medicine, dentistry, optometry, podiatry, pharmacy, or veterinary medicine, and pursuing a course of study which constitutes a full-time academic workload leading to a degree of Doctor of

Medicine, Dentistry, Osteopathic Medicine, Optometry, Podiatric Medicine, Pharmacy or Veterinary Medicine, or Bachelor of Science in Pharmacy.

Financial Information: *Range and Average of Financial Assistance*: 2,650 students receive $25,000 to $150,000; $59,200 ave.

Literature: "*A Guide for Repayment and Deferment Provisions of Health Professions Student Loans*"; "*Health Professions Student Loan Fact Sheet; Loans for Disadvantaged Students Fact Sheet*."

Who To Contact: *Headquarters Office*: Mary Farrington, Division of Student Assistance, Bureau of Health Professions, Health Resources and Services Administration, Public Health Service, Department of Health and Human Services, Parklawn Building, Room 8-34, 5600 Fishers Lane, Rockville, MD 20857. (301) 443-4776. *Regional or Local Office*: Students apply at student aid office of school of their choice for assistance in applying for a loan.

Money—to Study to be a Professional Nurse

Professional Nurse Traineeships (93.358)

Description: This program provides grants to nurses who are studying full-time at a master's or doctoral degree level or a nurse midwifery program. Uncle Sam gives funds to eligible institutions which provide the grants to nurse recipients.

Beneficiary Eligibility: You must be:
- A currently licensed registered nurse in your State, or have completed basic nursing preparation;
- Enrolled full-time in graduate courses;
- Pursuing a master's or doctoral degree;
- And be in a program designed to prepare trainees as a nurse practitioner, nurse midwife, nurse educator, public health nurse, or other clinical specialty that requires advanced education.

Financial Information: Students may receive up to $8,800 plus tuition and other expenses. 301 awards were made in the latest reported year.

Literature: *"Fact Sheet; Program Guide for Professional Nurse Traineeship Program."*

Who To Contact:

- *Headquarters Office*: Bureau of Health Professions, Health Resources and Services Administration, Department of Health and Human Services, Room 9-36, Parklawn Building, 5600 Fishers Lane, Rockville, MD 20857. (301) 443-6193.

- *Grants Management Contact*: John R. Westcott, Grants Management Officer, Bureau of Health Professions, Health Resources and Services Administration, Department of Health and Human Services, Parklawn Building, Room 8C26, 5600 Fishers Lane, Rockville, MD 20857. (301) 443-6880.

- *Regional/Local Office*: Not applicable.

Nursing Student Loans
(93.364)

Description: Direct loans to schools of nursing to make long-term, low-interest loans to nursing students in need of financial assistance.

Beneficiary Eligibility: Nursing students who are pursuing a course of study in professional nursing education.

Financial Information: Loans have a maximum of $2,500 for an academic year, $4,000 for each of the final 2 years, or the amount of the student's financial need, whichever is less. The total is limited to $13,000. In the latest reporting year, $3,500,000 was awarded.

Literature: *"A Guide for Repayment and Deferment Provisions of Nursing Student Loans," "Nursing Student Loan Program Fact Sheet."*

Who To Contact: *Headquarters Office*: Mary Farrington, Division of Student Assistance, Bureau of Health Professions, Health Resources and Services Administration, Public Health Service, Department of Health and Human Services, Parklawn Building, Room 8-34, 5600 Fishers Lane, Rockville, MD 20857. (301) 443-4776. *Regional or Local Office*: Not applicable.

$18,000 a Year—to Health Professions Students of Exceptional Need
Scholarships for Students of Exceptional Financial Need (93.820)

Description: This program makes funds available to authorized health professions schools so they can award scholarships to full-time students of exceptional financial need. Scholarships are awarded with a service obligation or with penalties for failure to serve.

Beneficiary Eligibility: Students who are citizens, nationals or lawful permanent residents of the United States, territories or possessions.

Financial Information: The average award per student for the latest reported year was $18,985. Currently no new applications are being accepted.

Literature: *"Exceptional Financial Need Scholarship Fact Sheet."*

Who To Contact: *Headquarters Office*: Division of Student Assistance, Bureau of Health Professions, Health Resources and Services Administration, Public Health Service, Department of Health and Human Services, Parklawn Building, Room 8-34, 5600 Fishers Lane, Rockville, MD 20857. (301) 443-4776. *Regional or Local Office*: Not applicable.

Scholarships—to Health Professions Students from Disadvantaged Backgrounds
Scholarships for Health Professions Students from Disadvantaged Backgrounds (93.925)

Description: Scholarships to students from disadvantaged backgrounds who are enrolled or accepted for enrollment as full-time students in schools of medicine, dentistry, pharmacy, podiatric medicine, optometry, veterinary medicine, allied health, public health, nursing.

Beneficiary Eligibility: Students who are citizens, nationals or lawful permanent residents of the United States, territories or possessions.

Financial Information: Scholarships may only be expended for tuition expenses, other reasonable educational expenses, and reasonable living expenses incurred while in attendance for the year. In the latest reported year, $41,000,000 was awarded.

Literature: Program guidelines and related application materials.

Who To Contact: *Headquarters Office*: Mary Farrington, Division of Student Assistance, Bureau of Health Professions, Health Resources and Services Administration, Public Health Service, Parklawn Building, Room 8-34, 5600 Fishers Lane, Rockville, MD 20857. (301) 443-4776. *Regional or Local Office*: Students apply to the Financial Aid Office at their school.

ADDITIONAL PROGRAMS

Summer Government Jobs for College and High School Students
Federal Summer Employment (27.006)

Description: This program provides summer jobs in federal agencies for college and high school students. The jobs may be clerical, crafts and trades, administrative or subprofessional related to career interests. Employees are paid at the regular Federal pay rate for the position.

Eligibility Requirements: U.S. Citizens, 16 years old at time of appointment.

Financial Information: Not available.

literature: Information about open examinations and/or Job Vacancy Announcements are available from sources listed below.

Who to Contact: *Headquarters Office*: The program is coordinated by the Office of Personnel and Management (OPM), but carried out by numerous Federal agencies.

Federal employment information is available nationwide from the following sources:

- USAJOBS - OPM's Web site: www.usajobs.opm.gov;

- Federal Job Opportunities Board: (912) 757-3100;

- Touch Screen Computer Kiosks: Located in OPM offices and Federal buildings throughout the country.

- Career America Connection (CAC) Telephone Listing System:
  Atlanta, GA, (404) 331-4315
  Chicago, IL, (312) 353-6192
  Dayton, OH, (937) 225-2720
  Denver, CO, (303) 969-7050
  Detroit, MI, (313) 226-6950
  Honolulu, HI, (808) 541-2791
  Huntsville, AL, (205) 837-0894
  Kansas City, MO, (816) 426-5702
  Norfolk, VA, (757) 441-3355
  Philadelphia, PA, (215) 597-7440
  Raleigh, NC, (919) 790-2822
  San Antonio, TX, (210) 805-2402
  San Francisco, CA, (415) 744-5627
  Seattle, WA, (206) 553-0888
  Twin Cities, MN, (612) 725-3430
  Washington, DC, (202) 606-2700
  Nationwide, (912) 757-3000

Application forms and instructions are available at individual Federal agency personnel offices.

Money—to Graduate Students to Study Abroad
Educational Exchange—Graduate Students (Fulbright Program) (82.001)

Description: Fulbright Fellowships are made to eligible U.S. students to give them the opportunity to live and study in a foreign country for one academic year with possible renewals or extensions. There are two kinds of grants:

- **Full grants** that include round trip transportation, tuition, books, maintenance for one academic year in one country, and health and accident insurance;

- **Travel grants** that supplement

maintenance and tuition scholarships granted to American students by universities, private donors, and foreign governments which do not cover the cost of transportation.

Beneficiary Eligibility: U.S. citizens who are graduate students and who want to live and study in a foreign country for one academic year. Language proficiency must be sufficient to communicate with the people of the host country and to carry out the proposed study;

Financial Information: $12,324,000 is budgeted for this year to award 820 grants. *Range and Average of Financial Assistance*: $1,200 to $61,000; $25,000 average.

Literature: Annual announcement *"Grants for Graduate Study Abroad,"* issued by Institute of International Education, 809 United Nations Plaza, New York, NY 10017.

Who to Contact: *Headquarters Office*: Institute of International Education, 809 United Nations Plaza, New York, NY 10017. *Application Procedure*: Applicants who are enrolled in U.S. colleges and universities should contact their Fulbright program advisers on campus. Others should write to the nearest office of the Institute of International Education: 401 North Wabash Avenue, Suite 722, Chicago, IL 60611; 515 Post Oak Boulevard, Suite 150, Houston, TX 77027; 41 Sutter Street, Suite 510, San Francisco, CA 94108; 700 Broadway, Suite 112, Denver, CO 80203.

Earn Money for College as a Volunteer
AmeriCorps (94.006)

Description: AmeriCorps is the national service program that allows people of all ages and backgrounds to earn money for college in exchange for a year of service. AmeriCorps members help meet community needs by augmenting the efforts of private and public non-profit organizations and government agencies to eliminate poverty and poverty-related problems.

AmeriCorps pays a living allowance to its volunteers. In addition, volunteers may also receive education awards for qualified postsecondary education expenses or to pay off qualified student loans.

The vast majority of AmeriCorps projects are in the areas of education, public safety, and human and environmental needs, with a special emphasis on children and youth. For example, its members serve in elementary schools as teaching assistants, tutors, mentors, and role models; assist in developing community service projects; renovate housing in low-income areas.

Eligibility: Graduate and undergraduate students, faculty members.

Financial Information: For the latest reported year, the program has a $284,000,000 budget. 45,000 Americans of all ages will serve in over 600 AmeriCorps projects.

Literature: Contact the Corporation's headquarters office for further details.

Who to Contact: *Headquarters Office*: Corporation for National and Community Service, 1201 New York Avenue, NW., Washington, DC 20525. (202)-606-5000, ext. 474. *Regional or Local Office*: See Table 4b

Army, Navy & Marine, and Air Force ROTC

Description: ROTC (Reserve Officer Training Corps) is the largest source of officers for the U.S. Armed Forces. ROTC units of the Army, Navy & Marines, and Air Force are found on hundreds of college and university campuses in every state.

Students, in exchange for possible tuition assistance and stipends of up to $1,500 a year, and eligibility for scholarships worth as much as $64,000 or more, take two or four years of special military courses that require an average five hours a week plus some summer training.

Normally, ROTC covers 4 years, with 2 years devoted to the Basic Course and 2 years to the Advanced. College freshmen can try Army ROTC without making any commitment to join the Army. That commitment does not usually come until the junior year. By entering the Advanced Course, you agree to complete your ROTC instruction.

Once you complete 4-year degree and commission requirements. you then join the active service as an officer. For example, if you take Army ROTC you'll join the Army as a Second Lieutenant with pay and allowances of almost $26,000 a year. After two years, this increases to $32,000.

There are also programs in which you can serve in the Army National Guard or the Army Reserve or a combination of the two for a total of eight years, serving part time, generally one weekend a month and two weeks during the summer, while pursuing your chosen civilian careers.

Who to Contact:
- *Army*: Telephone (800) USA-ROTC
- *Navy & Marines*: (800) USA-NAVY
- *Air Force*: (800) 522-0033 ext. 2091

Or contact the program director at your college or university, or see your local recruiting office.

Social Security Checks for Students under 19

Description: If you're a full-time elementary or high school student not over 19 years old, you can receive monthly Social Security checks if one of your parents is receiving Social Security Disability or Retirement Benefits. You can also get checks if a parent dies after working under social security long enough to be insured.

Such payments usually end when the child reaches 18 unless he has become disabled before 18. But if you are an unmarried, full-time student, you can receive benefits up to age 19.

Until recently, full-time students up to age 22 attending a university, college or junior college were eligible for such Social Security payments. But "because of the availability of other student financial assistance, and the need to restore the financial soundness of the social security system, the law was changed."

Who to Contact: Local Social Security office.

Table 4a: # DEPARTMENT OF EDUCATION, REGIONAL REPRESENTATIVES

Region I
Michael Sentance
McCormack P.O. and Courthouse
Room 540
Boston, MA 02109
(617) 223-9317

Region II
Daniel Cassidy
65 Court Street 12th Floor
Brooklyn, New York, NY 11201
(718) 935-5953

Region III
Beth Brinly
The Wanamaker Building
100 Penn Square East-Suite 505
Philadelphia, PA 19107
(215) 656-6010

Region IV
Dennis Bega

61 Forshyth Street S.W., Room 19T40
Atlanta, GA 30303
(404) 562-6225

Region V
Sunny Penedo-Chico
111 North Canal Street, Room 1094
Chicago, IL 60606
(312) 353-8192

Region VI
Susan Bonesteel
1999 Bryan Street, Suite 2700
Dallas, TX 75202-6817
(214) 880-3011

Region VII
Mary Cohen
10220 North Executive Hills
Boulevard, Suite 720
Kansas City, MO 64153

(816) 880-4000

Region VIII
Patricia Chlouber
Federal Regional Office Building
1244 Speer Boulevard, Room 310
Denver, CO 80204
(303) 844-3544

Region IX
Mary Jane Pearson
50 United Nations Plaza, Room 205
San Francisco, CA 94102
(415) 556-4120

Region X
Donna Foxely
915 Second Avenue, Room 3362
Seattle, WA 98174
(206) 220-7800

Table 4b: CORPORATION FOR NATIONAL AND COMMUNITY SERVICE, STATE PROGRAM OFFICES

Alabama
Betty Platt, Director
Medical Forum
950 22nd Street, North, Suite 428
Birmingham, AL 35203
(205) 731-0027

Alaska
Billy Joe Caldwell, Director
915 Second Avenue, Suite 3190
Seattle, WA 98174-1103
(206) 220-7736

Arizona
Richard Persely, Director
522 North Central, Room 205A
Phoenix, AZ 85004-2190
(602) 379-4825

Arkansas
Opal Sims, Director
700 West Capitol St., Room 2506
Little Rock, AR 72201
(501) 324-5234

California
Kristen Haggins, Director
11150 W. Olympic Blvd.
Suite 670
Los Angeles, CA 90064
(310) 235-7709

Colorado
Bruce Cline, Director
999 Eighteenth Street
Suite 1440 South
Denver, CO 80202
(303) 312-7950

Connecticut
Romero A. Cherry, Director
280 Trumball Street, 21st Floor
Hartford, CT 06103-3510
(860) 240-3237

Delaware (and MD)
Jerry E. Yates, Director
Fallon Federal Bldg.
31 Hopkins Plaza, Suite 400-B
Baltimore, MD 21201
(410) 962-4443

District of Columbia (and VA)
Rosetta Freeman-Busby, Director
1201 New York Ave. NW,

Suite 9107
Washington, DC 20525
(202) 606-5000, x485

Florida
Warren Smith, Director
3165 McCrory Street, Suite 115
Orlando, FL 32803-3750
(407) 648-6117

Georgia
Daryl James, Director
75 Piedmont Ave., N.E., Suite 902
Atlanta, GA 30303-2587
(404) 331-4646

Hawaii/Guam/American Samoa
Lynn Dunn, Director
300 Ala Moana Blvd., Rm. 6213
Honolulu, HI 96850-0001
(808) 541-2832

Idaho
Van Kent Griffitts, Director
304 North 8th Street, Room 344
Boise, ID 83702-5835
(208) 334-1707

Illinois
Timothy Krieger, Director
77 West Jackson Blvd., Suite 442
Chicago, IL 60604-3511
(312) 353-3622

Indiana
Thomas L. Haskett, Director
46 East Ohio Street, Room 226
Indianapolis, IN 46204
(317) 226-6724

Iowa
Joel Weinstein, Director
210 Walnut Street, Room 917
Des Moines, IA 50309-2195
(515) 284-4816

Kansas
Bruce Cline, Director
444 S.E. Quincy, Room 260
Topeka, KS 66683-3572
(785) 295-2540

Kentucky
Betsy Irvin Wells, Director
600 Martin Luther King Place, #372-D

Louisville, KY 40202-2230
(502) 582-6384

Louisiana
Willard L. Labrie, Director
707 Florida Street, Suite 316
Baton Rouge , LA 70801
(225) 389-0473

Maine (NH and VT)
Shireen Tilley, Director
1 Pillsbury Street, Suite 201
Concord, NH 03301
(603) 225-1450

Maryland (and DE)
Jerry E. Yates, Director
Fallon Federal Bldg.
31 Hopkins Plaza, Suite 400-B
Baltimore, MD 21201
(410) 962-4443

Massachusetts
Mal Coles, Director
10 Causeway Street, Room 467
Boston, MA 02222-1038
(617) 565-7000

Michigan
Mary Pfeiler, Director
211 West Fort Street, Suite 1408
Detroit, MI 48226-2799
(313) 226-7848

Minnesota
Robert Jackson, Director
431 South 7th Street, Room 2480
Minneapolis, MN 55415-1854
(612) 334-4083

Mississippi
Roktabija Abdul-Azeez, Director
100 West Capitol St., Room 1005A
Jackson, MS 39269-1092
(601) 965-5664

Missouri
Zeke Rodriguez, Director
801 Walnut Street, Suite 504
Kansas City, MO 64106-2009
(816) 374-6300

Montana
John Allen, Director
208 North Montana Ave., Suite 206
Helena, MT 59601-3837
(406) 449-5404

Nebraska
Anne C. Johnson, Director
100 Centennial Mall North, Rm. 156
Lincoln, NE 68508-3896
(402) 437-5493

Nevada
Craig Warner, Director
4600 Kietzke Lane, Suite E-141
Reno, NV 89502-5033
(775) 784-5314

New Hampshire (ME and VT)
Shireen Tilley, Director
1 Pillsbury Street, Suite 201
Concord, NH 03301
(603) 225-1450

New Jersey
Stanley Gorland, Director
44 South Clinton Ave., Room 312
Trenton, NJ 08609-1507
(609) 989-2243

New Mexico
Ernesto Ramos, Director
120 S. Federal Place, Room 315
Santa Fe, NM 87501-2026
(505) 988-6577

New York
Donna Smith, Director
Leo O'Brien Federal Bldg.
1 Clinton Square, Suite 900
Albany, NY 12207
(518) 431-4150

North Carolina
Robert L. Winston, Director
300 Fayetteville St. Mall, Rm. 131
Raleigh, NC 27601-1739
(919) 856-4731

North Dakota (and SD)
John Pohlman, Director
225 S. Pierre Street, Room 225
Pierre, SD 57501-2452
(605) 224-5996

Ohio
Paul Schrader, Director
51 North High Street, Suite 800
Columbus, OH 43215
(614) 469-7441

Oklahoma
H. Zeke Rodriguez, Director
215 Dean A. McGee, Suite 324
Oklahoma City, OK 73102
(405) 231-5201

Oregon
Robin Sutherland, Director
2010 Lloyd Center
Portland, OR 97232

(503) 231-2103

Pennsylvania
Jorina Ahmed, Director
Robert N.C. Nix Federal Bldg.
900 Market St., Rm 229,
P.O. Box 04121
Philadelphia , PA 19107
(215) 597-2806

Puerto Rico/Virgin Island
Loretta de Cordova, Director
U.S. Federal Building, Suite 662
150 Carlos Chardon Avenue
Hato Rey, PR 00918-1737
(787) 766-5314

Rhode Island
Vincent Marzullo, Director
400 Westminster Street, Room 203
Providence, RI 02903
(401) 528-5426

South Carolina
Jerome J. Davis, Director
1835 Assembly Street, Suite 872
Columbia, SC 29201-2430
(803) 765-5771

South Dakota (and ND)
John Pohlman, Director
225 S. Pierre Street, Room 225
Pierre, SD 57501-2452
(605) 224-5996

Tennessee
Jerry Herman, Director
233 Cumberland Bend Dr.
Suite 112
Nashville, TN 37228
(615) 736-5561

Texas
Jerry G. Thompson, Director
300 East 8th Street, Suite G-100
Austin, TX 78701
(512) 916-5671

Utah
Rick Crawford, Director
350 South Main Street, Room 504
Salt Lake City, UT 84101-2198
(801) 524-5411

Vermont (ME and NH)
Shireen Tilley, Director
1 Pillsbury Street, Suite 201
Concord, NH 03301
(603) 225-1450

Virginia (and DC)
Rosetta Freeman-Busby, Director
1201 New York Ave. NW,
Suite 9107
Washington, DC 20525

(202) 606-5000, x485

Washington
John Miller, Director
915 Second Avenue, Suite 3190
Seattle, WA 98174-1103
(206) 220-7745

West Virginia
Judith Russell, Director
10 Hale Street, Suite 203
Charleston, WV 25301-1409
(304) 347-5246

Wisconsin
Linda Sunde
310 W. Wisconsin Ave., Rm. 1240
Milwaukee, WI 53203-2211
(414) 297-1118

Wyoming
Patrick Gallizzi, Director
308 West 21st Street, Room 206
Cheyenne, WY 82001-3663
(307) 772-2385

CORPORATION SERVICE CENTERS
Altantic Cluster: CT,DE,MA,MD, ME,NH,NJ,NY, PA,PR,RI,VT
Rocco Gaudio, Director
801 Arch Street, Suite 103
Philadelphia, PA 19107-2416
(215) 597-9972

Southern Cluster: AL,DC,FL, GA,KY,MS,NC,SC,TN,VA,WV
Harold Williams, Director
101 Marietta St., NW, Suite 1003
Atlanta, GA 30323-2301
(404) 331-2860

North Central Cluster: IA,IL, IN,MI,MN,NE,ND,OH, SD,WI
Mary Lubertozzi, Director
77 West Jackson Blvd., Suite 442
Chicago, IL 60604-3511
(312) 353-7705

Southeast Cluster: AR,AZ,CO, KS, LS,MO,NM, OK,TX
James Parker, Director
1999 Bryan Street, Room 2050
Dallas, TX 75201
(214) 880-7050

Pacific Cluster: AK,CA,HI,ID, MT, NV,OR,UT, WA,WY
Thomas Joyce, Director
PO Box 29996
Presidio of San Francisco, CA
94129-0996
(415) 561-5960

Chapter 5
VETERANS BENEFITS

DEPARTMENT OF VETERANS AFFAIRS

Are you a military veteran? Or the spouse or child of a veteran? If so, then you should know that because veterans served our country, now it's our country's turn to serve them. From medical care to money for education to help in buying homes, there is a whole slew of valuable programs funded by the government to help veterans and their spouses and dependents. The Department of Veterans Affairs is the government agency most concerned with our veterans. As a veteran, check out what could be available to you from the department.

Veterans Health Administration

The Veterans Health Administration, an agency of the Dept. of Veteran Affairs, provides hospital, nursing home and domiciliary care, and outpatient medical and dental care to eligible veterans of military service in the Armed Forces. Dependents of certain veterans are provided medical care supplied by non-VA institutions and physicians.

Veterans Benefits Administration

The Veterans Benefits Administration conducts an integrated program of veterans benefits, including: claims for disability compensation and pension; claims for specially adapted housing; special clothing allowances; emergency officer's retirement pay; eligibility determinations based on military service for other VA benefits and services or those of other Government agencies; survivor's claims for death compensation, dependency and indemnity compensation, death pension, burial and plot allowance claims.

It also has responsibility for: rehabilitation of disabled veterans, readjustment educational benefits for veterans of post-Korean conflict service, and educational assistance for spouses, surviving spouses, and children of veterans who are totally disabled or die from disability incurred in active service. Special restorative training is also available to eligible children.

It also provides housing credit assistance or, in some cases, direct loans on more liberal terms than generally available to non-veterans. Assistance is provided chiefly through substituting the Government's guaranty on loans made by private lenders in lieu of the downpayments, shorter terms, and other requirements generally required in conventional home mortgage transactions. In addition, it makes direct financial grants to help certain permanently disabled veterans to acquire specially adapted housing.

VA life insurance operations are for the benefit of service members, veterans, and their beneficiaries. In addition, the VA is responsible for various other insurance programs for veterans, including supervision of the Veterans Mortgage Life Insurance Program for those disabled veterans who receive a VA grant for specially adapted housing.

Through the Veterans Services, information, advice, and assistance are provided to veterans, their dependents and beneficiaries, representatives and others in applying for benefits administered by the Department of Veterans Affairs.

National Cemetery System

The National Cemetery System administers the National Cemetery system, which provides cemeterial services to veterans and other eligibles. These services also include providing headstones and markers for the graves of eligibles in national and State veterans cemeteries and for veterans interred in private cemeteries.

MEDICAL CARE

Perhaps the most visible of all veteran benefits and services is the VA's health-care system. It is the largest in the nation. From 54 hospitals in 1930, the VA health-care system has grown to include 171 medical centers; more than 362 outpatient, community and outreach clinics; 128 nursing home care units and 35 domiciliaries.

VA health-care facilities provide a broad range of medical, surgical and rehabilitative care. It operates at least one medical center in each of the 48 contiguous states, Puerto Rico and the District of Columbia. VA hospitals contain approximately 80,000 beds. VA's outpatient clinics register approximately 23 million visits a year..

Since 1979, the VA has operated outreach **Veteran Centers**, which provide readjustment counseling services to veterans who served in the Vietnam era, the Persian Gulf War, and veterans who served during other periods of armed hostilities following the Vietnam War —Lebanon, Grenada and Panama. Currently, there are 201 Vet Centers nationwide. More than one million veterans and another 300,00 family members have visited Vet Centers since the program began. Counseling is provided for a variety of problems, including employment, marital difficulties and post-traumatic stress disorder.

Generally, any needy veteran can receive medical care from the VA who has been dis-

charged or released under conditions other than dishonorable.

Inpatient Medical Care for Vets
Veterans Domiciliary Care (64.008)

Description: This program provides specialized inpatient domiciliary medical care for ambulatory veterans disabled by age or illness who are not in need of more acute hospitalization and who do not need the skilled nursing services provided in nursing homes. VA domiciliaries provide shelter, food and necessary medical care to veterans who are self-sufficient and able to handle daily living activities without assistance.

The goal is to rehabilitate the veteran in anticipation of his/her return to the community in a self-sustaining and independent or semi-independent living situation.

Eligibility Requirements:
(1) Veterans discharged for a disability or receiving disability compensation and suffering from a permanent disability, have no adequate means of support, are incapacitated from earning a living and meet certain other requirements;

(2) Veterans with nonservice-connected disabilities that incapacitate them from earning a living, but which are not so severe as to require hospitalization, are also eligible

if they are unable to defray the expense of domiciliary care and if they meet certain other requirements for care in a domiciliary.

An income limitation criterion is applied to all applicants.

Financial Information: In the latest reported year, 49,987 patients were provided care with an average daily census of 10,662.

Literature: VA Manual M-5, Part IV "*Domiciliary Program, Extended Care*"; VA IS-1 Fact Sheet "*Federal Benefits for Veterans and Dependents,*" available from the Superintendent of Documents, Government Printing Office, Washington, DC 20402.

Who To Contact: *Headquarters Office*: VA Domiciliary Care Program Chief, Geriatrics and Extended Care Strategic Healthcare Group (114A), Department of Veterans Affairs, Washington, DC 20420. (202) 273-8543. *Regional or Local Office*: Contact the nearest VA medical facility (see Table 5a).

Hospital Outpatient Medical Care for Vets
Veterans Medical Care Benefits (64.009)

Description: Veterans and certain of their dependents can receive specialized hospital outpatient medical and dental services, medicines and medical supplies in a VA medical care facility, including reimbursements for some travel costs.

Outpatient medical services include:
- Examination
- Treatment
- Certain home health services
- Podiatric
- Optometric
- Dental
- Supportive medical services and surgical services provided to veterans in VA facilities or under fee basis hometown care programs when properly authorized.

Eligibility Requirements: Any veteran who has a service-connected disability falling under specific VA classifications; or is a former prisoner of war;

and is receiving VA pension benefits. Veterans with incomes above certain limits may be furnished outpatient care and or medical services but only to the extent resources and facilities are available and the veteran agrees to make a copayment.

Financial Information: In the latest reported year, there were 35,777,000 outpatient visits, including 1,555,000 for contract visits.

Literature: "*Federal Benefits for Veterans and Dependents,*" VA Pamphlet IS-1, $2.25, available from Superintendent of Documents, Government Printing Office, Washington, DC 20420.

Who To Contact: *Headquarters Office*: Director, Health Administration Services (10C3), Department of Veterans Affairs, Washington, DC 20420. (202) 273-8302. *Regional or Local Office*: Contact the nearest VA Medical Center. (See Table 5a.)

Veterans Nursing Home Care
(64.010)

Description: Veterans who are not acutely ill and not in need of hospital care, but who require skilled nursing care may be eligible for skilled nursing home care in a VA, State Home, or Contract Nursing Home Care Unit.

Eligibility Requirements: Veterans requiring long term nursing supervision, observation and care by an interdisciplinary team, and/or long term rehabilitative programs and supportive health services found only in a hospital based nursing home program.

Two categories of veterans are eligible:

1) All veterans having a service-connected disability plus those nonservice-connected disabled with annual incomes below $22,064 for a single veteran and below $26,480 for a veteran with one dependent plus $1,467 for each additional dependent;

2) Nonservice-connected veterans with incomes above these limits may be treated by the VA on a resource-available basis if they agree to pay a copayment.

Financial Information: In the latest reported year, 96,568 patients were treated, with a 33,670 average daily census.

Literature: VA Manual M-1, Part I, Chapter 12 *"Nursing Home Care"*; VA Manual M-5, Part II, Chapter 2; VA IS-1 *"Fact Sheet, Federal Benefits for Veterans and Dependents,"* available from the Superintendent of Documents, Government Printing Office, Washington, DC 20402.

Who To Contact: *Headquarters Office*: VA Nursing Home Care Program Chief, Geriatrics and Extended Care Strategic Health Group (114), Dept of Veterans Affairs, Wash., DC 20420. (202) 273-8544. *Regional or Local Office*: Table 5a.

Medical and Dental Care for Eligible Veterans
Veterans Outpatient Care (64.011)

Description: Eligible veterans can receive medical and dental services, medicines, and medical supplies on an outpatient basis in VA facilities or under a fee basis hometown care program when properly authorized. Drugs, medicines, prosthetic appliances, transportation, and such supplies as determined to be reasonable and necessary are also provided to eligible veterans.

Eligibility Requirements: These distinctive groups of veterans are eligible:
- Veterans who require care for service-connected disabilities;
- Veterans who are 50 percent or more service-connected disabled requiring care for any condition;
- Veterans who have a disability for which they receive compensation;
- Pre-bed care, post-hospital care, and care to obviate the need for hospitalization for any condition for veterans rated 30 percent or 40 percent service-connected disabled, whose annual income does not exceed the pension rate of a veteran in need of regular aid and attendance;
- Veterans whose income exceeds the pension rate of a veteran in need of regular aid and attendance may be treated by the

VA on a resource-available basis if they agree to pay a copayment.

Financial Information: In the latest reported year, there were 296,000 visits.

Literature: *"Federal Benefits for Veterans and Dependents,"* VA Pamphlet IS-1, $2.25, available from Superintendent of Documents, Government Printing Office, Washington, DC 20402.

Who To Contact: *Headquarters Office*: VA Central Office Administration Service (10C3), Department of Veterans Affairs, Washington, DC 20420. (202) 273-8303. *Regional or Local Office*: Any VA Medical Center (Table 5a).

State Veterans' Homes
Veterans State Domiciliary Care (64.014)

Description: This program gives financial assistance to States to furnish domiciliary care in State Veterans' Homes to eligible veterans disabled by age or illness, in order to assist eligible veterans to attain physical, mental, and social well-being through rehabilitative programs.

Eligibility Requirements: Eligible veterans must meet one of the following conditions:
- Have a service-connected disability for which such care is being provided;
- Have a nonservice-connected disability and cannot pay the expenses of necessary care;
- Was discharged or released from active service for a disability incurred or aggravated in line of duty;
- Is receiving or entitled to receive disability compensation. A veteran must also meet State admission criteria.

Financial Information: In the latest reported year, 6,230 patients were provided care with an average daily census of 3,898.

Literature: VA Manual M-1, Part I, Chapter 3 *"State Veterans' Homes."*

Who To Contact: *Headquarters Office*: Chief, State Home Per Diem Program, Geriatrics and Extended Care Strategic Healthcare Group, 114B, Dept. of Vet. Affairs, Wash., DC 20420. (202) 273-8538. *Regional or Local Office*: Table 5a.

Nursing Home Care for Vets in State Veterans' Homes
Veterans State Nursing Home Care (64.015)

Description: This program gives financial assistance to States to furnish nursing home care to eligible veterans in State Veterans' Homes.

Eligibility Requirements: Veterans eligible for care in a VA facility, needing nursing home care, and meeting the eligibility conditions of **64.014**.

Financial Information: In the latest reported year, 21,823 patients were treated in 84 State veterans nursing homes with an average daily census of 15,407.

Literature: VA Manual M-1, Part I, Chapter 3 *"State Veterans' Homes."*

Who To Contact: *Headquarters Office*: Chief, State Home Per Diem Program, Geriatrics and Extended Care Strategic Healthcare Group (114), Department of Veteran's Affairs, Washington, DC 20420. (202) 273-8538. *Regional or Local Office*: Table 5a.

Hospital Care for Vets in State Veterans' Homes
Veterans State Hospital Care (64.016)

Description: This program gives financial assistance to States to furnish hospital care to eligible veterans in State Veterans' Homes,

Eligibility Requirements: Veterans eligible for care in a VA facility, needing hospital care, and meeting the eligibility conditions of **64.014**.

Financial Information: In the latest reported year, 1,695 patients were treated in five State homes with an average daily census of 244.

Literature: VA Manual M-1, Part I, Chapter 3, *"State Veterans' Home."*

Who To Contact: *Headquarters Office*: Chief, State Home Per Diem Program, Geriatrics and Extended Care Strategic Healthcare Group (114), Department of Veterans Affairs, Washington, DC 20420. (202) 273-8538. *Regional or Local Office*: Table 5a.

Personal and Medical Services for Blind Vets
Blind Rehabilitation Centers and Clinics (64.007)

Description: Eligible blind veterans can receive personal and social adjustment services and medical or health-related services at selected VA Medical Centers maintaining blind rehabilitation centers.

Eligibility Requirements: Any blind veteran who requires treatment for a service-connected disability or disease; or has a service-connected, compensable disability; or who meets other specific criteria.

Financial Information: Approximately 1,700 veterans have benefited from the personal and social rehabilitation program at the nine Blind Rehabilitation Centers.

Literature: *"Federal Benefits for Veterans and Dependents,"* VA Fact Sheet IS-1, $2.00, available from Superintendent of Documents, Government Printing Office, Washington, DC 20402. *"Coordinated Services for Blinded Veterans,"* IB 11-59, available from Director, Blind Rehabilitation Service (117B), Department of Veterans Affairs, Central Office, Washington, DC 20420.

Who To Contact: *Headquarters Office*: Patient Care Services (117B), Department of Veterans Affairs, Washington, DC 20420. (202) 273-8481. *Regional or Local Office*: Initial contact should be made at the nearest VA facility (Table 5a).

Vocational and Rehabilitation Help for Alcoholic Vets
Veterans Rehabilitation—Alcohol and Drug Dependence (64.019)

Description: This program provides medical, social, vocational and rehabilitation therapies to eligible alcohol and drug dependent veterans, including substance abuse treatment in VA medical centers and clinics.

Eligibility Requirements: Any veteran is eligible

who has served in the active military, naval or air service; was discharged or released under conditions other than dishonorable, and meets general eligibility requirements.

Financial Information: In the latest reported year, over 131,800 veterans were provided outpatient substance abuse treatment services, and 20,100 veterans were treated on inpatient units.

Who To Contact: *Headquarters Office*: Director, Mental Health and Behavioral Sciences Services (11C), Department of Veterans Affairs, Washington, DC 20420. (202) 273-8437. *Application Procedure*: Apply personally to any VA medical center, outpatient clinic, or regional office, through any veterans service organization representative, or by mailing VA Form 10-10 ("*Application for Medical Benefits*") to nearest medical center (Table 5a).

At-Home Medical and Nursing Care for Eligible Veterans
Veterans Home–Based Primary Care (64.022)

Description: Veterans discharged from inpatient status in a Veterans Affairs facility are eligible for home-based primary care. Such care includes medical, nursing, social and rehabilitative services to eligible veterans in their homes by VA health care.

Eligibility Requirements: Veterans requiring intermittent skilled nursing care and related medical services for a protracted period, and meeting the eligibility requirements of Program **64.009**, Page 149.

Financial Information: 6,348 veterans receive care on the average day.

Literature: VA Manual M-1 Part 1, Chapter 30, Section II, "*Hospital Based Home Care*."

Who To Contact: Headquarters Office: Home Based Primary Care Program Coordinator, Geriatrics and Extended Care Strategic Healthcare Group (114), Department of Veterans Affairs, Washington, DC 20420. (202) 273-6488. *Regional or Local Office*: Not applicable.

Medical Care for Dependents of Disabled Vets
Civilian Health and Medical program, Veterans Affairs (CHAMPVA).

Description: CHAMPVA is a healthcare benefits program for:
1) Dependents of veterans who have been rated by VA as having a total and permanent disability;
2) Survivors of veterans who died from VA-rated service-connected conditions; or
3) Survivors of veterans who, at the time of death, were rated permanently and totally disabled from a VA-rated service-connected condition.

It is intended to serve as a *safety net* for dependents and survivors of severely disabled veterans who, because of their disabilities, were unable to provide health insurance benefits to their families through their jobs. Under this program, CHAMPVA's safety net protection only kicks in after the application of most other health insurance policies and programs.

The Department of Defense has a similar program called TRICARE for military retirees as well as families of active duty, retired, and deceased service members. The two programs are easily and often mistaken for each other.

Please note that CHAMPVA is separate from TRICARE and that there are distinct differences between them. (CHAMPVA is explained below. TRICARE is described in the next section.)

Eligibility: The following persons are eligible for CHAMPVA benefits, providing they are not eligible for TRICARE or Medicare Part A as a result of reaching the age of 65:
- Spouse or child of a veteran who has a permanent and total service-connected condition/disability;
- Surviving spouse or child of a veteran who died as a result of a service-connected condition; or who, at the time of death, was permanently and totally disabled from a service-connected condition;
- Surviving spouse or child of a person who died in the line of duty and not due to misconduct.

To be eligible, the child must be unmarried and: under the age of 18; or who, before reaching age 18, became permanently incapable of self-support; or who, after reaching age 18 and continuing up to age 23, is enrolled in a full-time course of instruction at an approved educational institution.

Financial Information: In general, CHAMPVA covers most healthcare services and supplies that are medically and psychologically necessary. General Exclusions:

- Care determined by VA to be medically unnecessary;
- Care for persons eligible for benefits under other government agency programs, except Medicaid and State Victims of Crime Compensation programs,
- Custodial, domiciliary, or rest cures,
- Dental care
- Over-the-counter medications.

As with most insurance policies, there may be a deductible charge the dependent has to meet. However, if treated in a VA facility (on a space-available basis), treatment is free.

Who to Contact: *Headquarters Office*: The administration of CHAMPVA is centralized to the Health Administration Center in Denver, Colorado. *How to Apply*: Prospective applicants are encouraged to contact the Health Administration Center using the below listed toll-free telephone number for assistance or to obtain an Application for CHAMPVA Benefits (VA Form 10-10D); (800) 733-8387.

Health Care for Veterans and Their Families
"TRICARE"

Description: TRICARE is the government's main healthcare program for military retirees and their family members. Technically, this is not a program administered by the Veterans Administration, but by the U.S. Department of Defense.

The TRICARE Standard program allows you to see any civilian physician you choose and the government will pay for part of the cost. It is a typical fee for service plan. There are two other plans that are more like HMO plans: TRICARE Extra and TRICARE Prime (the most restrictive, and thus cheapest, of the three).

Eligibility: All military retired personnel under age 65, and their family members and survivors under age 65.

Persons reaching age 65 are expected to get their health care under the Medicare system.

Financial Information: Under the Tricare Standard Plan, there is an annual deductible you have to spend on medical care first: $150 for an individual policy; $300 for a family. You only pay it if you seek treatment. After paying the initial amount, the government pays 75 percent of an approved-rate amount afterwards. You have to pay 25 percent of hospital charges.

The two other TRICARE plans are less expensive because your choice of doctors is restricted, much like with a managed-care HMO plan. Under the most restrictive plan, you pay only $11 a day for a hospital stay at a military hospital. However, there are annual enrollment fees of a few hundred dollars. So in deciding which of the three plans you want, you have to consider freedom to choose versus cost.

Literature: "*Member Handbook.*"

Who to Contact: Call the TRICARE Service Center toll-free at 1-888-999-5195.

LIFE INSURANCE

The Veterans Administration operates one of the largest life insurance programs in the world and the fourth largest in the United States. It administers seven life insurance programs with 3.1 million policies with a face value of $26.5 billion

In addition, VA supervises the Servicemen's Group Life Insurance and the Veterans' Group Life Insurance programs, which provide some $336 billion in insurance coverage to some 3.5 million veterans and members of the uniformed services.

Veterans Group Life Insurance
(VGLI)

Description: This is the VA's current and most important life insurance program for veterans. It is a conversion of the life insurance policy that was in effect while you were in the military, and provides up to $200,000 coverage through a five-year renewable term policy with reasonable premiums.

You can keep this insurance throughout your life or convert it to an individual commercial life insurance policy with any one of about 128 participating commercial insurance companies.

Veterans are encouraged to apply within 120 days from their release from active duty. If you apply after the 120-day period, you have one additional year to apply but will be required to submit medical evidence of insurability.

Eligibility: Veterans Group Life Insurance is available to:
A) Individuals being released from active duty or the Ready Reserves
B) Ready Reservists who have part-time coverage, and who suffer a disability while performing active duty or inactive duty training for up to 31 days, that makes them uninsurable at standard premium rates
C) Members of the Individual Ready Reserves and Inactive National Guard

Financial Information: Benefits may be paid in a lump sum or over a 36-month period, depending upon which option you select for your beneficiary.

Who to Contact: Same as **64.103** below.

GI Life Insurance
Life Insurance for Veterans— "GI Insurance" (64.103)

Description: This program offers life insurance protection for World Wars I, II, and Korean war veterans and for service-disabled veterans separated from active duty on or after April 25, 1951.

It also provides mortgage protection life insurance for those disabled veterans who were given a VA grant to secure specially adapted housing.

In addition, the insured may be granted a loan up to 94 percent of the cash surrender value of a permanent plan policy, at a low interest rate.

Eligibility Requirements: All of the programs are closed for new issues except Service-Disabled Veterans Insurance and the Mortgage Protection Life Insurance.

Financial Information: Not available.

Literature: "*National Service Life Insurance Information about Waiver of Premium and Total Disability Income Provision*," VA Pamphlet 29-14; "*Veterans Mortgage Life Insurance Information and Premium Rates*," VA Pamphlet 29-79-2; "*Federal Benefits for Veterans and Dependents*," VA Pamphlet 80-97-1, $5.50, available from Superintendent of Documents, PO Box 371954, Pittsburgh, PA 15250-7954.

Who To Contact:
Headquarters Office: Dept. of Veterans Affairs Regional Office and Insurance Center, P.O. Box 8079, Philadelphia, PA 19101. (800) 669-8477.

Regional or Local Office:
- For States east of the Mississippi River, contact the Department of Veterans Affairs Regional Office and Insurance Center, PO Box 8079, Philadelphia, PA 19101.
- For States west of the Mississippi River, contact Dept. of Veterans Affairs Regional Office and Insurance Center, Federal Bldg., Fort Snelling, St. Paul, MN 55111.
- Only the headquarters office or the St. Paul Office should be contacted about Mortgage Protection Life.

COMPENSATION AND PENSION

There are some 2.7 million veterans receiving disability compensation or pension payments from the VA. And some 774,000 widows, children and parents of deceased veterans being paid survivor compensation or death pension benefits.

Total VA disability and death compensation and pension payments came to $16.8 billion in the latest reported year.

Payments—to Vets with Service–Connected Disabilities

Veterans Compensation for Service–Connected Disability (64.109)

Description: The VA compensation program provides monthly payments to veterans for disabilities incurred or aggravated during military service. Payments are based on the average impairment in earning capacity such disability would cause in civilian occupations. If your service-connected disabilities are evaluated as 30 percent or more, you are entitled to additional allowances for your dependents.

Eligibility Requirements: Disabled veterans released from active duty with an other than dishonorable discharge. There is no time limit to apply, but you are encouraged to apply within one year of release from active duty.

Financial Information: Basic rates of compensation range from $101 a month for a 10 percent degree of disability, to a maximum of $6,027 a month for specified very severe disabilities.

In the latest reported year, 2,371,834 disabled veterans received compensation.

Other Related Benefits: In addition to cash benefits, disabled vets may be entitled to:
- priority inpatient and outpatient medical care
- prosthetics, sensory and rehabilitative aids
- clothing allowance
- vocational grant
- vocational rehabilitation
- disabled veterans life insurance
- preference for federal government jobs
- job finding assistance
- specially adapted housing grant
- burial benefits
- Dependents Educational Assistance Program
- Medical Care for Dependents and Survivors (CHAMPVA)
- certain State and local benefits

Literature: *"Federal Benefits for Veterans and Dependents,"* VA Pamphlet 80-97-1, $5.50, available from Superintendent of Documents, P.O. Box 371954, Pittsburgh, PA 15250-7954.

Who To Contact: *Headquarters Office*: Department of Veterans Affairs, Washington, DC 20420. (202) 273-7210. *Application Procedure*: An application (VA Form 21-526) may be obtained from any VA office or regional office and submitted to the regional benefits office (see Table 5a).

Payments—to Eligible Vets with Non-Service-Connected Disabilities

Pension for Non-Service-Connected Disability for Veterans (64.104)

Description: This program provides pensions to assist wartime veterans in need with permanent and total non-service-connected disabilities that prevent them from working. The amount the VA will pay you depends on the type and amount of income you and your family members receive from other sources. Payments are made to bring your total annual income up to an established support level.

Eligibility Requirements:
- Veterans who have had 90 days or more of honorable service of which at least one day must have been during a period of war;
- If less than 90 days service, were released or discharged from such service because of a service-connected disability;
- Or who are permanently and totally disabled for reasons not necessarily due to service.

You must have a disability that the VA evaluates as permanent and total (meaning, for VA purposes, it's not likely you will be able to maintain a substantially gainful job). Income restrictions apply. Pension is not payable to those whose estates are so large that it is reasonable they use the estate for maintenance.

Financial Information:
Veteran without dependents. $8,898 a year, reduced by other income; $14,999 if in need of aid and attendance; $10,987 if housebound.

Veteran with one dependent. $11,773 a year, reduced by other income; $17,782 if in need of aid and attendance; and $13,771 if housebound. Plus $1,533 for each additional dependent;

In addition, veterans of World War One receive an additional $1,922 a year. Currently, 409,900 veterans receive pensions.

Literature: *"Federal Benefits for Veterans and Dependents,"* VA Pamphlet 80-97-1, $5.50, available from Superintendent of Documents, P.O. Box 371954, Pittsburgh, PA 15250-79054.

Who To Contact: *Headquarters Office*: Department of Veterans Affairs, Washington, DC 20420. (202) 273-7210. *Application Procedure*: An application (VA Form 21-526) may be obtained from any local or regional VA Office and submitted to the regional benefits office (Table 5a).

Payments—to Needy Surviving Spouses and Children
Pension to Veterans Surviving Spouses, and Children (64.105)

Description: Pensions are paid to needy surviving spouses and children of deceased war-time veterans whose deaths were not due to service.

Eligibility Requirements: Unmarried surviving spouses and children of deceased veterans who had at least 90 days of honorable active war-time service or, if less than 90 days during war-time, were discharged for a service-connected disability. Income restrictions apply.

A child must be unmarried and under 18, or between 18 and 23 if in school, or disabled before 18 and continuously incapable of self-support.

Pension is not payable to those whose estates are so large that it is reasonable they use the estate for maintenance.

Financial Information:
Spouse without children. $6,237 a year, reduced by other income; $9,973 if in need of aid and attendance; $7,625 if housebound

Surviving spouse with one child. $8,168 a year, reduced by other income; $11,900 if in need of aid and attendance; $9,551 if housebound; plus $1,586 for each additional child.

In the latest reported year, 235,415 survivors cases received pensions.

Literature: *"Federal Benefits for Veterans and Dependents,"* VA Pamphlet 80-97-1, $5.50, available from Superintendent of Documents, P.O. Box 371954, Pittsburgh, PA 15250-7954.

Who To Contact: *Headquarters Office*: Department of Veterans Affairs, Washington, DC 20420. (202) 273-7210. *Application Procedure*: An application (VA Form 21-534) may be obtained from any VA office or regional office and submitted to the regional benefits office (Table 5a).

Payments—to Surviving Spouses and Dependents of Servicepersons
Veterans Dependency and Indemnity Compensation for Service-Connected Death—"DIC" (64.110)

Description: Pensions are paid to surviving spouses, children and parents for the death of any veteran who died because of a service-connected disability, or while in the active military, naval or air service.

Eligibility Requirements: The unmarried surviving spouse, unmarried children, and parent or parents of deceased veterans who died on or after January 1, 1957 because of a service-connected disability.

Survivors of veterans who died before January 1, 1957 **while serving on active duty** may elect to receive payments under this program. Such payments may also be authorized for the surviving spouse and children of certain veterans who were totally service-connected disabled at time of death and whose deaths were not the result of their service-connected disability.

Income restrictions are applied for parents.

Financial Information: *Rang of benefits*:
- From $386 monthly for one child when no

spouse is entitled;

- From $911 to $2,083 for a surviving spouse (with $229 additional if the surviving spouse is in need of aid and attendance, or $110 if housebound);
- A surviving spouse is also entitled to an additional $229 monthly for each child under age 18;
- Monthly rates for parents range from $5 to $445 depending upon income and whether single or married (with $239 additional if the parent is in need of aid and attendance).

In the latest reported year, survivors of 305,851 servicepersons were receiving benefits.

Literature: "*Federal Benefits for Veterans and Dependents,*" VA Pamphlet 80-97-1, $5.50, available from Superintendent of Documents, P.O. Box 371954 Pittsburgh, PA 15250-7954.

Who To Contact: *Headquarters Office*: Department of Veterans Affairs, Washington, DC 20420. (202) 273-7203. *Application Procedure*: An application (VA Form 21-534 for surviving spouses, and/or children; VA Form 21-535 for parents) may be obtained from any VA office or regional office and submitted to the regional benefits office (Table 5a).

Payments to Spouses and Dependants of Certain Deceased Vets

Compensation for Service–Connected Deaths for Veterans' Dependents (64.102)

Description: Pensions are paid to surviving spouses, children and dependent parents for the death of any veteran who died before January 1, 1957 because of a service-connected disability. For deaths on or after January 1, 1957, Dependency and Indemnity Compensation (**64.110**) is payable.

Eligibility Requirements: Unmarried surviving spouse, unmarried children and dependent parents of the deceased veteran.

Financial Information: From $87 monthly for a surviving spouse to $121 for a widow or widower with one child; plus $29 for each additional child. An additional monthly allowance of $79 if widow, widower or dependent parent is in need of aid and attendance. Assistance for dependent parent(s) is $75 for one alone and $80 for two. In the latest reported year, 15 widows and 2,450 parents received survivor's compensation.

Literature: "*Federal Benefits for Veterans and Dependent,*" VA Pamphlet 80-97-1, $5.50, available from Superintendent of Documents, P.O. Box 371954, Pittsburgh, PA 15250-7954.

Who To Contact: *Headquarters Office*: Department of Veterans Affairs, Washington, DC 20420. (202) 273-7210. *Application Procedure*: An application (VA Form 21-534 for surviving spouses, and/or children; VA Form 21-535 for parents) may be obtained from any local or regional VA office and submitted to the regional benefits office (see Table 5a).

HOME LOAN ASSISTANCE

The VA's 49-year-old loan guaranty program has benefited some 14 million veterans and their dependents. Since 1944, when this program was established as part of the original GI Bill, through September 1992, VA home loan guarantees have totaled approximately $400 billion. In the latest reported year, the VA guaranteed 266,000 loans valued at $23 billion and assisted more than 400 disabled veterans with grants totaling $15.6 million for specially adapted housing.

Most VA home loan programs provide for loans to be made by a lender, such as a mortgage company, savings and loan, or bank, with the VA guaranteeing the lender against loss if payment are not made. This encourages lenders to offer veterans loans with more favorable terms:

- Lower interest rate;
- No downpayment required in most cases;
- Loan maximum may be up to 100 percent. But generally loans may not exceed $203,000.
- No monthly mortgage insurance premium to pay.

- Thirty year loans with a choice of repayment plans.

Money—for Disabled Vets to Buy Specially Adapted Housing

Specially Adapted Housing for Disabled Veterans—Paraplegic Housing (64.106)

Description: The Veterans Administration has a variety of programs to help veterans obtain homes, condominiums and mobile homes. This particular program gives money to eligible disabled vets so they can obtain suitable housing units with special fixtures and facilities made necessary by the nature of their disabilities.

The program pays half the cost of a new or suitably remodeled housing unit, land, fixtures, and allowable expenses, up to a maximum grant of $43,000. It provides up to $8,250 for adaptations to the veteran's residence.

Eligibility Requirements: Permanently and totally disabled veterans.

Financial Information: In the latest reported year, 600 grants were made to disabled veterans.

Literature: "*Questions and Answers on Specially Adapted Housing for Veterans*," VA Pamphlet 26-69-1, no charge; "*Federal Benefits for Veterans and Dependents*," VA Pamphlet 80-97-1, $5.50, available from Superintendent of Documents, P.O. Box 371954, Pittsburgh, PA 15250-7954; "*Handbook for Design, Specially Adapted Housing*," VA Pamphlet 26-13, available to eligible veterans.

Who To Contact: *Headquarters Office*: Department of Veterans Affairs, Washington, DC 20420. (202) 273-7355. *Regional or Local Office*: Information may be obtained from the nearest regional benefits office (Table 5a) or by calling toll free (800) 827-1000.

Money—for Veterans to Buy a Home

Veterans Housing—Guaranteed and Insured Loans— "VA Home Loans" (64.114)

Description: The Department of Veterans Affairs provides home mortgage loan guarantees to assist veterans, certain service personnel, and certain unremarried surviving spouses of veterans obtain credit for the purchase, construction or improvement of homes on more liberal terms than are generally available to non-veterans.

Generally such loans, because they are guaranteed by the government, are made on more liberal terms than generally available to non-vets. Interest rates are lower, there may be no down payment required, and the repayment period may be longer.

Home loans can be used to
- Buy or build or improve a home or condominium;
- Purchase a manufactured home and a lot on which it will be permanently placed;
- Refinance a mortgage or existing VA loan or other lien on a house owned by the applicant.

Applicants must have sufficient present and prospective income to meet loan repayment terms and have a satisfactory credit record.

Eligibility Requirements: The following categories of veterans are eligible:

a) Veterans who served on active duty on or after 9/16/40, and were discharged under conditions other than dishonorable. Veterans who served any time during World War II, the Korean Conflict, the Vietnam War, or the Persian Gulf War must have served on active duty 90 days or more; veterans with peacetime service only must have served a minimum of 181 days continuous active duty;

b) All veterans separated from enlisted service which began after 9/7/80, or service as an officer which began after 10/16/81, must also have served at least 24 months of continuous active duty or the full period for which the person was ordered to active duty. Veterans of such recent service may qualify with less service time if they have a compensable service-connected disability or were discharged after at least 181 days (90 days during Persian Gulf War;

c) Members of the Selected Reserve who are not otherwise eligible for home loan benefits and who have completed a total of six years in the reserves, followed by an honorable discharge, placement on the retired list, or continued service. Individuals who completed less than 6 years may be eligible if discharged for a service connected disability;

d) Unremarried surviving spouses of otherwise eligible veterans who died in service or whose deaths were attributable to service-connected disabilities; or are listed as missing in action, or as prisoners of war

Financial Information: *Range and Average of Financial Assistance*: The home loan guarantee is for the following amounts:
1) 50 percent for loans of $45,000 or less;
2) $22,500 for loans over $45,000 and not more than $56,250;
3) $36,000 or 40 percent, whichever is less, for loans of $56,251 to $144,000;
4) $50,750, or 25 percent, whichever is less, for loans over $144,000 or to refinance the outstanding balance of an existing VA guaranteed home loan at a lower interest rate.

Literature: "*Federal Benefits for Veterans and Dependents*," VA Pamphlet 80-97-1, $5.50, available from Superintendent of Documents, P.O. Box 371954, Pittsburgh, PA 15250-7954; "*VA-Guaranteed Home Loans For Veterans*," VA Pamphlet 26-4; "*Pointers For the Veteran Homeowner*," VA Pamphlet 26-5; "*To the Homebuying Veteran*," VA Pamphlet 26-6.

Who To Contact: Headquarters Office: Department of Veterans Affairs, Washington, DC 20420. (202) 273-7390. *Regional or Local Office*: Loan applications are processed completely by the Veterans Benefits Administration field offices for their respective geographic area jurisdictions. Initial contact should be made with the appropriate office listed in Table 5a.

Money—for Disabled Vet to Buy a House
64.118

Description: Under this program, the VA makes loans or grants to certain severely disabled veterans for specially adaptive housing with special features or movable facilities made necessary by the nature of their disabilities.

The VA may make loans up to $33,000 to eligible applicants for any of the following purposes:
a) Purchase or construction of a dwelling to be owned and occupied by the veteran as his or her home;
b) Construction on land owned by the veteran of a farm residence to be occupied as his or her home;
c) Repair, alteration or improvement of a farm residence or other dwelling owned by the veteran and occupied as his or her home.

Applicant Eligibility: Veterans who served on active duty who have permanent, total and compensable disabilities due to:
- loss or loss of use of both lower extremities; or
- blindness in both eyes, having only light perception, plus loss or loss of use of one lower extremity; or
- loss or loss of use of one lower extremity, together with (a) residuals of organic disease or injury, or (b) the loss or loss of use of one upper extremity which so affect the functions of balance or propulsion as to preclude locomotion without the aid of braces, crutches, canes or a wheelchair.

It must be medically feasible for the veteran to reside in the proposed or existing housing unit, and in the locality. The housing unit must be so adapted as to be suitable to the veteran's needs for dwelling purposes.

Financial Information: *Range of Financial Assistance:* Up to $33,000. Last year, one loan was made.

Literature: "*Questions and Answers on Specially Adapted Housing for Veterans*," VA Pamphlet 26-

69-1, no charge; "*Federal Benefits for Veterans and Dependents,*" VA Pamphlet 80-96-1, $3.25, available from Superintendent of Documents, P.O. Box 371954, Pittsburgh, PA 15250-7954; "*Handbook For Design, Specially Adapted Housing,*" VA Pamphlet 26-13, available to eligible veterans only.

Who to Contact: *Headquarters Office*: Department of Veterans Affairs, Washington, DC 20420. (202) 273-7390. *Regional or Local Office*: See Veterans Benefits Administration field office listed Table 5a. *Application Procedure*: The veteran should apply to the VA regional office or center having jurisdiction over the property location. No specific initial application form is prescribed. The VA office will respond with appropriate formal application blanks with instructions for further processing.

Money—for Veterans to Buy Manufactured Mobile Homes
(64.119)

Description: Guaranteed/insured loans (of up to approximately 20 years) to assist veterans, servicepersons, and certain unremarried surviving spouses of veterans to purchase a manufactured home on more liberal terms than are available to non-veterans.

Eligibility Requirements: Same as for **64.114.** Applicants must have sufficient present and prospective income to meet loan repayment terms and have a satisfactory credit record.

Financial Information: *Range and Average of Financial Assistance*: The guaranty is $20,000 or 40 percent, whichever is less. The average loan amount is $29,596.

Literature: VA Pamphlet 26-71-1, "*Questions and Answers on Manufactured Home Loans to Veterans.*"

Who To Contact: *Headquarters Office*: Department of Veterans Affairs, Washington, DC 20420. (202) 273-7390. *Regional or Local Office*: See Veterans Benefits Administration field office listed Table 5a.

Loans to Native American Veterans to Acquire a Home
VA Native American Veteran Direct Loan Program (64.126)

Description: This program makes direct loans to certain Native American veterans for the purchase, construction, or repair of the veteran's home on Indian trust lands. Also for the purchase of a manufactured home to be permanently affixed to a lot that is already held in leasehold by the applicant.

Applicant Eligibility: Native American veterans recognized by a Federally Recognized Tribal Government as a Native American and who meet certain conditions, such as

- Served on active duty on or after September 16, 1940, and was discharged or released under conditions other than dishonorable;
- If service was any time during WW II, the Korean Conflict, the Vietnam War, or the Persian Gulf War, then the Native American Veteran must have served on active duty for 90 days or more; peacetime service only, he must have served a minimum of 181 days continuous active duty;
- If separated from enlisted service which began after September 7, 1980, or service as an officer which began after October 16, 1981, a veteran must also have served at least 24 months of continuous active duty or the full period for which called or ordered to active duty;
- Native American members of the Selected Reserve and who are not otherwise eligible for home loan benefits and who have completed a total of 6 years in the Selected Reserves followed by an honorable discharge, placement on the retired list, or continued service.

Also, certain unremarried surviving spouses of veterans.

Financial Information: Loans are limited to $80,000, except where, because of significantly higher than average housing costs in certain geographic areas, higher loans may be made. Annual totals: 34 loans for $3.3 million.

Literature: VA Pamphlet 26-93-1, "*VA Direct Home Loan for Native American Veterans Living on Trust Lands.*"

Who to Contact: *Headquarters Office*: Department of Veterans Affairs, Washington, DC 20420. (202) 273-7377. *Regional or Local Office*: Loan applications are processed completely by the Veterans Benefits Administration field offices for their respective geographic area jurisdiction. Initial contact should by made with the appropriate office listed in Table 5a.

EDUCATION AND TRAINING

Since 1944, when the first GI Bill became law, more than 20 million beneficiaries have participated in veterans' education and training programs. This includes 7.8 million World War II veterans, 2.4 million Korean Conflict veterans, and 8.2 million Post-Korean and Vietnam War veterans and active-duty service personnel.

The VA also has assisted in the education of more than 671,000 eligible dependents of veterans whose deaths or permanent and total disabilities were service-connected.

Money—for Disabled Vets to Go to College, Get Vocational Rehabilitation or Start a Small Business
Vocational Rehabilitation for Disabled Veterans (64.116)

Description: The purpose of this program is to help disabled veterans achieve independence in daily living and to the maximum extent feasible, to become employable.

The program provides direct payments, direct loans, advisory services and counseling. It pays the entire cost of tuition, books, fees, supplies, job-placement and other services, and a monthly subsistence allowance for up to four years.

Veterans who meet certain requirements may receive an initial supply of goods and commodities to start a small business.

Eligibility Requirements: Veterans of World War II and later service with a compensable service-connected disability; certain service-disabled servicepersons pending discharge or release from service in need of vocational rehabilitation because they have a serious employment handicap.

Financial Information: Monthly full-time allowances range from $433.06 for a single veteran to $633.04 for a veteran with two dependents, plus $46.14 for each dependent in excess of two; No-interest loans of up to $866.12; Work-study allowances not higher then 25 times the minimum hourly wage times the number of weeks in the veteran's period of enrollment.

Literature: "*Federal Benefits for Veterans and Dependents,*" VA Pamphlet 80-97-1, $5.50, available from Superintendent of Documents, P.O. Box 371954, Pittsburgh, PA 15250-7954; "*Vocational Rehabilitation—Your Key to an Independent Future,*" VA Pamphlet 28-82-1, free, available from any VA regional office.

Who To Contact: *Headquarters Office*: Department of Veterans Affairs, Veterans Benefits Administration, Vocational Rehabilitation and Counseling Service (28), Washington, DC 20420. (202) 273-7419. *Application Procedure*: Obtain an application (VA Form 28-1900) from any VA office or regional office and submit it to the nearest VA regional benefits office (see Table 5a).

Money—for Surviving Spouse and Children to Go to College
Survivors and Dependents Educational Assistance (64.117)

Description: This program help dependents of certain veterans continue their education. It pays monthly payments to qualifying spouses, surviving spouses, or children of deceased or disabled veterans to be used for degree and certificate programs, apprenticeships, and on-the-job training.

Benefits may be paid for up to a maximum of 45 months, to be used for tuition, books, living expenses, etc.

Eligibility Requirements: Spouses, surviving spouses, and children between age 18 and 26 of veterans who died or who are permanently and totally disabled due to military service; or died because of any cause while such service-connected disabilities were in existence.

Financial Information: *Range and Average of Financial Assistance for institutional training:* full time, $588 a month; three-quarters time, $441 a month; half-time, $294 a month. Tutorial assistance up to a maximum of $1,200. *Work-Study Allowance:* payment based on the minimum wage.

During the latest reported year, there were 52,120 participants.

Literature: "*Federal Benefits for Veterans and Dependents*," VA Pamphlet 80-97-1, $5.50, available from Superintendent of Documents, P.O. Box 371954, Pittsburgh, PA 15250-7954.

Who To Contact: *Headquarters Office*: Department of Veterans Affairs, Central Office, Washington, DC 20420. (202) 273-7132. *Application Procedure*: An application (VA Form 22-5490) may be obtained from any VA Regional Office and submitted to the VA Regional Benefits Office with jurisdiction over the state where you will get your education. See Table 5a.

Money for Post–Vietnam Vets to Go to College

Post–Vietnam Era Veterans' Educational Assistance—"Voluntary–Contributory Matching Program" (64.120)

Description: Direct payments to persons entering the Armed Forces after December 31, 1976, and before July 1, 1985, to help them get the educational, professional or vocational training they might otherwise not be able to afford.

Eligibility Requirements: Post-Vietnam era veterans who served honorably on active duty for more than 180 continuous days beginning on or after January 1, 1977, or have been discharged

after such date because of a service-connected disability. Participants must have contributed to the program a monthly deduction of $25 to $100 from military pay, up to a maximum of $2,700, for deposit in a special training fund.

No individuals on active duty in the Armed Forces may initially begin contributing to this program after March 31, 1987. Generally, eligibility ceases at the end of 10 years from the date of the participant's last discharge.

Financial Information: *Range and Average of Financial Assistance*: Up to a maximum of $8,100 of basic benefits. Tutorial assistance up to a maximum of $1,200.

Literature: "*Federal Benefits For Veterans and Dependents*," VA Pamphlet 80-97-1, $5.50, available from Superintendent of Documents, P.O. Box 371954, Pittsburgh, PA 15250-7954.

Who To Contact: *Headquarters Office*: Department of Veterans Affairs, Central Office, Washington, DC 20420. (202) 273-7132. *Application Procedure*: Application form (VA Form 22-1990) may be obtained from any VA office and submitted to the appropriate VA regional benefits office (Table 5a).

College Money for Recently Retired Vets

All-Volunteer Force Educational Assistance—Montgomery GI Bill Active Duty (64.124)

Description: The Montgomery GI bill is the VA's main education program for veterans. It provides up to 36 months of educational benefits. Veterans receive monthly payments for educational expenses if enrolled in an educational, professional, or vocational program of education at an approved educational institution. Benefits may be used for degree and certificate programs, apprenticeship or on-the-job training, and correspondence courses. Benefits may not be paid for elementary or secondary courses, or farm cooperative courses.

Eligibility Requirements: Veterans and servicepersons initially entering military service on or after July 1, 1985 and had their basic pay reduced by $100 a month for the first 12 months in service unless they specifically elect not to participate. (If an individual elected not to participate, he or she may not decide at a later date to participate except for certain situations.)

An individual must have received a high school degree or the equivalent before completing the initial obligated period of active duty, or successfully completed 12 college credits. Veterans generally have 10 years after release from service to complete their education.

Financial Information: Active duty for 3 years, or 2 years active duty plus 4 years in the Selected Reserve or National Guard will entitle a veteran to $528 monthly basic benefits for 36 months.

Two years active duty would entitle the individual to $429 monthly for 36 months.

Total maximum basic assistance is $19,296. Plus, the Department of Defense may provide a supplemental assistance benefit of up to $300 monthly to individuals who serve an additional five continuous years of active duty.

Literature: "*Federal Benefits for Veterans and Dependents,*" VA Pamphlet 80-97-1, $5.50, available from Superintendent of Documents, P.O. Box 371954, Pittsburgh, PA 15250-7954.

Who To Contact: *Headquarters Office*: Department of Veterans Affairs, Central Office, Washington, DC 20420. (202) 273-7132. *Application Procedure*: Application (VA Form 22-1990) may be obtained from any VA Regional Office and submitted to the VA Regional Benefits Office for the state where you will receive your education. See Table 5a.

ADDITIONAL BENEFITS

$150–$1,500 Burial Allowance for Vets
Burial Expenses Allowance for Veterans (64.101)

Description: Uncle Sam will pay up to $150 toward the plot or interment expenses for certain veterans not buried in a national cemetery. Up to $300 as a burial allowance is payable toward the burial expense of certain veterans. If death is service-connected, payments can be made to reimburse burial and funeral expenses generally up to $1,500.

In addition, the cost of transporting the veterans' remains from place of death to site of burial, a headstone or marker, and an American flag to drape the casket may be authorized. Application for the burial allowance must be filed within 2 years of the veteran's burial. There is no deadline on receipt of the flag.

Applicant Eligibility: The person who bore the veteran's burial expense or the Funeral Director, if unpaid, is eligible for reimbursement of the burial expense. The next of kin, friend or associate of the deceased veteran is eligible for the flag.

Financial Information: In the latest reported year, there were 93,740 burial allowances and 532,000 burial flags.

Literature: "*Federal Benefits for Veterans and Dependents,*" VA Pamphlet 80-97-1, $5.50, available from Superintendent of Documents, P.O. Box 371954, Pittsburgh, PA 15250-7954.

Who To Contact: *Headquarters Office*: Department of Veterans Affairs, Washington, DC 20420. (202) 273-7210. *Application Procedure*: For burial benefits, application (VA Form 21-530) may be obtained from any VA regional or local office and submitted to the nearest regional office (see Table 4a). Headstones and markers must be applied for (on VA Form 40-1330) to the Director of the National Cemetery System, Department of Veterans Affairs, 810 Vermont Ave, NW, Washington, DC 20420. (202) 273-5146

Free Headstones for Veterans
Procurement of Headstones and Markers (64.202)

Description: The Government furnishes headstones and markers for deceased eligible veterans in national, post and State veterans cemeteries, or for the unmarked graves of eligible veterans in private cemeteries. This includes inscription, cost of shipment to destination, installation and maintenance cost in national, State and post cemeteries, and replacement of illegible headstones or markers.

Beneficiary Eligibility: Any deceased vet who was discharged under conditions other than dishonorable and meets the following qualifications:

- Service after 9/7/80 for enlisted personnel and 10/16/81 for commissioned officers, must be for a minimum of 24 months or the period for which ordered, unless completed under special circumstances such as death on active duty;
- Any active duty during the Persian Gulf War qualifies for this benefit;
- Members of the Reserve and the Army and Air National Guard who die while performing active duty, or are entitled to retirement pay subsequent to 10/27/92;
- All persons, including Reservists and National Guard members having 20 years of qualifying service, who are entitled to retired pay or would be entitled, if at least 60 years of age, and their eligible dependents;
- Commissioned officers of the Public Health Service and the National Oceanic and Atmospheric Administration;
- Merchant Mariners and certain other categories of individuals who participated in wartime activities whose service has been classified as active duty.
- Spouses and certain other dependents of those eligible for a headstone or marker and buried in a national, State or post cemetery are also eligible.

If a burial plot is in a national cemetery or State veterans cemetery, the Cemetery Director orders the headstone or marker. When burial is in a private cemetery, the applicant is normally the next of kin. In the absence of relatives, the applicant need not be a member of the deceased's family, but must certify in writing that the grave is unmarked and that a Government headstone or marker is preferred in lieu of a privately purchased one.

Financial Information: In the latest reported year, 361,200 applications were processed for standard government headstones and markers.

Literature: "*Headstone and Marker Program for Veterans*" (VA Pamphlet 40-107) and "*Application for Standard Government Headstone or Marker*" (VA Form 40-1330).

Who To Contact: *Headquarters Office*: Director, Memorial Programs Service (403), National Cemetery System, Department of Veterans Affairs, 810 Vermont Avenue, NW., Washington, DC 20420-0001. Contact: David K. Schettler. Phone: (202) 501-3100. *Application Procedure*: Applicant should complete VA Form 40-1330, Application for Standard Government Headstone or Marker, in accordance with instructions provided and mail it to the Director, at the above Headquarters address. Application forms are available at all Department of Veterans Affairs Regional Offices and State and County Veterans Service Offices.

Free Help with Veterans Benefits
Veterans Information and Assistance—Vet Services (64.115)

Description: Information and assistance to vets about veterans benefits and to provide locations within each State where this assistance can be obtained.

Eligibility Requirements: Veterans, their dependents and beneficiaries, their representatives, other interested parties, including veterans of the Public Health Service, the National Oceanic and Atmospheric Administration, and certain World War II Merchant Marines.

Financial Information: Not applicable.

Literature: "*Federal Benefits for Veterans and Dependents*," VA Pamphlet 80-97-1, $5.50, available from Superintendent of Documents, P.O. Box 371954, Pittsburgh, PA 15250-7954; "*A Summary of VA Benefits*," VA Pamphlet 27-82-2; "*Un Resumen De Beneficios Del VA*," VA Pamphlet 27-82-2(S); "*Vocational Rehabilitation, Making It All Possible*," VA Pamphlet 28-82-1; "*Veterans Benefits for Older Americans*," VA Pamphlet 27-80-2; "*Veteran-Student Work-Study Programs*," VA Pamphlet 27-80-3.

Who To Contact: *Headquarters Office*: Department of Veterans Affairs, Washington, DC 20420. (202) 273-7210. *Regional or Local Office*: Contact the nearest Veterans Benefits Administration field office as shown in Table 5a

Legal Services for Veterans

Description: If you need help getting veterans benefits you think are due you, you can get help from the National Veterans Legal Service Project.

This is a non-profit organization that provides legal aid to veterans.

Who to Contact: National Veterans Legal Service Project, 2001 "S" St., NW, Washington, DC 20009. (202) 265-8305.

Table 5a: VETERANS ADMINISTRATION FACILITIES, BY STATE

The Veterans Benefits Administration provides toll-free telephone service throughout the 50 States, Washington, DC and Puerto Rico: (800) 827-1000.

(Note 1: The following symbols indicate additional programs are available at medical centers: *for nursing-home care units; #for domiciliaries.)

(Note 2. For each listing, the 5-digit zip code immediately follows the name of the city.)

ALABAMA
Medical Centers:
Birmingham 35233 (700 S. 19th St., 205-933-8101)
Montgomery 36109 (215 Perry Hill Rd., 334-272-4670)
*Tuscaloosa 35404 (3701 Loop Rd. East, 205-554-2000)
*Tuskegee 36083 (2400 Hospital Rd., 334-727-0550)

Clinics:
Anniston 36207 (413 Quintard Ave., 256-231-7980)
Decatur 35601 (401 Lee St. N.E., Suite 606, 256-350-1531)
Dothan 36303 (1785 East Main, 334-677-7823)
Florence 35630 (401 E. Spring St., 205-766-5683)
Gadsden 35906 (3006 Rainbow Drive, 256-413-7154)
Huntsville 35801 (201 Governor's Dr. S.W., 256-535-3100)
Huntsville 35801 (2006 Franklin St. SE, #104, 205-534-1691)
Jasper 35501 (3400 Highway 78, 205-221-7384)
Mobile 36604 (1359 Springhill Ave., 205-415-3900)
Shoals 35660 (422 Cox Blvd., 256-381-9055)
Tuscaloosa (2017 Rainbow Dr., 205-546-9239)

Regional Office:
Montgomery 36109 (345 Perry Hill Rd., local, 279-4866; statewide, (800) 827-1000)

Vet Centers:
Birmingham 35205 (1500 5th Ave. S., 205-731-0550)
Mobile 36608 (3725 Airport Blvd., Ste. 143, 205-304-0108)

National Cemeteries:
Fort Mitchell (Seale 36875, 553 Hwy 165, 205-855-4731)
Mobile 36604 (1202 Virginia St.; for information, call Barrancas, FL, NC, 904-452-3357)

ALASKA
Clinics:
Anchorage Outpatient Clinic and Regional Office 99508-2989 (2925 DeBarr Rd., 907-257-4700)

Regional Office:
Anchorage 99508-2989 (2925 DeBarr Rd., local, 257-4700; statewide, (800) 827-1000)

Benefits Office:
Juneau 99802 (709 W. 9th St., #263, 907-586-7472)

Vet Centers:
Anchorage 99508 (4201 Tudor Ctr. Dr., #115, 907-563-6966)
Fairbanks 99701 (540 4th Ave., Suite 100, 907-456-4238)
Kenai 99669 (Bldg F, Ste 4, Red Diamond Ctr, 43335 K-Beach Road, 907-260-7640)
Wasilla 99654 (851 E. Westpoint Ave., #111, 907-376-4318)

National Cemeteries:
Fort Richardson 99505 (PO Box 5-498, Bldg. 997, Davis Highway, 907-384-7075)
Sitka 99835 (PO Box 1065; for information, call Ft. Richardson, AK, NC, 907-384-7075)

ARIZONA
Medical Centers:
*Phoenix 85012 (650 E. Indian School Rd., 602-277-5551)
#Prescott 86313 (Highway 89 North, 928-445-4860)
*Tucson 85723 (3601 S. 6th Ave., 520-792-1450)

Clinics:
Bellemont 86015 (PO Box 16916, 520-226-1056)
Buckeye 85326 (1209 N. Miller Road, 623-386-5785)
Casa Grande 85222 (900 E. Florence Blvd., 520-629-4900)
Cottonwood 86326 (203 Candy Lane Bdg. 5B, 982-649-1523)
Kingman 86401 (1726 Beverly Ave., 520-692-0080)
Lake Havasu 86403 (2035 Mesquite, Ste. E, 520-680-0090)
Mesa 85212 (6950 E. Williams Rd., Bldg. 23, 602-222-6568)
Stafford 85546 (711 S. 14th Ave., 520-629-4900)
Show Low 85901 (2450 Show Low Lake Rd., 520-532-1069)
Sun City 85351 (10147 Grand Ave., Ste. C1, 602-222-2630)
Yuma 85365 (2555 E. Gila Ridge Rd., 520-629-4900)

Regional Office:
Phoenix 85012 (3225 N. Central Ave., local, 263-5411; statewide, (800) 827-1000)

Vet Centers:
Phoenix 85012 (77 E. Weldon, Ste. 100, 602-640-2981)
Prescott 86303 (161 E. Granite St., Ste. B, 520-778-3469)
Tucson 85719 (3055 N. 1st Ave., 520-882-0333)

National Cemeteries:
National Memorial Cemetery of Arizona (Phoenix 85024, 23029 N. Cave Creek Rd., 602-379-4615)
Prescott 86301 (VA Med. Ctr., 500 Hwy 89 N., 602-445-4860)

ARKANSAS

Medical Centers:
Fayetteville 72703 (1100 N. College Ave., 479-443-4301)
#*Little Rock 72205 (4300 W. 7th St., 501-257-1000)

Regional Office:
N. Little Rock 72115 (2200 Ft. Roots Dr., 501-257-1000)

Vet Center:
North Little Rock 72114 (201 W. Broadway, #A, 501-324-6395)

National Cemeteries:
Fayetteville 72701 (700 Government Ave., 501-444-5051)
Fort Smith 72901 (522 Garland Ave., 501-783-5345)
Little Rock 72206 (2523 Confederate Blvd., 501-324-6401)

CALIFORNIA
Medical Centers:
*Fresno 93703 (2615 E. Clinton Ave., 559-225-6100)
*Livermore 94550 (4951 Arroyo Rd., 925-447-2560)
*Loma Linda 92357 (11201 Benton St., 800-741-8387)
*Long Beach 90822 (5901 E. 7th St., 562-826-8000)
Mather 95655 (10535 Hospitol Way, 916-366-5366)
#*Palo Alto 94304 (3801 Miranda Ave., 650-493-5000)
*San Diego 92161 (3350 La Jolla Village Dr., 858-552-8585)
San Francisco 94121 (4150 Clement St., 415-221-4810)
Santa Ana 92704 (2740 S. Bristol St., 714-825-3500)
*Sepulveda 91343 (1611 Plummer St., 818-891-7711)
West Los Angeles 90073 (Wilshire & Sawtelle Blvds., 310-478-3711)

Clinics:
Bakersfield 93301 (1801 West Wind Dr., 661-632-1871)
Berkeley 94710 (841 Folger Ave., 510-486-3902)
Capitola 95010 (1350 N. 41st St., Ste. 102, 831-464-5519)
Chico 95926 (280 Cohasset Rd., 530-879-5000)
Eureka 95501 (727 E. St., 707-442-5335)
East Los Angeles 90040 (5400 E. Olympic Blvd., Suite 150, 323-725-7557)
Los Angeles 90012 (351 E. Temple, 213-253-2677)
Fairfield 94535 (103 Bodin Circle, 707-437-5660)
Martinez 94553 (150 Muir Rd., 925-370-4701)
Modesto 95330 (1524 McHenry Ave., 209 557-6200)
Pleasant Hill 94523 (N. Calif. System of Clinics, 2300 Contra Costa Blvd., 510-372-2000)
Oakland 94612 (2221 Martin Luther King Jr. Way, 510-267-7820)
Oakland, 94612 (427 13th St., 510-273-7096)
Redding 96002 (351 Hartnell Ave., 530-226-7555)
Sacramento 95820 (4600 Broadway, 916-731-7360)
San Jose 95119 (80 Great Oaks Blvd., 408-363-3000)
Santa Barbara 93110 (4440 Calle Real, 805-683-1491)
Santa Rosa 95404 (3315 Chanate Rd., 707-570-3855)
Sonora 95370 (720 Pauline Ct., 209-533-5470)

Regional and Benefits Offices:
East Los Angeles 90022 (5400 E. Olympic Blvd., 213-722-4927)
Los Angeles 90024 (Fed. Bldg., 11000 Wilshire Blvd. serving counties of Inyo, Kern, Los Angeles, Orange, San Bernardino, San Luis Obispo, Santa Barbara and Ventura; local, 479-4011; statewide, (800) 827-1000)
Oakland 94612 (1301 Clay St., Rm. 1300 North, local, 637-1365; statewide, 800-827-1000; recorded benefits, 24-hour availability, 637-1325)
San Diego 92108 (2022 Camino Del Rio North, serving counties of Imperial, Riverside and San Diego, local, 297-8220; statewide, 800-827-1000)
Counties of Alpine, Lassen, Modoc and Mono served by Regional Office in Reno, NV.

Vet Centers:
Anaheim 92805 (859 S. Harbor Blvd., 714-776-0161)
Burlingame 94010 (1234 Howard Ave., 415-344-3126)
Chico 95928 (25 Main St., 530-899-8549)
Commerce 90022 (VA East L.A. Clinic, 5400 E. Olympic Blvd., Ste. 140, 213-728-9966)
Concord 94520 (1899 Clayton Rd., Ste. 140, 925-680-4526)
Culver City 90230 (5730 Uplander Way, 310-641-0326)
Eureka 95501 (2839 G St., 707-444-8271)
Fresno 93726 (3636 N. 1st St., Suite 112, 559-437-5660)
Los Angeles 90003 (S. Central L.A., 251 W. 85th Pl., 310-215-2380)
Los Angeles 90025 (West L.A., 2000 Westwood Blvd., 310-475-9509)
Marina 93933 (455 Reservation Rd., Ste. E, 408-384-1660)
Oakland 94612 (1504 Franklin St., 510-763-3904)
Redwood City 94062 (2946 Broadway St., 650-299-0672)
Riverside 92571 (4954 Arlington Ave., Ste. A, 909-276-6342)
Rohnert Park 94928 (6225 State Farm Dr., Suite 101, 707-586-3295)
Sacramento 95825 (1111 Howe Ave., Ste. 390, 916-566-7430)
San Diego 92103 (2900 6th Ave., 858-294-2040)
San Francisco 94102 (505 Polk St., 415-441-5051)
San Jose 95112 (278 N. 2nd St., 408-993-0729)
Santa Barbara 93101 (1300 Santa Barbara St., 805-564-2345)
Sepulveda 91343 (16111 Plummer St., 818-891-7711)
Upland 91786 (1238 E. Arrow Hwy., #100, 909-946-5348)
Vista 92083 (1830 West Dr., Suite 103, 619-945-8941)

National Cemeteries:
Fort Rosecrans (San Diego 92166, Point Loma, P.O. Box 6237, 619-553-2084)
Golden Gate (San Bruno 94066, 1300 Sneath Ln., 415-589-7737)
Los Angeles 90049 (950 S. Sepulveda Blvd., 310-824-4311)
Riverside 92508 (22495 Van Buren Blvd., 909-653-8417)
San Francisco 94129 (P.O. Box 29012, Presidio of San Francisco, 415-561-2008)
San Joaquin Valley (Gustine 95322, 32053 W. McCabe Rd., 209-854-1040)

COLORADO
Medical Centers:
Alamosa 81101 (1847 2nd St., 719-589-4488)
*Denver 80220 (1055 Clermont St., 303-399-8020)
*Fort Lyon 81038 (C St., 719-384-3100)
*Grand Junction 81501 (2121 North Ave., 970-242-0731)

Clinic:
Aurora 80045 (13001 E. 17th Pl. Bld. 500, 303-724-0190)
Colorado Springs 80905 (25 North Spruce St., 719-327-5660)
Greeley 80631 (2020 16th St., 970-313-0027)
Fort Collins 80524 (1100 Poudre River Dr., 970-224-1550)
La Junta 81050 (1100 Carson Ave., Ste. 104, 719-383-5195)
Lakewood 80225 (155 Van Gordon St., 303-914-2680)
Montrose 81401 (4 Hillcrest Plaza Way, 970-249-7791)
Pueblo 81008 (4112 Outlook Blvd., 719-553-1000)

Regional and Benefits Offices:

Denver 80225 (44 Union Blvd., P.O. Box 25126; local, 980-1300; statewide, (800) 827-1000)
Lakewood 80228 (155 Van Gordon St.)

Vet Centers:
Boulder 80302 (2336 Canyon Blvd., 303-440-7306)
Colo. Springs 80903 (416 E. Colorado Ave., 719-471-9992)
Denver 80230 (7465 E. First Ave., 303-328-0645)
Pueblo 81003 (909 N. Elizabeth St., 719-543-8343)

National Cemeteries:
Fort Logan (Denver 80235, 3698 S. Sheridan Blvd., 303-761-0117)
Fort Lyon 81038 (VA Medical Center, C St., 719-384-3152, ext. 231)

CONNECTICUT
Medical Centers:
Newington 06111 (555 Willard Ave., 860-666-6951)
*West Haven 06516 (950 Cambell Ave., 203-932-5711)

Clinics:
Danbury 06810 (7 Germantown Road)
New London 06320 (S. 15 Mohegan Ave., 860-437-3611)
Stamford 06904 (128 Strawberry Hill Ave., 888-844-4441)
Waterbury 06706 (133 Scovill St., 203-465-5292)
Willimantic 06226 (96 Mansfield St., 860-450-7583)
Winsted 06908 (115 Spencer St., 860-738-6985)

Regional and Benefits Office:
Hartford 06103 (450 Main St.; local, 278-3230; statewide, 800-827-1000)

Vet Centers:
Hartford 06109 (30 Jorden Lane, 860-240-3543)
New Haven 06516 (141 Captain Thomas Blvd., 203-932-9899)
Norwich 06360 (100 Main St., 203-887-1755)

DELAWARE
Medical Center
*Wilmington 19805 (1601 Kirkwood Hwy., 302-994-2511)

Regional and Benefits Office:
Wilmington 19805 (1601 Kirkwood Hwy.; local, 998-0191; statewide, 800-827-1000)

Vet Center:
Wilmington 19805 (VAMROC Bldg. 2, 1601 Kirkwood Highway, 302-994-1660)

DISTRICT OF COLUMBIA:
Medical Center:
*Washington, D.C. 20422 (50 Irving St., NW, 202-745-8000)

Clinic:
Wash., D.C. 30032 (820 Chesapeake SE 202-745-8685)

Regional and Benefits Office:
Wash., D.C. 20421 (1120 Vermont Ave., NW, 418-4343)

Vet Center:
Wash., D.C. 20002 (911 Second St., 202-543-8821)

FLORIDA
Medical Centers:
#*Bay Pines 33708 (10000 Bay Pines Blvd., N., 727-398-6661)
*Gainesville 32608 (1601 Southwest Archer Rd., 352-376-1611)

*Lake City 32025 (801 S. Marion St., 386-755-3016)
*Miami 33125 (1201 N.W. 16th St., 305-324-4455)
*Tampa 33612 (13000 Bruce B. Downs Blvd., 813-972-2000)
West Palm Bch. 33410 (7305 N. Military Trail, 561-882-8262)

Clinics:
Avon Park 33825 (950 C.R., 17A, West, 863-452-3000)
Coral Springs 33065 (9900 W. Sample Rd., 954-575-4940)
Daytona Beach 32114 (551 Natl. H.C. Dr., 904-274-4600)
Deerfield Beach 33442 (2100 S.W. 10th St., 954-570-5572)
Fort Myers 33916 (3033 Winkler Extension., 239-939-3939)
Hallandale Beach 33009 (2500 E. Hallandale Beach Blvd., Penthouse 2, 954-454-7788)
Jacksonville 32206 (1833 Boulevard, 904-232-2751)
Key West 33040 (1111 12th St., Suite 207, 305-536-6696)
Miami 33130 (900 Southwest 2nd Ave., 305-324-4455)
New Port Richey 34654 (9912 Little Road, 727-869-4100)
Oakland Park 33334 (5599 N. Dixie Hwy., 954-771-2101)
Orlando 32806 (83 W. Columbia St., 407-425-7521)
Pensacola 32514 (312 Kenmore Rd., 850-476-1100)
Port Richey 34668 (8911 Ponderosa, 813-869-3203)
Riviera Beach 33404 (301 Broadway, 407-845-2800)
Tallahassee 32308 (1607 St. James Ct., 850-878-0191)
Viera 32940 (2900 Veterans Way, 321-637-3788)

Regional and Benefits Offices:
Fort Myers 33901 (2070 Carrell Rd.)
Jacksonville 32206 (1833 Boulevard, Rm. 3109)
Miami 33130 (Federal Bldg., Rm. 120, 51 S.W. 1st Ave.)
Oakland Park 33334 (5599 N. Dixie Highway)
Orlando 32806 (83 W. Columbia St.)
Pensacola 32503-7492 (312 Kenmore Rd., Rm. 1G250)
Riviera Beach 33404 (Executive Plaza, 310 Broadway)
St. Petersburg 33701 (144 1st Ave. S.; local, 898-2121; statewide, 800-827-1000)

Vet Centers:
Ft. Lauderdale 33304 (713 N.E. 3rd Ave., 954-356-7926)
Jacksonville 32206 (1833 Boulevard St., 904-232-3621)
Miami 33129 (2700 SW 3rd Ave., Suite 1A, 305-859-8387)
Orlando 32809 (5001 S. Orange Ave., Suite A, 407-857-2800)
Palm Beach 33461 (2311 10th Ave., North #13, 561-585-0441)
Pensacola 32501 (202 W. Jackson St., 904-435-8761)
Sarasota 34231 (4801 Swift Rd., 941-927-8285)
St. Petersburg 33713 (2880 1st Ave., N., 727-893-3791)
Tallahassee 32303 (249 E. 6th Ave., 850-942-8810)
Tampa 33604 (1507 W. Sligh Ave., 813-228-2621)

National Cemeteries:
Barrancas (Pensacola 32508, Naval Air Sta., 904-452-3357)
Bay Pines 33504 (P.O. Box 477, 813-398-9426)
Florida (Bushnell 33513, P.O. Box 337, 904-793-7740)
St. Augustine 32084 (104 Marine St.; for information, call Florida NC, 904-793-7740)

GEORGIA
Medical Centers:
*Augusta 30904 (1 Freedom Way, 706-733-0188)
*Decatur 30033 (1670 Clairmont Rd., 404-321-6111)
#*Dublin 31021 (1826 Veterans Blvd., 478-272-1210)

Regional and Benefits Office:
Atlanta 30365 (730 Peachtree St., N.E.; local, 881-1776; statewide, 800-827-1000)

Clinics:
Albany 31701 (521 Third Ave., 229-446-9000)
Atlanta 30309 (77 Peachtree Place, 404-321-6111)
Columbus 31902 (1310 13th St., 706-649-7879)
Macon 31210 (140 N. Crest Blvd., 478-476-8868)
Oakwood 30566 (3931 Munday Mill Rd., 404-728-8210)
Savannah 31406 (325 W. Montgomery Crossroad, 912-920-0214)

Vet Centers:
Atlanta 30309 (77 Peachtree Pl., N.W., 404-347-7264)
Savannah 31406 (8110 White Bluff Rd., 912-652-4097)

National Cemetery:
Marietta 30060 (500 Washington Ave., 404-428-5631)

HAWAII
Medical, Regional and Benefit Office:
Honolulu 96850-001 (P.O. Box 50188, 300 Ala Moana Blvd., Rm. 1004; Medical Office, 808-566-1000; Regional Office: from Oahu, 808-566-1000; toll-free from Hawaiian neighbor islands, 800-827-1000; toll-free service from Guam, 800-475-8387; toll-free from American Samoa, 800-844-7928)

Vet Centers:
Hilo 96720 (120 Keawe St., Suite 201, 808-969-3833)
Honolulu 96814 (1680 Kapiolani Blvd., Suite F, 808-566-1764)
Kailua-Kona 96740 (Pottery Terrace, Fern Bldg., 75-5995 Kuakini Hwy., #415, 808-329-0574)
Lihue 96766 (3367 Kuhio Hwy., Ste. 101, 808-246-1163)
Wailuku 96793 (35 Lunaliho St., Ste. 101, 808-242-8557)

National Cemetery:
National Memorial Cemetery of the Pacific (Honolulu 96813, 2177 Puowaina Dr., 808-566-1430)

IDAHO
Medical Center:
*Boise 83702 (500 West Fort St., 208-422-1000)

Clinic:
Pocatello 83201 (444 Hospitol Way., 208-232-6214)

Regional and Benefits Office:
Boise 83702 (805 W. Franklin St.; local, 334-1010; statewide, 800-827-1000)

Vet Centers
Boise 83705 (5440 Franklin Rd., Ste. 100, 208-342-3612)
Pocatello 83201 (1800 Garett Way., 208-232-0316)

ILLINOIS
Medical Centers:
Chicago 60611 (Lakeside, 333 E. Huron St., 312-569-8387)
Chicago 60612 (Westside, 820 S. Damen Ave., 312-569-8387)
*Danville 61832 (1900 E. Main St., 217-442-8000)
*Hines 60141 (Roosevelt Rd. & 5th Ave., 708-202-8387)
*Marion 62959 (2401 W. Main St., 618-997-5311)
#*North Chicago 60064 (3001 Green Bay Rd., 847-688-1900)

Clinics:
Aurora 60506 (1700 N. Landmark Rd., 630-859-2504)
Chicago 60637 (1502 E. 63rd St., 773-363-5748)
Chicago Heights 60411 (30 E. 15th St., 708-756-5454)
Decatur 62526 (3035 East Mound Rd., 217-875-2670)
Effingham 62401 (1901 South 4th St., 217-347-7600)

Elgin 60123 (1231 W. Larkin, 847-742-5920)
Evanston 60202 (107-109 Clyde St., 847-869-6315)
Galesburg 61401 (695 N. Kellog St., 309-343-0311)
Joliet 60435 (2000 Glenwood Ave., 815-744-0492)
LaSalle 61301 (2970 Chartres, 815-223-0196)
Manteno 60950 (1 Veterans Dr., 815-468-1027)
McHenry 60050 (620 S. Route 31, 815-759-2306)
Oak Lawn 60453 (4700 W. 95th St., 708-499-3675)
Oak Park 60302 (149 S. Oak Park Ave., 708-386-3008)
Quincy 62301 (1707 N. 12th St., 217-224-3366)
Rockford 61108 (4940 E. State St., 815-227-0081)
Peoria 61605 (411 W. Martin Luther King Jr. Dr., 309-671-7350)
Springfield 62701 (326 N. 7th St., 217-522-9730)

Regional and Benefits Office:
Chicago 60680 (536 S. Clark St., P.O. Box 8136; local 663-5510; statewide, 800-827-1000)

Vet Centers:
Chicago 60637 (1514 E. 63rd. St., 773-684-5500)
Chicago Heights 60411 (1600 Halsted St., 708-754-0340)
East St. Louis 62203 (1269 N. 89th St., Suite 1, 618-397-6602)
Moline 61265 (1529 16th Ave., Rm. 6, 309-762-6954)
Oak Park 60302 (155 S. Oak Park Ave., 708-383-3225)
Peoria 61603 (3310 N. Prospect St., 309-671-7300)
Springfield 62701 (624 S. 4th St., 217-492-4955)
Evanston 60602 (565 Howard St., 847-332-1019)

National Cemeteries:
Alton 62003 (600 Pearl St.; for information, call Jefferson Barracks, MO, NC 314-263-8691/2)
Camp Butler (Springfield 62707, R.R. #1, 217-522-5764)
Danville 61832 (1900 E. Main St., 217-431-6550)
Mound City 62963 (P.O. Box 38; for information, call Jefferson Barracks, MO, NC, 314-263-8691/2)
Quincy 62301 (36th & Maine Sts.; for information, call Keokuk, IA, NC, 319-524-1304)
Rock Island (Moline 61265, P.O. Box 737, 309-782-2094)

INDIANA
Medical Centers:
*Fort Wayne 46805 (2121 Lake Ave., 260-426-5431)
Indianapolis 46202 (1481 W. 10th St., 317-554-0000)
*Marion 46952 (E. 38th St., 317-674-3321)

Clinics:
Bloomington 47401 (200 E. Winslow Rd., 812-353-2600)
Crown Point 46307 (9330 Broadway, 219-662-5000)
Evansville 47713 (500 E. Walnut, 812-865-6202)
Hagerstown 47346 (State Route 1, 765-489-3950)
Lawrenceburg 47025 (710 Eads Parkway, 812-539-2313)
Muncie 47304 (3500 W. Purdue Ave., 765-284-6860)
Napanee 46550 (2521 E. Market St., 219-773-4101)
Richmond 47374 (4351 S. A St., 765-973-6915)
South Bend 46635 (53830 Generations Dr., 574-273-0848)
Terre Haute 47804 (1632 N. Third St., 812-232-2890)
West Lafayette 47906 (3851 N. River Rd., 765-464-2280)

Regional and Benefits Office:
Indianapolis 46202 (575 N. Pennsylvania St.; local, 226-5566; statewide, 800-327-1000)

Vet Centers:
Evansville 47711 (311 N. Weinbach Ave., 812-473-5993)
Fort Wayne 46802 (528 West Berry St., 574-460-1456)
Gary 46408 (2236 West Ridge Rd., 219-887-0048)

Indianapolis 46408 (3833 Meridian, 317-927-6440)
Merrillville 46410 (6505 Broadway, 219-736-5633)

National Cemeteries:
Crown Hill (Indianapolis 46208, 700 W. 38th St.; for
information, call Marion, IN, NC, 317-674-0284)
Marion 46952 (1700 E. 38th St., 317-674-0284)
New Albany 47150 (1943 Ekin Ave.; for information, call
Zachary Taylor, KY, NC, 502-893-3852)

IOWA
Medical Centers:
#Des Moines 50310 (3600 30th St., 515-699-5999)
Iowa City 52246 (Hwy. 6 West, 319-338-0581)
#*Knoxville 50138 (1515 W. Pleasant St., 515-842-3101)

Clinic:
Bettendorf 52722 (2979 Victoria Dr., 319-332-8528)
Dubuque 52001 (250 Mercy Dr., 319-589-8899)
Fort Dodge 50501 (804 Kenyon Rd., 515-576-2235)
Mason City 50402 (910 N. Eisenhower 515-421-8077)
Sioux City 51104 (1551 Indian Hills Dr., 712-258-4700)
Waterloo 50703 (2055 Kimball Ave., 319-272-2424)

Regional and Benefits Office:
Des Moines 50309 (210 Walnut St.; local, 284-0219;
statewide, 800-827-1000)

Vet Centers:
Des Moines 50310 (2600 Martin Luther King Jr. Pkwy.,
515-284-4929)
Sioux City 51101 (706 Jackson, 712-255-3808)

National Cemetery:
Keokuk 52632 (1701 J St., 319-524-1304)

KANSAS
Medical Centers:
#*Leavenworth 66048 (4101 S. 4th St., Trafficway, 913-
682-2000)
*Topeka 66622 (2200 Gage SW Blvd., 785-350-3111)
*Wichita 67218 (5500 E. Kellogg, 316-685-2221)

Clinic:
Liberal 67901 (2130 N Kansas Ave., 316-626-5574)

Regional and Benefits Office:
Wichita 67211 (5500 E. Kellogg; local, 682-2301;
statewide, 800-827-1000)

Vet Center:
Wichita 67211 (413 S. Pattie, 800-478-3381)

National Cemeteries:
Fort Leavenworth 66027 (For information, call
Leavenworth, KS, NC, 913-758-4105)
Fort Scott 66701 (P.O. Box 917, 316-223-2840)
Leavenworth 66048 (P.O. Box 1694, 913-758-4105)

KENTUCKY
Medical Centers:
*Lexington 40502 (1101 Veterans Dr., 859-233-4511)
Louisville 40206 (800 Zorn Ave., 502-895-3401)

Clinic:
Bellevue 41073 (103 Landmark Dr., 859-392-3840)

Regional and Benefits Office:

Louisville 40202 (545 S. Third St.; local, 584-2231;
statewide, 800-827-1000)

Vet Centers:
Lexington 40503 (301 E. Vine St., Suite C, 606-253-0717)
Louisville 40208 (1347 S. 3rd St., 502-634-1916)

National Cemeteries:
Camp Nelson (Nicholasville 40356, 6980 Danville Rd.,
606-885-5727)
Cave Hill (Louisville 40204, 701 Baxter Ave.; for
info. call Zachary Taylor, KY, NC, 502-893-3852)
Danville 40442 (377 N. First St.; for information, call
Camp Nelson, KY, NC, 606-885-5727)
Lebanon 40033 (R.R. 1, Box 616; for information, call
Zachary Taylor, KY, NC, 502-893-3852)
Lexington 40508 (833 W. Main St.; for information, call
Camp Nelson, KY, NC, 606-885-5727)
Mill Springs (Nancy 42544; for information, call Camp
Nelson, KY, NC, 606-885-5727)
Zachary Taylor (Louisville 40207, 4701 Brownsboro Rd.,
502-893-3852)

LOUISIANA
Medical Centers:
*Alexandria 71360 (2495 Shreveport Hwy., 318-473-0010)
New Orleans 70112 (1601 Perdido St., 504-568-0811)
Shreveport 71101 (510 E. Stoner Ave., 318-221-8411)

Clinics:
Baton Rouge 70806 (216 S. Foster Dr., 318-389-0628)
Jennings 70546 (1907 Johnson St., 318-824-1000)
Lafayette 70501(2100 Jefferson St., 337-261-0734)

Regional and Benefits Office:
New Orleans 70113 (701 Loyola Ave.; local, 589-7191;
statewide, 800-827-1000)

Vet Centers:
New Orleans 70116 (1529 N. Claiborne Ave., 504-943-8386)
Shreveport 71104 (2800 Youree Dr., 318-861-1776)

National Cemeteries:
Alexandria (Pineville 71360, 209 Shamrock Ave., 318-449-
1793)
Baton Rouge 70806 (220 N. 19th St.; for information, call
Port Hudson, LA, NC, 504-654-3767)
Port Hudson (Zachary 70791, 20978 Port Hickey Rd., 504-
654-3767)

MAINE
Medical Center:
*Togus 04330 (Route 17 East, 207-623-8411)

Clinics:
Caribou 04736 (163 Van Buren Dr., Ste. 6, 207-498-8785)
Bangor 04401 (304 Hancock St., Ste. 3B, 207-941-8160)
Calais 04619 (1 Palmer St., 207-454-7849)
Rumford 04726 (209 Lincoln Ave., 207-364-4-98)
Saco 04072 (655 Main St., 207-294-3100)

Regional and Benefits Offices:
Portland 04101 (475 Stevens Ave., 207-780-3569)
Togus 04330 (Route 17 East; local, 623-8000; statewide,
800-827-1000)

National Cemetery:

Togus 04330 (VA Medical & Regional Office Center; for information, call MA, NC, 508-563-7113)

MARYLAND
Medical Centers:
Baltimore 21201 (10 N. Green St., 410-605-7000)
Baltimore 21201 (Prosthetic Assessment Information Center, 103 S. Gay St., 410-962-3934)
*Fort Howard 21052 (9600 N. Point Rd., 410-477-1800)
*Perry Point 21902 (410-642-2411)

Clinic:
Baltimore 21218 (3901 The Alameda, 410-605-7651)
Cambridge 21613 (830 Chesapeake Dr., 410-228-6243)
Charlotte Hall 20622 (29431 Charlotte Hall Rd., 301-884-7102)
Cumberland 21502 (710 Memorial Ave., 301-724-0061)
Glen Burnie 21061 (1406 S. Crain Hwy., 410-590-4140)
Greenbelt 20770 (7525 Greenway Center Dr., Ste. T-4, 301-345-2463)
Hagerstown 21742 (1101 Opal Ct., 301-665-1462)
Pocomoke 21851 (101B Market St., 410-957-6718)

Regional and Benefits Offices:
Baltimore 21201 (31 Hopkins Plaza Fed. Bldg.; local, 685-5454; counties of Montgomery, Prince Georges served by Washington, DC, Regional Office, 202-418-4343; other areas, 800- 827-1000)

Vet Centers:
Baltimore 21207 (6666 Security Blvd., 410-227-3600)
Cambridge 21613 (5510 W. Shore Dr., 410-228-6305)
Elkton 21921 (103 Chesapeake Blvd., 410-392-4485)
Silver Spring 20910 (1015 Spring St., Suite 101, 301-589-1073)

National Cemeteries:
Annapolis 21401 (800 West St.; for information, call Baltimore, MD, NC, 410-644-9696)
Baltimore 21228 (5501 Frederick Ave., 410-644-9696)
Loudon Park (Baltimore 21229, 3445 Frederick Ave.; for information, call Baltimore, MD, NC, 410-644-9696)

MASSACHUSETTS:
Medical Centers:
#*Bedford 01730 (200 Springs Rd., 781-687-2000)
Boston 02130 (150 S. Huntington Ave., 617-232-9500)
*Brockton 02301 (940 Belmont St., 508-583-4500)
Northampton 01053 (421 N. Main St., 413-584-4040)
West Roxbury 02132 (1400 VFW Pkwy., 617-323-7700)

Clinics:
Boston 02114 (251 Causeway St., 617-248-1000)
Dorchester 02121 (895 Blue Hill Ave., 617-880-7946)
Fitchburg 01420 (275 Nichols Rd., 978-342-9781)
Framingham 01702 (61 Lincoln St., 508-628-0205)
Gloucester 01930 (298 Washington St., 978-282-0676)
Greenfield 01301 (51 Sanderson St., 413-773-8428)
Haverhill 01830 (108 Merrimack St., 978-372-5207)
Hyannis 02601 (145 Falmouth Rd., 508-771-3190)
Lowell 01851 (130 Marshall Rd., 978-671-9000)
Lynn 01904 (225 Boston Rd., Ste. 107, 781-595-9818)
Martha's Vinyard 02557 (Martha's Vinyard Hospitol Rd., 508-693-0410)
Nantucket 02554 (57 Prospect St., -508-825-VETS)
New Bedford 02740 (174 Elm St., 508-994-0217)

Pittsfield 01201 (73 Eagle St., 413-443-4878)
Quincy 02169 (114 Whitwell St., 617-376-2010)
Springfield 01103 (1550 Main St., 413-785-0301)
Worcester 01605 (605 Lincoln St., 508-856-0104)

Regional and Benefits Offices:
Boston 02203 (JFK Federal Bldg., Government Center; local, 227-4600; statewide, 800-827-1000)
Towns of Fall River & New Bedford, counties of Barnstable, Dukes, Nantucket, Bristol, part of Plymouth served by Providence, RI, Regional Office)

Vet Centers:
Boston 02215 (665 Beacon St., 617-424-0665)
Brockton 02401 (1041-L Pearl St., 508-580-2730)
Lowell 01852 (81 Bridge St., 508-934-9124)
Springfield 01103 (1985 Main St., 508-737-5167)
Worcester 01605 (605 Lincoln St., 508-856-7046)

National Cemeteries:
Massachusetts (Bourne 02532, 508-563-7113/4)

MICHIGAN
Medical Centers:
*Allen Park 48101 (Southfield & Outer Drive, 313-562-6000)
*Ann Arbor 48105 (2215 Fuller Rd., 734-769-7100)
*Battle Creek 49015 (5500 Armstrong Rd., 616-966-5600)
Detroit 48201(4646 John Rd., 313-576-1000)
*Iron Mountain 49801 (H Street, 906-774-3300)
*Saginaw 48602 (1500 Weiss St., 989-497-2500)

Clinics:
Benton Harbor 49022 (960 Agard Ave., 616-925-5912)
Flint 48532 (G-3267 Beecher Rd., 810-720-2913)
Gaylord 49735 (806 S. Otsego, 989-732-6555)
Grand Rapids 49505 (3019 Colt, N.E., 616-365-9575)
Hancock 49930 (200 Michigan Ave., 906-482-7762)
Iron Mountain 49801 (325 E. H St., 906-774-3300)
Ironwood 49938 (N10565 Grand View Ln., 906-932-6161)
Jackson 49202 (2200 Springport Rd., 517-787-8010)
Marquette 49855 (425 Fisher St., 906-226-4618)
Menominee 49858 (1101 11th Ave., Ste. 2, 906-863-1286)
Muskegon 49442 (165 E. Apple St., Bldg F, 231-725-4105)
Lansing 48910 (2727 S. Pennsylvanina, 517-374-4295)
Oscoda 48750 (5671 Skeel Ave., Ste. 4, 989-747-0026)
Pontiac 48342 (950 University Dr., 248-409-0585)
Sault Ste. Marie 49783 (2864 Ashmun Rd., 906-253-9564)
Traverse City 49648 (745 S. Garfield, 231-932-9720)
Yale 48097 (7470 Brockway Rd., 810-387-3211)

Regional and Benefits Office:
Detroit 48226 (Patrick V. McNamara Federal Bldg., 477 Mich. Ave., 964-5110; statewide, 800-827-1000)

Vet Centers:
Dearborn 48124 (2881 Monroe St., 313-277-1428)
Detroit 48201 (4161 Cass Ave., 313-831-6509)
Grand Rapids 49507 (1940 Eastern Ave., SE, 616-243-0385)
Lincoln Park 48146 (1766 Fort St., 313-381-1370)
Oak Park 48237 (20820 Greenfield Rd., 313-967-0040)

National Cemetery:
Ft. Custer (Augusta 49012, 15501 Dickman Rd., 616-731-4164)

MINNESOTA
Medical Centers:

Minneapolis 55417 (One Veterans Dr., 612-725-2000)
#*St. Cloud 56303 (4801 Veterans Dr., 320-252-1670)

Clinics:
Arlington 55307 (607 W. Chandler St.)
Blue Earth 56013 (435 S. Grove, Ste., 1)
Brainerd 56401 (17771 Hwy. 18 E., 218-855-1115)
Bricelyn 56014 (311 N. Main St.)
Chisholm 55719 (101 S.W. 1st Ave., 218-254-3316)
Elmore 56027 (201 E. Willis St.)
Fergus Falls 56537 (1821 N. Park St., 218-739-1400)
Gaylord 55334 (315 4th St.)
Hibbing 55746 (150 E. 34th St., 218-262-3441)
Janesville 56048 (312 N. Main St.)
Lake Crystal 56055 (102 S. Main St.)
Madelia 56062 (4 E. Main St.)
Maplewood 55109 (2785 White Bear Ave., 651-290-3040)
Mountain Iron 55768 (39 Enterprise Dr., S.)
Nashwauk 55769 (402 Platt Ave. E)
Rochester 55902 (1617 Skyline Dr., 507-252-0885)
Springfield 56087 (602 N. Jackson)
St. James 56081 (1205 6th Ave. S.)
Trimont 56176 (11 E. Chestnut)
Waseca 56093 (100 5th Ave. N.W.)
Waterville 56096 (212 Lake St. E.)
Winnebago 56098 (1 N. Main St.)
Winthrop 55396 (223 N. Carver St.)

Regional and Benefits Office and insurance Center:
St. Paul 55111 (Bishop Henry Whipple Federal Bldg., 1
    Federal Dr., Fort Snelling; local 726-1454; statewide,
    800-827-1000; insurance, 800-669-8477)
Counties of Becker, Beltrami, Clay, Clearwater, Kittson,
    Lake of the Woods, Mahnomen, Marshall, Norman,
    Otter Tail, Pennington, Polk, Red Lake, Roseau, Wilkin
    served by Fargo, ND, Regional Office)

Vet Centers:
Duluth 55802 (405 E. Superior St., 218-722-8654)
St. Paul 55114 (2480 University Ave., 612-644-4022)

National Cemetery:
Ft. Snelling (Mnpls. 55450, 7601 34 Ave. S., 612-726-1127)

MISSISSIPPI
Medical Centers:
#*Biloxi 39531 (400 Veterans Dr., 228-523-5000)
*Jackson 39216 (1500 E. Woodrow Wilson Dr., 601-362-4471)

Regional and Benefits Office:
Jackson 39269 (100 W. Capitol St.; Local, 965-4873;
    statewide, 800-827-1000)

Vet Centers:
Biloxi 39531 (313 Abbey Ct., 228-388-9938)
Jackson 39206 (4436 N. State St., Suite A3, 601-965-5727)

National Cemeteries:
Biloxi 39535 (P.O. Box 4968, 601-388-6668)
Corinth 38834 (1551 Horton St.; for information, call
    Memphis, TN, NC, 901-386-8311)
Natchez 39120 (41 Cemetery Rd., 601-445-4981)
MISSOURI
Medical Centers:
*Columbia 65201 (800 Hospital Dr., 573-814-6000)
Kansas City 64128 (4801 Linwood Blvd., 816-861-4700)

*Poplar Bluff 63901 (1500 N. Westwood Blvd., 573-686-
    4151)
St. Louis 63106 (John Cochran Div., 915 N. Grand Blvd.,
    314-652-4100)
*St. Louis 63125 (Jefferson Barracks Div., 314-652-4100)
Clinic:
Mt. Vernon 65712 (600 N. Main St., 417-466-4000)

Regional and Benefits Offices:
Kansas City 64106 (Federal Office Bldg., 601 E. 12th St.)
St. Louis 63103 (Federal Bldg., 400 South 18th St.; local,
    342-1171; statewide, (800) 827-1000)

Vet Centers:
Kansas City 64111 (3931 Main St., 816-753-1866)
St. Louis 63103 (2345 Pine St., 314-231-1260)

National Cemeteries:
Jefferson Barracks (St. Louis 63125, 2900 Sheridan Rd.,
    314-263-8691/2)
Jefferson City 65101 (1024 E. McCarty St.; for
    information, call Jefferson Barracks, MO, NC, 314-
    263-8691/2)
Springfield 65804 (1702 E. Seminole St., 417-881-9499)

MONTANA
VA Medical & Regional Office
Fort Harrison 59636 (William St. off Hwy. 12 W., 406-
    442-6410)

Medical Center:
*Miles City 59301 (210 S. Winchester, 406-232-3060)
Missoula 59801 (900 N. Orange, Ste. 206, 406-327-0912)

Clinics:
Anaconda 59711 (118 E. 7th St., 406-563-6090)
Billings 59102 (2345 King Ave. W., 406-651-5670)
Bozeman 300 N. Wilson, Ste. 2004, 406-522-8923)
Glasgow 59230 (621 3rd St., S., 406-228-3554)
Great Falls 59405 (1417-9th St. S., 406-761-0179)
Kalispell 59901 (66 Claremont St., 406-751-5980)
Sidney 216-14th Ave. S.W., 406-488-2307)

Regional and Benefits Office:
Fort Harrison 59636 (local, 447-7975; statewide, 800-
    827-1000)

Vet Centers:
Billings 59102 (1234 Ave. C., 406-657-6071)
Missoula 59802 (500 N. Higgins Ave., 406-721-4918)

NEBRASKA
Medical Centers:
*Grand Island 68803 (2201 N. Broadwell, 308-382-3660)
Lincoln 68510 (600 S. 70th St., 402-489-3802)
Omaha 68105 (4101 Woolworth Ave, 402-346-8800)

Clinics:
Sidney 69162 (645 Osage St., 308-254-5544)
Alliance 69301 (815 Flak St.)
Gering 69341 (1825 10th St.)
Norfolk 68701 (2600 Norfolk Ave., 402-346-8800)
North Platte 69101 (220 W. Liota St., 308-532-6906)
Rushville 69360 (307 Conrad St., 402-346-6735)

Regional and Benefits Office:
Lincoln 68516 (5631 S. 48th St.; local, 437-5001;

statewide, 800-827-1000)

Vet Centers:
Lincoln 68508 (920 L St., 402-476-9736)
Omaha 68131 (2428 Cuming St., 402-346-6735)

National Cemetery:
Fort McPherson (Maxwell 69151, HCO 1, Box 67, 308-582-4433)

NEVADA
Medical Center:
*Reno 89520 (1000 Locust St., 702-786-7200)
Las Vegas 89102 (1703 W. Charleston, 702-385-3700)
Pahrump 89048 (1501 Calvada Blvd., 775-727-6060)

Regional and Benefits Offices:
Las Vegas 89102 (3233 W. Charleston Blvd., Suite 101)
Reno 89520 (1201 Terminal Way; local, 329-9244; statewide, 800-827-1000)

Vet Centers:
Las Vegas 89101 (704 S. 6th St., 702-388-6368)
Reno 89503 (1155 W. 4th St., Suite 101, 702-323-1294)

NEW HAMPSHIRE
Medical Center:
*Manchester 03104 (718 Smyth Rd., 603-624-4366)

Clinics:
Conway 03818 (7 Greenwood Ave., 603-447-3500)
Littleton 03561 (600 St. Johnsbury Rd., 603-444-9328)
Portsmouth 03803 (302 Newmarket St., 603-624-4366)
Tilton 03276 (139 Winter St., 603-624-4366)
Wolfeboro 03894 (183 N. Main St., 603-569-4336)

Regional and Benefits Office:
Manchester 03101 (Norris Cotton Federal Bldg., 275 Chestnut St.; local, 666-7785; statewide, 800-827-1000)

Vet Center:
Manchester 03104 (103 Liberty St., 603-668-7060/61)

NEW JERSEY
Medical Centers:
*East Orange 07018 (385 Tremont Ave., 973-676-1000)
#*Lyons 07939 (151 Knollkroft Rd., 908-647-0180)

Clinics:
Brick 08724 (970 Rt. 70, 732-206-8900)
Elizabeth 07206 (654 E. Jersey St., 908-994-0120)
Hackensack 07601 (385 Prospect Ave., 201-487-1390)
Linwood 08221 (222 New Rd., Bldg. 2, Suite 2, 609-926-1180)
Morris Plains 07950 (540 W. Hanover Ave.)
New Brunswick 08901 (317 George St., 732-729-9555)
Newark 07102 (20 Washington Pl., 3rd Floor)
Vineland 08360 (New Jersey Vets Memorial Home, Northwest Blvd., 609-692-2881)

Regional and Benefits Office:
Newark 07102 (20 Washington Pl.; local, 645-2150; statewide, 800-827-1000)

Vet Centers:
Jersey City 07302 (115 Christopher Columbus Dr., Rm. 200, 201-645-2038)
Linwood 08221 (222 New Rd., Bldg. 2, # 4-5, 609-927-8387)
Newark 07102 (157 Washington St.)

Trenton 08611 (171 Jersey St., Bldg. 36, 609-989-2260)
Ventnor 08406 (6601 Ventnor Ave., Ste. 401, 609-927-8387)

National Cemeteries:
Beverly 08010 (R.D. # 1, Bridgeboro Rd., 609-989-2137)
Finn 's Point (Salem 08079, R.F.D. # 3, Fort Mott Rd., Box 542; for info. call Beverly, NJ, NC, 609-989-2137)

NEW MEXICO
Medical Center
*Albuquerque 87108 (1501 San Pedro Dr., SE, 505-265-1711)

Clinics:
Alamogordo 88310 (1410 Aspen, 505-437-7000)
Artesia 88210 (1700 W. Main St., 505-746-3531)
Clovis 88101 (100 E. Manana, 505-763-4335)
Espanola 87532 (620 Coronado St., Ste. B, 505-753-7395)
Farmington 87401 (1001 W. Broadway, 505-326-4383)
Gallup 87301 (1806 E. 66th Ave., 505-722-7234)
Hobbs 88340 (1601 N. Turner, 505-391-0354)
Las Cruces 88001 (1635 Don Roser, 505-522-1241)
Las Vegas 87701 (3031 Hot Springs Blvd., 505-425-6788)
Raton 87740 (1275 S. 2nd St., 505-445-2391)
Santa Fe 87505 (465 St. Michaels Dr., 505-954-8740)
Silver City 88061 (1302 32nd St., 505-538-2921)

Regional and Benefits Office:
Albuquerque 87102 (Dennis Chavez Federal Bldg., 500 Gold Ave., S.W.; local, 766-3361; statewide, 800-827-1000)

Vet Centers:
Albuquerque 87104 (2209 Brothers Rd., 505-346-6562)
Farmington 87402 (4251 E. Main, Suite B, 505-327-9684)
Santa Fe 87505 (1996 Warner St., Suite 5, 505-988-6562)

National Cemeteries:
Fort Bayard 88036 (P.O. Box 189; for information, call Fort Bliss, TX, NC, 915-564-0201)
Santa Fe 87504 (501 N. Guadalupe St., 505-988-6400)

NEW YORK
Medical Centers:
*Albany 12208 (113 Holland Ave., 518-626-5000)
*Batavia 14020 (222 Richmond Ave., 716-343-7500)
#*Bath 14810 (76 Veterans Ave., 607-664-4000)
*Bronx 10468 (130 W. Kingsbridge Rd., 718-584-9000)
#*Brooklyn 11209 (800 Poly Place, 718-836-6600)
*Buffalo 14215 (3495 Bailey Ave., 716-834-9200)
#*Canandaigua 14424 (400 Fort Hill Ave., 585-394-2000)
*Castle Point 12511 (Rte. 9D, 845-831-2000)
#*Montrose 10548 (Rte. 9A, 914-737-4400)
New York City 10010 (423 E. 23rd St., 212-686-7500)
*Northport 11768 (79 Middleville Rd., 631-261-4400)
*Syracuse 13210 (800 Irvine Ave., 315-476-7461)

Clinics:
Albany 12206 (91 Central Ave., 518-432-1068)
Auburn 13021 (17 Lansing St., 315-255-7002)
Bainbridge 13733 (109 N. Main St., 607-967-8590)
Binghampton 13901 (425 Robinson St., 607-772-9100)
Brooklyn 11208 (1205 Sutter Ave., 718-647-2600)
Bronx 10459 (953 Southern Blvd., 718-741-4900)
Buffalo 14209 (2963 Main St., 716-834-4270)
Carmel 10512 (65 Gleneida Ave., 914-228-5291)

Catskill 12414 (Columbia Green Medical Arts Bldg., Ste. 102, 518-943-7515)

Clifton Park 12065 (1673 Route 9, 518-393-8506)

Cortland 13045 (1104 Commons Ave., 607-662-1517)

Dunkirk 14048 (325 Central Ave., 716-366-2122)

Elizabethtown 12932 (Community Hospital, Park St., 518-873-3295)

Elmira 14901 (200 Madison Ave., Ste. 2E, 877-845-3247)

Fonda 12068 (2623 State Hwy. 30A, 518-853-1247)

Fort Drum 13602 (Bldg. T2407, Dunn Ave., 315-773-7231)

Glens Falls 12801 (84 Broad St., 518-798-6066)

Harris 12472 (Bushville Road, 914-791-1337)

Islip 11751 (39 Nassau Ave., 631-581-5330)

Jamestown 14701 (890 E. 2nd St., 716-661-1447)

Kingston 12401 (63 Hurley Ave., 914-331-8322)

Lackawanna 14218 (227 Ridge Rd., 716-822-5944)

Lindenhurst 11757 (560 N. Deleware Ave., 631-884-1133)

Lockport 14094 (5875 S. Transit Rd., 716-433-2025)

Lynnbrook 11563 (235 Merrick Rd., 516-887-3666)

Malone 12953 (133 Park St., 518-481-2545)

Massena 13662 (1 Hospital Dr., 315-764-1711)

Middletown 10949 (110 Crystal Rd. Run, 914-692-0551)

Monticello 12601 (275 Broadway, 845-791-4936)

Mt. Sinai 11766 (North County Rd., 631-473-4068)

Mt. Vernon 10550 (12 N. 7th Ave, Rm 635, 914-664-8000)

New City 10970 (20 Squadron Blvd., 845-634-8942)

New York 10027 (55 W. 125th St., 212-828-5265)

New York 10014 (245 W. Houston St., 212-337-2569)

New York 10036 (423 E. 23rd St., 212-951-5983)

Niagra Falls 14301 (620 10th St., Ste. 709, 716-283-2000)

Olean 14760 (500 Main St., 716-375-7555)

Oswego 13126 (105 County Route 45A. 315-343-0925)

Patchogue 11772 (269 Baker St. & S. Ocean Ave., 631-475-6610)

Plainview 11803 (1425 Old Country Rd., 516-572-8567)

Plattsburgh 12901 (206 Cornelia St., 518-566-8563)

Port Jervis 12771 (150 Pike St., 914-856-5396)

Poughkeepsie 12603 (488 Freedom Plains Rd, 914-452-5151)

Riverhead 11901 (89 Hubbard Ave., 631-727-7171)

Rochester 14620 (465 Westfall Rd., 585-242-0160)

Rome 13441 (125 Brookley Rd., Bldg. 510, 315-336-3389)

Sayville 11782 (40 Lakeland Ave., 631-563-1105)

Schenectady 12309 (1475 Balltown Rd., 518-346-3334)

Sidney 13838 (39 Pearl St. West, 607-563-3970)

Somers 10589 (Rt. 100, 914-227-3418)

St. Albans 11425 (179 St. & Linden Blvd., 718-526-1000)

Staten Island 10304 (21 Water St., 718-630-3550)

Sunnyside 11104 (41-03 Queens Blvd., 718-741-4800)

Syracuse 13210 (1031 E. Fayette St., 315-423-5690)

Troy 12180 (500 Federal St., 518-274-7707)

Watertown 13601 (218 Stone St., 315-788-5050)

Wellsville 14895 (15 Loder St., 585-596-4111)

White Plains 10601 (23 S. Broadway, 914-421-1951)

Yonkers 10705 (124 New Main St., 914-375-8055)

Regional and Benefits Offices:
Albany 12207 (Leo W. O'Brian Federal Bldg., Clinton Ave. & N. Pearl St.)
   Buffalo 14202 (Federal Bldg., 111 W. Huron St.; local, 846-5191; statewide, 800-827-1000) Serves counties not served by New York City Regional Office.)
New York City 10001 (245 West Houston St.; local, 807-

7229; NYC, 212-807-7229; statewide, 800-827-1000) Serves counties of Albany, Bronx, Clinton, Columbia, Delaware, Dutchess, Essex, Franklin, Fulton, Greene, Hamilton, Kings, Montgomery, Nassau, New York, Orange, Otsego Putnam, Queens, Rensselaer, Richmond, Rockland, Saratoga, Schenectady, Schoharie, Suffolk, Sullivan, Ulster, Warren, Washington, Westchester.

Rochester 14614 (Fed. Office Bldg./Courthouse, 100 State St.)

Syracuse 13202 (344 W. Genessee St.)

Vet Centers:
Albany 12206 (875 Central Ave., 518-438-2505)

Babylon 11702 (116 West Main St., 516-661-3930)

Brooklyn 11201 (25 Chapel St., Ste. 604, 718-330-2825)

Bronx 10468 (226 E. Fordham Rd., 718-367-3500)

Buffalo 14202 (564 Franklin St., 716-882-0505)

Harlem 10027 (55 W. 125 St., 212-870-8126)

New York 10014 (201 Varick St., Rm. 707, 212-620-3306)

Rochester 14614 (134 S. Fitzhugh St., 716-263-5710)

Staten Island 10301 (150 Richmond Terr., 718-816-4499)

Syracuse 13203 (716 E. Washington St., 315-478-7127)

White Plains 10601 (300 Hamilton Ave., 914-682-6250)

Woodhaven 11421 (75-10B 91st Ave., 718-296-2871)

National Cemeteries:
Bath 14810 (VA Medical Center, 607-776-5480)

Calverton 11933 (210 Princeton Blvd., 516-727-5410)

Cypress Hills (Brooklyn 11208, 625 Jamaica Ave.; for information, call Long Island, NY, NC, 516-454-4949)

Long Island (Farmingdale 11735, 516-454-4949)

Woodlawn (Elmira 14901, 1825 Davis St.; for information, call Bath, NY, NC, 607-776-5480)

NORTH CAROLINA
Medical Centers:
*Asheville 28805 (1100 Tunnel Rd., 828-298-7911)

*Durham 27705 (508 Fulton St., 919-286-0411)

*Fayetteville 28301 (2300 Ramsey St., 910-488-6252)

*Salisbury 28144 (1601 Brenner Ave., 704-638-9000)

Clinic:
Winston-Salem 27103 (190 Kimel Park Dr., 336-768-3296)

Regional and Benefits Offices:
Winston-Salem 27155 (Federal Bldg., 251 N. Main St.; local, 748-1800; statewide, 800-827-1000)

Vet Centers:
Charlotte 28202 (223 S. Brevard St., Ste. 103, 704-333-6107)

Fayetteville 28301 (4 Market Square, 910-323-4908)

Greensboro 27406 (2009 Elm-Eugene St., 910-355-5366)

Greenville 27858 (150 Arlington Blvd., #B, 919-355-7920)

National Cemeteries:
New Bern 28560 (1711 National Ave., 919-637-2912)

Raleigh 27610 (501 Rock Quarry Rd., 919-832-0144)

Salisbury 28144 (202 Government Rd., 704-636-2661)

Wilmington 28403 (2011 Market St.; for information, call New Bern, NC, NC, 919-637-2912)

NORTH DAKOTA
Medical Center:
*Fargo 58102 (2101 Elm St., 701-232-3241)

Clinics:
Bismarck 58503 (115 W. Century Ave., 701-255-2252)
Grafton 58237 (Hlth Serv. Bldg, W. 6th St., 701-352-4594)
Minot 58705 (10 Missle Ave., 701-727-9800)

Regional and Benefits Offices:
Fargo 58102 (2101 Elm St.; local, 293-3656; statewide, 800-827-1000)

Vet Centers:
Bismarck 58501 (1684 Capitol Way, 701-224-9751)
Fargo 58103 (3310 Fiechtner Dr., Ste. 100, 701-237-0942)
Minot 58703 (3041 3rd St. N.W., 701-852-0177)

OHIO
Medical Centers:
#*Brecksville 44141 (10000 Brecksville Rd., 216-526-3030)
*Chillicothe 45601 (17273 State Route 104, 740-773-1141)
#*Cincinnati 45220 (3200 Vine St., 513-861-3100)
Cleveland 44106, 10701 East Blvd., 216-791-3800)
#*Dayton 45428 (4100 W. 3rd St., 937-268-6511)

Clinics:
Akron 44311 (676 S Broadway St., Ste 203, 330-344-4177)
Ashtabula 44004 (4314 Main Ave., 440-993-1318)
Athens 45701 (510 W. Union St., 740-593-7314)
Canton 44702 (221 Third St., S.E., 330-489-4660)
Cincinniti 45245 (4355 Ferguson Dr., 513-943-3680)
Cleveland 44113 (4242 Lorain Ave., 216-939-0699)
Columbus 43203 (543 Taylor Ave., 614-257-5200)
East Liverpool 43920 (332 W. 6th St., 330-386-4303)
Grove City 43123 (1953 Ohio Ave., 614-257-5800)
Lancaster 43130 (1550 Sheridan Dr., 740-653-6145)
Lima 45804 (1220 E. Elm St., 419-227-9676)
Lorain 44052 (205 W. 20th St., 440-244-3833)
Mansfield 44906 (1456 Park Ave. W., 419-529-4602)
Marrieta 45750 (418 Colegate Dr., 740-568-0412)
Middletown 45042 (675 N. University Blvd., 513-423-8387)
Painsville 44077 (W. 7 Jackson St., 440-357-6740)
Portsmouth 45662 (621 Broadway St., 740-353-3236)
Sandusky 44870 (3416 Columbus Ave., 419-625-7350)
Springfield 45505 (512 S. Burnett Rd., 937-328-3385)
Toledo 43614 (3333 Glendale Ave., 419-259-2000)
Warren 44485 (1400 Tod Ave. N.W., 330-392-0311)
Youngstown 44505 (2031 Belmont, 330-740-9200)

Regional and Benefits Offices:
Cincinnati 45202 (36 E. 7th St., Suite 210)
Cleveland 44199 (Anthony J. Celebrezze Fed. Bldg., 1240 E. 9th St.; local, 621-5050; statewide, 800-827-1000)
Columbus 43215 (Federal Bldg., Rm. 309, 200 N. High St., 800-827-8272)

Vet Centers:
Cincinnati 45203 (801 W. 8th St., Ste. 126, 513-569-7140)
Cleveland 44111 (11511 Lorain Ave., 440-845-5023)
Cleveland Heights 44118 (2134 Lee Rd., 216-932-8476)
Columbus 43215 (30 Spruce St., 937-461-9150)
Dayton 45402 (111 W. 1st St., 513-461-9150)

National Cemetery:
Dayton 45428 (VA Med. Ctr., 4100 W. 3 St., 513-262-2115)

OKLAHOMA
Medical Centers:
Muskogee 74401 (1011 Honor Heights Dr., 918-683-3261)
Oklahoma City 73104 (921 N.E. 13th St., 405-270-0501)

Clinics:
Ardmore 73401 (1015 S. Commerce, 405-223-2266)
Clinton 73601 (1/4 mile south of I-40 on Highway 183, P.O. Box 1209, 405-323-5540)
Lawton 73502 (Comanche Co. Hospital, P.O. Box 49, 405-357-6611)
Tulsa 74101 (1855 E. 15th St., 918-581-7105)

Regional and Benefits Offices:
Muskogee 74401 (Federal Bldg., 125 S. Main St.; local 687-2500; statewide, 800-827-1000)
Oklahoma City 73105 (200 N.W. 5th St.)

Vet Centers:
Oklahoma City 73105 (3033 N. Walnut, Suite 101W, 405-270-5184)
Tulsa 74112 (1408 S. Harvard, 918-748-5105)

National Cemetery:
Fort Gibson 74434 (Rt. 2, Box 47, 918-478-2334)

OREGON
Medical Centers:
#*Portland 97207 (3710 S.W. U.S. Veterans Hospital Rd., 503-220-8262)
Roseburg 97470 (913 N.W. New Garden Valley Blvd., 541-440-1000)

Clinics:
Bandon 97411 (1010 1st St. S.E., Suite 100, 541-347-4736)
Brookings 97415 (412 Alder St., 541-412-1152)
Eugene 97404 (100 River Ave., 541-465-6918)
Portland 97207 (8909 S.W. Barbur Blvd., 503-293-2946)

Domiciliary:
White City 97503 (8495 Crater Lake Hwy., 541-826-2111)

Regional and Benefits Offices:
Portland 97204 (Federal Bldg., 1220 S.W. 3rd Ave.; local, 221-2431; statewide, 800-827-1000)

Vet Centers:
Eugene 97401 (1255 Pearl St., 541-465-6918)
Grants Pass 95726 (211 S.E. 10th St., 541-479-6912)
Portland 97220 (8383 N.E. Sandy Blvd., Suite 101, 503-273-5370)
Salem 97301 (617 Chemeketa St. N.E., 503-362-9911)

National Cemeteries:
Eagle Point 97524 (2763 Riley Rd., 503-826-2511)
Roseburg 97470 (VA Medical Center, 913 N.W. Garden Valley Blvd., 503-440-1000)
Willamette (Portland 97266, 11800 S.E. Mt. Scott Blvd., 503-273-5250)

PENNSYLVANIA
Medical Centers:
*Altoona 16602 (2907 Pleasant Valley Blvd., 814-943-8164)
#*Butler 16001 (325 New Castle Rd., 724-287-4781)
#*Coatesville 19230 (1400 Black Horse Hill Rd., 610-384-7711)
*Erie 16504 (135 E. 38th St., 814-868-8661)
*Lebanon 17042 (1700 S. Lincoln Ave., 717-272-6621)
*Philadelphia 19104 (Univ. & Woodland Aves., 215-823-5800)
Pittsburgh 15206 (7180 Highland Dr., 412-365-4900)
*Pittsburgh 15240 (University Drive C, 412-688-6000)

*Wilkes-Barre 18711 (1111 East End Blvd., 570-824-3521)

Clinics:
Allentown 18103 (3110 Hamilton Blvd., 610-776-4304)
Berwick 18603 (301 W. 3rd St., 570-759-0351)
Camp Hill 17011 (25 N. 32 N. 32nd St., 717-730-9782)
Sayre 18840 (301 N. Elmira St., 877-470-0920)
Springfield 19064 (1489 Baltimore Pike, 215-543-1588)

Regional and Benefits Offices:
Philadelphia 19101 (Regional Office and Insurance Center, P.O. Box 8079, 5000 Wissahickon Ave.; local, 438-5225; statewide, 800-827-1000; insurance, 800-669-8477; recorded benefits information, 215-951-5368, 24-hour availability) Serves counties of Adams, Berks, Bradford, Bucks, Cameron, Carbon, Centre, Chester, Clinton, Columbia, Cumberland, Dauphin, Delaware, Franklin, Juniata, Lackawanna, Lancaster, Lebanon, Lehigh, Luzerne, Lycoming, Mifflin, Monroe, Montgomery, Montour, Northampton, Northumberland, Perry, Philadelphia, Pike, Potter, Schuylkill, Snyder, Sullivan, Susquehanna, Tioga, Union, Wayne, Wyoming, York.
Pittsburgh 15222 (1000 Liberty Ave.; local, 281-4233; statewide, 800-827-1000) Serves the remaining counties of Pennsylvania.
Wilkes-Barre 18702 (Jewelcor Bldg., 2nd Floor, 100 N. Wilkes-Barre Blvd.)

Vet Centers:
Erie 16501 (1000 State St., Suite 1-2, 814-543-7955)
Harrisburg 17102 (1500 N. 2nd St., 717-782-3954)
McKeesport 15132 (2001 Lincoln Way., 412-678-7704)
Philadelphia 19107 (801 Arch St., 215-627-0238)
Phila. 19120 (101 E. Olney Ave., Box C-7, 215-924-4670)
Pittsburgh 15222 (954 Penn Ave., 412-765-1193)
Scranton 18509 (959 Wyoming Ave., 570-344-2676)

National Cemeteries:
Indiantown Gap (Annville 17003, R.R. 2, Box 484, 717-865-5254/5)
Philadelphia 19138 (Haines St. & Limekiln Pike; for information, call Beverly, NJ, NC, 609-989-2137)

PHILIPPINES
Regional and Benefits Office:
Manila 1000 (1131 Roxas Blvd., Manila 1300, APO San Francisco CA 9640, airmail)

Outpatient Clinic:
Pasay City 1300 (2201 Roxas Blvd., Pasay City, 011-632-833-4566)

PUERTO RICO
Medical Center:
*San Juan 00921 (10 Casia St., 787-641-7582)

Clinics:
Mayaguez 00680 (Avenida Hostos #345, 787-265-8805)
Ponce 00716 (Paseo Del Veterano #1010, 787-812-3030)
St. Croix 00853 (Box 12 RR 02, 809-778-5553)

Regional and Benefits Office:
San Juan 00936 (U.S. Courthouse/Fed. Bldg., Carlos E. Chardon St., Hato Rey, GPO Box 4867, 766-5141)
All other San Juan areas and the Virgin Islands, 800-827-1000; to call San Juan from Virgin Islands, 800-827-1000)

Vet Centers:
Arecibo 00612 (52 Gonzalo Marin St., 809-879-4510)
Ponce 00731 (35 Mayor St., 809-841-3260)
San Juan 00921 (Condomino Medical Center Plaza, Suite LCBA and LC9, La Riviera, 787-783-8794)

National Cemetery:
Puerto Rico (Bayamon 00960, Box 1298, 809-785-7281)

RHODE ISLAND
Medical Center:
Providence 02908 (830 Chalkstone Ave., 401-273-7100)

Regional and Benefits Office:
Providence 02903 (380 Westminster Mall; local, 273-4910; statewide, 800-827-1000)

Clinic:
Middletown 02842 (One Corporate Place, 401-847-6239)

Vet Centers:
Cranston 02910 (789 Park Ave., 401-528-5271)
Providence 02904 (909 N. Main St., 401-528-5271)

SOUTH CAROLINA
Medical Centers:
Charleston 29401 (109 Bee St., 843-577-5011)
*Columbia 29209 (6439 Garners Ferry Rd., 803-776-4000)

Clinics:
Florence 29501 (514-H Dargan St., 843-292-8383)
Greenville 29605 (3510 Augusta Rd., 864-299-1600)
Rock Hill 29730 (124 Glenwood Dr., 803-328-3622)
Savannah 31406 (325 W. Montgomery Crossroads, 912-920-0214)

Regional and Benefits Office:
Columbia 29201 (1801 Assembly St.; local, 765-5861; statewide, 800-827-1000)

Vet Centers:
Columbia 29201 (1513 Pickens St., 803-765-9944)
Greenville 29601 (14 Lavinia St., 803-271-2711)
North Charleston 29418 (5603A Rivers Ave., 803-747-8387)

National Cemeteries:
Beaufort 29902 (1601 Boundary St., 803-524-3925)
Florence 29501 (803 E. Nat'l Cemetery Rd., 803-669-8783)

SOUTH DAKOTA
Medical Centers:
*Fort Meade 57741 (113 Comanche Rd., 605-347-2511)
#Hot Springs 57747 (500 N. 5th St., 605-745-2000)
*Sioux Falls 57117 (2501 W. 22nd St., 605-336-3230)

Clinics:
Aberdeen 57401 (1440 15th Ave., 605-622-2640)
Eagle Butte 57625 (15 Main St.)
McLaughlin 57642 (Veterans Industries, P.O. Box 519)
Pierre 57501 (1601 N. Harrison, Ste. 1A)
Rapid City 57701 (3625 5th St., 605-718-1095)
Rosebud 57570 (Soldier Creek Rd./Hwy. 18)
Winner 57580 (311 Jefferson Ave.)

Regional and Benefits Offices:
Sioux Falls 57117 (PO Box 5046, 2501 W. 22nd St.;

local, 336-3496; statewide, 800-827-1000)

Vet Centers:
Rapid City 57701 (621 6th St., Ste. 101, 605-348-0077)
Sioux Falls 57102 (601 S. Cliff Ave., #C, 605-332-0856)

National Cemeteries:
Black Hills (Sturgis 57785, P.O. Box 640, 605-347-3830)
Fort Meade 57785 (VA Medical Center; for information, call Black Hills, SD, NC, 605-347-3830)
Hot Springs 57747 (VA Med. Ctr., 605-745-4101, ext. 2054)

TENNESSEE
Medical Centers:
*Memphis 38104 (1030 Jefferson Ave., 901-523-8990)
#*Mountain Home 37684 (Sidney & Lamont St., 615-926-1171)
*Murfreesboro 37129 (3400 Lebanon Rd., 615-893-1360)
Nashville 37212 (1310 24th Ave., South, 615-327-4751)

Clinics:
Chattanooga 37411 (Bldg. 6200 E. Gate Ctr., 423-855-6550)
Cookville 38501 (121 S. Dixie Ave., 615-893-1360)
Knoxville 37923 (9031 Cross Park Dr., 423-545-4592)

Regional and Benefits Office:
Nashville 37203 (110 9th Ave. South; local, 736-5251; statewide, 800-827-1000)

Vet Centers:
Chattanooga 37404 (425 Cumberland St., Suite 140, 423-855-6570)
Johnson City 37604 (1615A Market St., 615-928-8387)
Knoxville 37914 (2817 E. Magnolia Ave., 423-545-4680)
Memphis 38104 (1835 Union, Suite 100, 901-722-2510)

National Cemeteries:
Chattanooga 37404 (1200 Bailey Ave., 615-855-6590)
Knoxville 37917 (939 Tyson St., N.W., 615-461-7935)
Memphis 38122 (3568 Townes Ave., 901-386-8311)
Mountain Home 37684 (PO Box 8, 615-461-7935)
Nashville (Madison 37115, 1420 Gallatin Rd. So., 615-327-5360)

TEXAS
Medical Centers:
*Amarillo 79106 (6010 Amarillo Blvd. W., 806-355-9703)
*Big Spring 79720 (300 Veterans Blvd., 915-263-7361)
#*Bonham 75418 (1201 East Ninth, 903-583-2111)
#*Dallas 75216 (4500 S. Lancaster Rd., 214-742-8387)
*Houston 77030 (2002 Holcombe Blvd., 713-791-1414)
*Kerrville 78028 (3600 Memorial Blvd., 830-896-2020)
Marlin 76661 (1016 Ward St., 817-883-3511)
*San Antonio 78284 (7400 Merton Minter Blvd., 210-617-5300)
#*Temple 76504 (1901 S. First, 254-778-4811)
#*Waco 76711 (4800 Memorial Dr., 817-752-6581)

Clinics:
Abilene 79606 (6200 Regional Plaza, 915-695-3252)
Austin 78741 (2901 Montopolis Dr., 512-389-1010)
Beaumont 77707 (3420 Veterans Circle., 409-839-2482)
Childress 79201 (Hwy. 83 N., 940-937-3636)
Corpus Christi 78405 (5283 Old Brownsville Rd., 512-854-7392)
El Paso 79925 (5919 Brook Hollow Dr., 915-540-7811)
Fort Stockton 79735 (P.O. Box 1060, 915-336-8365)

Fort Worth 76104 (300 W. Rosedale St., 800-443-9672)
Laredo 78043 (2359 E. Saunders Ave., 956-725-7060)
Lubbock 79410 (4902 34th St., #10, 806-796-7900)
Lufkin 75901 (1301 Frank Ave., 936-637-1342)
McAllen 78501 (2101 S. Row Blvd., 956-618-7100)
Odessa 79761 (419 W. 4th St., 915-337-1586)
San Angelo 76905 (2018 Pulliam, 915-658-6138)
San Antonio 78240 (5788 Eckhert Rd., 210-699-2100)
Stamford 79553 (Hwy. 6 East, 915-773-2710)
Stratford 79084 (1220 Purnell, 806-396-2852)
Victoria 77901 (2710 E. Airline Dr., 512-572-0006)

Regional and Benefits Offices:
Dallas 75242 (Santa Fe Bldg., 1114 Commerce St.)
Houston 77054 (8900 Lakes at 610 Dr.; local 664-4664; statewide, 800-827-1000) Serves counties of Angelina, Aransas, Atacosa, Austin, Bandera, Bee, Bexar, Blanco, Brazoria, Brewster, Brooks, Caldwell, Calhoun, Cameron, Chambers, Colorado, Comal, Crockett, DeWitt, Dimitt, Duval, Edwards, Fort Bend, Frio, Galveston, Gillespie, Goliad, Gonzales, Grimes, Guadeloupe, Hardin, Harris, Hays, Hidalgo, Houston, Jackson, Jasper, Jefferson, Jim Hogg, Jim Wells, Karnes, Kendall, Kenedy, Kerr, Kimble, Kinney, Kleberg, LaSalle, Lavaca, Liberty, Live Oak, McCulloch, McMullen, Mason, Matagorda, Maverlck, Medina, Menard, Montgomery, Nacogdoches, Newton, Nueces, Orange, Pecos, Polk, Real, Refugio, Sabine, San Augustine, San Jacinto, San Patricio, Schleicher, Shelby, Starr, Sutton, Terrell, Trinity, Tyler, Uvalde, Val Verde, Victoria, Walker, Waller, Washington, Webb, Wharton, Willacy, Wilson, Zapata, Zavala)
Lubbock 79401 (4902 34th St., Suite 10, Room 134)
Waco 76799 (1400 N. Valley Mills Dr., local, 817-772-3060; statewide, 800-827-1000, serves rest of state)
Bowie County served by Little Rock, AR, Regional Office, 800-827-1000.

Vet Centers:
Amarillo 79109 (3414 E. Olsen Blvd., #E., 806-354-9779)
Austin 78723 (1110 W. William Cannon Dr., Suite 301, 512-416-1314)
Corpus Christi 78404 (3166 Reid Dr., #1, 512-854-9961)
Dallas 75244 (5232 Forest Lane, Suite 111, 214-361-5896)
El Paso 79925 (Sky Park II, 6500 Boeing, Suite L-112, 915-772-0013)
Fort Worth 76104 (1305 W. Magnolia, #B, 817-921-9095)
Houston 77006 (503 Westheimer, 713-523-0884)
Houston 77024 (701 N. Post Oak Rd., 713-682-2288)
Laredo 78041 (6020 McPherson Rd. #1A, 956-723-4680)
Lubbock 79410 (3208 34th St., 806-792-9782)
McAllen 78501 (1317 E. Hackberry St., 956-631-2147)
Midland 79703 (3404 W. Illinois, Suite 1, 915-697-8222)
San Antonio 78212 (231 W. Cypress St., 210-229-4025)

National Cemeteries:
Fort Bliss 79906 (5200 Fred Wilson Rd., 915-564-0201)
Fort Sam Houston (San Antonio 78209, 1520 Harry Wurzbach Rd., 210-820-3891)
Houston 77038 (10410 Vet. Memorial Dr., 713-447-8686)
Kerrville 78028 (VA Medical Center, 3600 Memorial Blvd.; for information, call Fort Sam Houston, TX, NC, 210-820-3891)
San Antonio 78202 (517 Paso Hondo St.; for information,

call Fort Sam Houston, TX, NC, 210-820-3891)

UTAH
Medical Center:
*Salt Lake City 84148 (500 Foothill Dr., 801-582-1565)
Clinics:
Fountain Green 84632 (300 W. 300 S., 435-623-3129)
Nephi 84648 (18 W. 1500 N., 435-623-3129)
South Ogden 84403 (982 Chambers St., 801-479-4105)
St. George 84770 (1100 E. Tabernacle, 435-634-7608)

Regional and Benefits Office:
Salt Lake City 84147 (PO Box 11500, Federal Bldg., 125 S. State St.; local, 524-5960; statewide, 800-827-1000)

Vet Centers:
Provo 84601 (750 North 200 West, Ste.105, 801-377-1117)
Salt Lake City 84106 (1354 E. 3300, South, 801-584-1294)

VERMONT
Medical Center:
*White River Jnct. 05009 (N. Hartland Rd., 802-295-9363)

Clinics:
Bennington 05201 (325 North St., 802-447-6913)
Burlington 05401 (Appletree Bay Medical Center, 1205 North Ave., 802-864-4492)
Colchester 05446 (74 Hegeman Ave., 802-655-1356)
North Troy 05859 (Mobile Clinic, American Legion Post, 802-296-6399)
Rutland 05702 (215 Stratton Rd., 802-773-3386)
St. Albans 05478 (Mobile Clinic, Highgate Shopping Center, 802-296-6399)

Regional and Benefits Office:
White River Junction 05009 (N. Hartland Rd.; local, 296-5177; statewide, 800-827-1000)

Vet Centers:
South Burlington 05403 (359 Dorset St., 802-862-1806)
White River Junction 05001 (Gilman Office Center, Bldg. #2, Holiday Inn Dr., 802-295-2908)

VIRGINIA
Medical Centers:
#*Hampton 23667 (100 Emancipation Dr., 757-722-9961)
*Richmond 23249 (1201 Broad Rock Blvd., 804-675-5000)
*Salem 24153 (1970 Roanoke Blvd., 540-982-2463)

Clinics:
Alexandria 22309 (8796-D Sacramento Plaza, 703-719-6797)
Harrisonburg 22802 (101 N. Main St., 540-442-1773)
Norfolk 23508 (6500 Hampton Blvd., 804-444-5517)
Stephens City 22655 (106 Hyde Ct., 540-869-0600)

Regional and Benefits Offices:
Roanoke 24011 (210 Franklin Rd., S.W.; local, 857-2109; statewide, 800-827-1000)
Northern Virginia counties of Arlington & Fairfax, cities of Alexandria, Fairfax, Falls Church served by Washington, D.C., Regional Office, 202-418-4343).

Vet Centers:
Alexandria 22309 (8796 Sacramento Dr., 703-360-8633)
Norfolk 23517 (2200 Colonial Ave., Ste. 3, 804-623-7584)
Richmond 23230 (3022 W. Clay St., 804-353-8958)

Roanoke 24016 (320 Mountain Ave., SW, 703-342-9726)
Springfield 22150 (7024 Spring Garden Dr., 703-866-0924)

National Cemeteries:
Alexandria 22314 (1450 Wilkes St.; for information, call Quantico, VA, NC, 703-690-2217)
Balls Bluff (Leesburg 22075; for information, call Culpeper, VA, NC, 703-825-0027)
City Point (Hopewell 23860, 10th Ave. & Davis St.; for information, call Richmond, VA, NC 804-222-1490)
Cold Harbor (Mechanicsville 23111, Rt. 156 North; for information, call Richmond, VA, NC, 804-222-1490)
Culpeper 22701 (305 U.S. Ave., 703-825-0027)
Danville 24541 (721 Lee St.; for information, call Salisbury, NC, NC, 704-636-2661)
Fort Harrison (Richmond 23231, 8620 Varina Rd.; for information, call Richmond, VA, NC, 804-222-1490)
Glendale (Richmond 23231, 8301 Willis Church Rd.; for information, call Richmond, VA, NC, 804-222-1490)
Hampton 23669 (Cemetery Rd. at Marshall Ave., 804-723-7104)
Hampton 23669 (VA Medical Center, 804-723-7104)
Quantico (Triangle 22172, 18424 Joplin Rd., 703-690-2217)
Richmond 23231 (1701 Williamsburg Rd., 804-222-1490)
Seven Pines (Sandston 23150, 400 E. Williamsburg Rd.; for info. call Richmond, VA, NC, 804-222-1490)
Staunton 24401 (901 Richmond Ave.; for information call Culpeper, VA, NC, 703-825-0027)
Winchester 22601 (401 National Ave.; for information, call Culpeper, VA, NC, 703-825-0027)

VIRGIN ISLANDS
For Information on VA benefits, call 800-827-1000.

Vet Centers:
St. Croix 00850 (Box 12, R.R. 02, Village Mall, #113, 809-778-5553)
St. Thomas 00801 (Buccaneer Mall, 809-774-6674)

WASHINGTON
Medical Centers:
*Seattle 98108 (1660 S. Columbian Way, 800-329-8387)
*Spokane 99205 (N. 4815 Assembly St., 509-434-7000)
#*Tacoma 98493 (9900 Veterans Dr., S.W., American Lake, 206-582-8440)
*Walla Walla 99362 (77 Wainwright Dr., 509-525-5200)

Clinics:
Bremerton 98312 (295 Adele Ave., 360-782-0129)
Longview 98632 (1801 1st Ave., Ste. 4C, 360-636-7822)
Richland 99352 (946 Stevens Dr., Ste. C, 509-946-1020)
Yakima 98908 (102 N. 56th Ave. 509-966-0199)

Regional and Benefits Office:
Seattle 98174 (Federal Bldg., 915 2nd Ave.; local, 624-7200; statewide, 800-827-1000)

Vet Centers:
Bellingham 98226 (3800 Byron, Ste. 124, 360-733-9226)
Seattle 98121 (2030 9th Ave., 206-553-2706)
Spokane 99206 (100 N. Mullian Rd., 509-444-VETS)
Tacoma 98409 (4916 Center St., Suite E, 253-565-7038)

WEST VIRGINIA
Medical Center:
*Beckley 25801 (200 Veterans Ave., 304-255-2121)

Clarksburg 26301 (1 Medical Center Dr., 304-623-3461)
Huntington 25704 (1540 Spring Valley Dr., 304-429-6741)
#*Martinsburg 25401 (Route 9, 304-263-0811)
Clinics:
Franklin 26807 (305 N. Main St., 304-358-2355)
Petersburg 26847 (Grant Mem. Hospital, 304-257-1026)

Regional and Benefits Office:
Huntington 25701 (4640 Fourth Ave.; local, 529-5720;
    statewide, 800-827-1000)
Counties of Brooke, Hancock, Marshall, Ohio, served by
    Pittsburgh, PA, Regional Office)

Vet Centers:
Beckley 25801 (101 Ellison Ave., 304-252-8220)
Charleston 25302 (512 Washington St. W., 304-343-3825)
Huntington 25701 (1005 6th Ave., 304-523-8387)
Martinsburg 25401 (900 Winchester Ave., 304-263-6776)
Morgantown 26508 (1083 Greenbag Rd., 304-291-4303)
Mt. Gay 25637 (304-752-4453)
Princeton 24740 (905 Mercer St., 304-425-5653)
Wheeling 26003 (1070 Market St., 304-232-0587)

National Cemeteries:
Grafton 26354 (431 Walnut St.; for information, call West
    Virginia NC, 304-265-2044)
West Virginia (Grafton 26354, Rt. 2, Box 127, 304-265-
    2044)

WISCONSIN
Medical Centers:
Madison 53705 (2500 Overlook Terrace, 608-256-1901)
#*Milwaukee 53295 (5000 W. Nat'l Ave., 414-384-2000)
*Tomah 54660 (500 E. Veterans St., 608-372-3971)

Clinics:
Appleton 54914 (10 Tri-Park Way, 920-831-0070)
Baraboo 53913 (626 14th St., 608-356-9318)
Beaver Dam 53916 (208 LaCrosse St., 920-356-9415)
Chippewa 54729 (2503 County Road I, 715-720-3780)
Cleveland 53015 (1205 North Ave., 920-693-3750)

Edgerton 53534 (92 E. Hwy. 59, 608-884-3417)
LaCrosse 54601 (300 4th St. N., 608-784-3886)
Loyal 54446 (141 N. Main St., 715-255-9799)
Rhinelander 54501 (5 W. Frederick St., 715-362-4080)
Superior 54880 (3520 Tower Ave., 715-392-9711)
Union Grove 53182 (21425 Spring St., 414-878-7820)
Wausau 54401 (995 Campus Dr., 715-675-3391)
Wisconsin Rapids 54494 (420 Dewey St., 715-422-7736)

Regional and Benefits Office:
Milwaukee 53295 (5000 W. National Ave., Bldg. 6; local,
    383-8680; statewide, 800-827-1000)

Vet Centers:
Madison 53703 (147 S. Butler St., 608-264-5342)
Milwaukee 53208 (3400 Wisconsin, 414-344-5504)

National Cemetery:
Wood (Milwaukee 53295, 5000 W. National Ave., Bldg.
    122, 414-382-5300)

WYOMING
Medical Center
*Cheyenne 82001 (2360 E. Pershing Blvd., 307-778-7550)
Sheridan 82801 (1898 Fort Rd., 307-672-3473)
Clinics:
Casper 82601 (111 S. Jefferson St., 307-235-4143)
Gillette 82718 (1701 Phillips Circle, Ste. A, 307-685-0676)
Green River 82935 (1400 Uinta Dr., 307-875-6010)
Newcastle 82701 (2990 W. Main St.)
Powell 82435 (777 Avenue H, 307-754-7257)
Riverton 82501 (2300 Rose Lane, 307-857-1211)

Regional and Benefits Office:
Cheyenne 82001 (2360 E. Pershing Blvd.; local 778-7396;
    statewide, 800-827-1000)

Vet Centers:
Casper 82601 (111 S. Jefferson, 307-261-5355)
Cheyenne 82001 (2424 Pioneer Ave., 307-778-7370)

Chapter 6
COLLECTING FROM SOCIAL SECURITY, MEDICARE AND MEDICAID

Though most of us know about Social Security, many think it is only for retired people. Think again: you may be eligible for various Social Security benefits and not even know it. The same goes for Medicare and Medicaid — you may be eligible for these programs right now.

SOCIAL SECURITY ADMINISTRATION
Social Security

Social Security is a national program of social insurance in which workers, their employers, and the self-employed pay contributions which are pooled in special trust funds. Social Security is paying monthly retirement benefits to more than 30 million retired workers and their families.

While people usually think of monthly retirement benefits when they think of Social Security, this program also protects workers who become severely disabled. When earnings cease or are reduced because the worker retires, dies, or becomes disabled, monthly cash benefits are paid to replace part of the earnings the family has lost. Studies show that a 20-year-old worker stands a nearly 3-in-1 chance of becoming disabled before age 65. Few workers have private, long-term disability insurance, but nearly all workers do have Social Security disability protection equal to a $201,000 disability policy.

The Social Security Administration has almost 1,300 district and branch offices. To find the address of the office near you, consult the telephone directory under Social Security Administration or U.S. Government, or ask at your post office.

Supplemental Security Income (SSI)

Needy persons are often not eligible for regular Social Security benefits because they have not worked the required period of time. Other persons are collecting Social Security but they are not getting enough to meet their needs. The Supplemental Security Income Program (SSI) was created by the government to help these people.

SSI is a federal welfare program that pays monthly checks to eligible Americans who have little or no income or resources. It covers needy persons who are 65 or older who don't own much or have a lot of income, and blind or disabled of any age. Monthly checks can also go to disabled and blind children. Sometimes, a person whose sight is not poor enough to qualify for benefits as a blind person may be able to get checks as a disabled person if his or her condition prevents him from working.

People who get SSI usually get Food Stamps and Medicaid too. Often, people can get both Social Security and SSI benefits.

Medicare

Medicare is a federal health insurance program for people who are 65 or older. You are eligible for Medicare at age 65 even if you don't retire, so you should apply at that time. People under age 65 who have been receiving Social Security disability benefits for at least two years or have kidney failure can also get Medicare. Medicare has two parts — hospital insurance (called Part A) and medical insurance (called Part B). Together, these two programs are often referred to as "Medicare."

Part A) Hospital Insurance. Part A coverage is usually free. When you were working, part of your Social Security taxes went into a special hospital insurance trust fund, so that when you and your dependents become 65 years old, you'll have help with hospital bills. Hospital Insurance covers inpatient hospital stays, skilled nursing care and certain follow-up care.

Part B) Medical Insurance. Medical Insurance covers doctors' bills, outpatient and emergency care, home medical equipment and some other services not covered by hospital insurance. It is optional, and a premium is charged. It's generally a good buy for most people.

Medicaid—Health Care Financing Administration (HCFA)

Medicaid is a federal-state program of cash matching grants to the States to provide medical assistance for cash assistance and welfare recipients, children, pregnant women, and the elderly who meet income and resource requirements. Medicaid helps pay their doctor and hospital costs, including the biggest of all, nursing home care..

SOCIAL SECURITY

Monthly Social Security Checks—to Retired Workers
Social Security—Retirement Insurance (96.002)

Description: Perhaps the most important benefit of Social Security is to pay monthly payments to retired workers who have worked long enough to be covered, and certain family members.

Eligibility Requirements: Retired workers age 62 and over who have worked the required number of years under Social Security are eligible for monthly benefits.

Also, certain family members can receive benefits, including the retired worker's:

1) wife or husband age 62 or over;

2) spouse at any age, if a child who is under age 16 or is disabled is in his or her care and is entitled to benefits based on the worker's record;

3) unmarried children under age 18 (or under age 19 for students in elementary or secondary school);

4) unmarried adult offspring at any age if disabled before age 22;

5) divorced wife or husband age 62 or over who was married to the worker for at least 10 years.

If you retire early, you can apply to start collecting Social Security from the age of 62. However, your monthly check will be permanently reduced. Or you can wait to age 65 to apply, and get full monthly checks.

Until the year 2001, all benefits, other than benefits to disabled beneficiaries, and to beneficiaries age 70 and older, were subject to an earnings test. Benefits were reduced $1 for each $2 of earnings over $10,800 for those under age 65 and $1 for each $3 of earnings over $17,000 for those ages 65 through 69. These deductions have now been eliminated for ages 65 through 69.

Financial Information: *Range and Average of Financial Assistance*: Monthly cash benefits depend on the retiree's average lifetime earnings. At the present time, monthly cash benefits for a worker retiring at age 65 range up to $1,536, and to a maximum of $2,690.40 for a family of such a worker receiving benefits.

The average benefit paid to a retired worker alone (no family members receiving benefits) is $830; the average amount payable to a retired worker with an eligible spouse is $1,410.

Literature: *"Your Social Security," "Thinking About Retiring,"* and many other publications are available free from any Social Security office.

Who To Contact: *Headquarters Office*: Office of Public Inquiries, Room 4100, Annex, Social Security Administration, Baltimore, MD 21235. (410) 965-2736. *Regional or Local Office*: Telephone or visit any Social Security office. It is to your advantage to apply for benefits in the three months before you retire.

Little-Known Higher Benefits For Divorces Spouses

Ordinarily, a retiree and spouse receive the working spouse's social security payment plus up to 50% of this amount for the spouse. To collect, the worker must be over 62 years of age. However, there is a way in which the worker's spouse can get a larger check by getting divorced: If the worker is not yet 62 but the divorced spouse is over 62, the spouse can collect social security if they get divorced. That's because the divorced spouse can begin receiving benefits even before the worker has begun receiving benefits. It is required that the divorced spouse be at least 62 years old and that the divorce have been final for at least two years if she or he has not yet reached full retirement age.

Monthly Checks—to a Deceased Worker's Dependents
Social Security—Survivors Insurance (96.004)

Description: Social Security is also an insurance program. It pays monthly cash checks to eligible family members of deceased workers if the deceased was paying into Social Security.

Eligibility Requirements: Survivors eligible for monthly cash benefits are the following:

- Widows or widowers age 60 or over — full benefits ate age 65, or reduced benefits as early as 60
- Surviving divorced spouses age 60 or over (married to the deceased worker for at least 10 years);
- Disabled widows, widowers or surviving divorced spouses ages 50-59;
- Widows, widowers, or surviving divorced spouses at any age who have in their care a child under age 16 or a disabled child and entitled to benefits on the deceased worker's Social Security record;
- Unmarried children under age 18 (under age 19 if a full time student in elementary or secondary school);
- Unmarried children age 18 or older who have a disability which began before age 22;
- Dependent parents age 62 and over.

All survivors benefits, except for beneficiaries age 70 and over, are subject to an earnings test.

Under certain conditions, a special one-time death payment of $255 is payable to the widow or children of the deceased worker.

Financial Information: *Range and Average of Financial Assistance*: Monthly cash benefits depend on the deceased's average lifetime earnings. They range up to $1,536 for the widow or widower of a worker who dies at age 65. The average benefit paid to an aged widow or widower alone is $811; the average amount paid to a widowed mother or father with two eligible children is $1,634.

Here are the most typical situations:

- Widow or widower age 65 or older: 100 percent of the deceased's basic Social Security benefit.
- Widow or widower age 60-64: About 71 to 94 percent.
- Widow any age with a child under age 16: 75 percent.
- Children: 75 percent.

Literature: "*Your Social Security*," and other publications available free from any Social Security office.

Who To Contact: *Headquarters Office*: Office of Public Inquiries, Room 4100, Annex, Social Security Administration, Baltimore, MD 21235. (410) 965-2736. *Application Procedure*: Telephone or visit any Social Security office.

Monthly Payments—if You Become Disabled
Social Security—Disability Insurance (96.001)

Description: Social Security Disability Insurance is a part of Social Security and pays monthly cash benefits, based on your lifetime earnings record, to replace part of the earnings lost if you receive a physical or mental impairment severe enough to prevent you from working. The amount you get paid is based on your average earnings over the previous several years

Benefits are paid to eligible disabled persons throughout the period of disability after a 5-month waiting period. Costs of vocational rehabilitation also are paid for certain beneficiaries.

Persons applying for Social Security Disability Insurance are often encouraged to apply for Supplemental Security Income (see the next section).

Eligibility Requirements: Disabled workers under age 65 if they worked for a sufficient period of time and made sufficient contributions to Social Security.

Under the definition of disability in the Social Security law, disability benefits are provided to a person who is unable to engage in any substantial gainful activity by reason of a medically determinable physical or mental impairment that has lasted or is expected to last at least 12 months, or to result in death. To meet the definition you must have a severe impairment that makes you unable to do your previous work or any other gainful work.

The sooner you file the better because benefits begin with the sixth month of disability. (If you expect your disability to be temporary, check out your state disability program. State programs bridge the gap for people who are disabled for less than a year.)

Certain family members of disabled workers also are eligible for benefits:
- unmarried children under age 18, or under age 19 for students in elementary or secondary school;
- unmarried adult offspring at any age if disabled before age 22;
- wife or husband at any age if a child in his or her care is receiving benefits on the worker's Social Security record and is under age 16 or disabled;
- spouse age 62 or over;
- divorced wives or husbands age 62 or over who were married to the worker for at least 10 years.

If a deceased covered worker's spouse becomes disabled, the disabled widow(er)s' benefits are covered under Survivors Insurance **96.004**.

When you apply for Disability Insurance, talk to your doctor first. Social Security agents will use his diagnosis to help make their decision. If your doctor thinks you're able to work, you can always find another doctor.

The Social Security benefit the spouse receives is based on his or her own work. Benefits are reduced $1 for each $2 of earnings over $10,080 for those under age 65.

Financial Information: *Range and Average of Financial Assistance:* Monthly cash benefit for a disabled worker is up to a maximum of $1,830, based on the level of the worker's earnings and the age at which he becomes disabled. The corresponding maximum for such a worker with a family is $2,745. The average benefit paid to a disabled worker alone is $773 and the average amount payable to a disabled worker with eligible dependents is $1,311.

Benefits may be reduced by amounts received under other programs. In addition, benefits to spouses and children of disabled workers are subject to an earnings test unless those beneficiaries are age 70 or older.

Literature: "*If You Become Disabled,*" "*Benefits For Children With Disabilities,*" and other publications available free from any Social Security office.

Who To Contact: *Headquarters Office*: Office of Public Inquiries, Room 4100, Annex, Social Security Administration, Baltimore, MD 21235. (410) 965-2736. *Regional or Local Office*: Telephone or visit any Social Security Office.

Supplemental Security Income (SSI)
"SSI" (96.006)

Description: SSI is a federal welfare program for poor people who are over 65, or are disabled or blind of any age, including infants and children. The money comes from the Social Security Administration. It provides monthly income payments to those who have not worked enough to be fully insured under the Social Security program. It's purpose is to assure a minimum level of income to such persons whose income and resources are below specified levels.

Eligibility Requirements: Individuals age 65 and over; or blind or disabled—with benefits based on the individual's income and certain other financial resources. Eligibility may continue for beneficiaries who engage in substantial gainful activity despite disabling physical or mental impairments.

1) Income. The amount of outside income you can have each month and still get SSI depends partly on where you live. You can call the Social Security Administration at (800) 772-1213 to find out the income limits in your state. Social Security doesn't count all of your income when deciding if you can get SSI. For example, it doesn't count:

- the first $20 of most income received in a month;
- the first $64 a month you earn from working and half the amount over $65;
- food stamps;
- most food, clothing, or shelter you get from private nonprofit organizations;
- most home energy assistance.

If you are a student, some of the wages or scholarships you receive may not count.

If you are disabled but work, Social Security does not count any wages you use to pay for items or services you need to work because of your disability For example, if you require a wheelchair in order to work, the wages you use to pay for the wheelchair don't count as income.

Also, Social Security doesn't count any wages a blind person uses to pay expenses that are caused by working. For example, if a blind person uses wages to pay for transportation to and from work, the transportation cost is not counted as income.

2) The Things You Own. Social Security considers such items as real estate, personal belongings, bank accounts, cash, stocks and bonds. Usually, you may be able to get SSI with items worth up to $2,000. Social Security doesn't count everything you own. For example:

- the home you live in and the land it's on do not count;
- your personal and household goods and life insurance policies may not count, depending on their value;
- your car usually does not count;
- wedding and engagement rings;
- property used for self-support including equipment, building, inventory, business bank account, farm land, livestock;
- burial plots do not count. And up to $1,500 in burial funds for you and up to $1,500 in burial funds for your spouse may not count.

If you have too many resources, you can spend them down or even give them away to meet the limits.

Financial Information: *Range and Average of Financial Assistance*: Monthly Federal cash payments range from $1 to $512 for an aged, blind, or disabled individual who does not have an eligible spouse, and from $1 to $769 for an aged, blind, or disabled individual and an eligible spouse. The average monthly benefit is $378.

In addition, some states provide supplemental monthly payments to certain categories of SSI recipients, often an extra couple of hundred dollars a month, and pay Medicare premiums.

About 6,499,000 recipients per month collect SSI.

Literature: *"SSI for Aged, Blind, and Disabled People"* and other publications available free from any Social Security office.

Who To Contact: *Headquarters Office*: Office of Public Inquiries, Room 4100, Annex, Social Security Administration, Baltimore, MD 21235. (410) 965-2736. *To Apply*, just visit your local Social Security office or call (800) 772-1213.

You may be encouraged to also apply for Medicaid and Social Security Disability Insurance.

State Money for the Disabled
State Supplementary Payments (SSPs)

Description: State Supplemental Payments are state welfare programs for low-income aged, blind, or disabled persons who need more than the federal Supplemental Security Income (SSI) income to live on. Such state payments thus raise the SSI level by adding state welfare funds.

Not all states have such programs. The richer and more industrialized the state, usually the better the programs offered.

Who to Contact: Your local Social Security office, or State and local welfare office.

MEDICARE

Medicare—to Pay Your Hospital Bills
Medicare Part A—Hospital Insurance (93.773)

Description: This is the basic government program to provide hospital insurance protection for covered services to persons age 65 or over, to certain disabled persons and to individuals with chronic renal disease.

Hospital insurance benefits are paid directly to participating and emergency hospitals, skilled nursing facilities, home health agencies, and hospice agencies to cover the prospective payment amount or reasonable cost of medically necessary services furnished to individuals entitled under this program.

Eligibility Requirements:
- Persons age 65 or over and certain disabled persons are eligible for hospital insurance protection. Nearly everyone who reached 65 before 1968 is eligible for hospital insurance, including people not eligible for cash Social Security benefits;
- A person reaching age 65 in 1968 or after, who is not eligible for cash benefits, needs some work credit to qualify for hospital insurance benefits. The amount of work credit needed depends on age.
- Hospital insurance is also available to persons, age 65 or over, not otherwise eligible, through payment of a monthly premium of about $301;
- Persons under age 65 who have been entitled for at least 24 months to Social Security disability benefits, or for 29 consecutive months to railroad retirement benefits based on disability, are eligible for hospital insurance benefits.
- Most people who have chronic kidney disease and require kidney dialysis or transplant are also eligible.
- Certain federal, state and local government employees are eligible.

Individuals entitled to Social Security or railroad retirement are enrolled automatically.

Financial Information: There is no annual fee, but there are deductibles and co-payments. You are responsible for a $792 inpatient hospital deductible, a $198 per day coinsurance amount for the 60th through 90th day of inpatient hospital care, a $396 per day coinsurance amount for inpatient hospital care during the 60 lifetime reserve days, and a $97 per day coinsurance amount for days 21 through 100 of care in a skilled nursing facility. Certain home health services are paid in full.

An estimated 39,702,000 persons are insured.

Literature: "*Your Medicare Handbook*" and other publications available free from any Social Security Office.

Who To Contact: *Headquarters Office*: Ms. Carol Cronin, Center for Beneficiary Services, Health Care Financing Administration, Room C5-19-07, 7500 Security Boulevard, Baltimore, MD 21244. (410) 786-2744. *Regional or Local Office*: Telephone or visit any Social Security office.

Medicare—to Pay Your Doctor Bills
Medicare Part B—Supplementary Medical Insurance (93.774)

Description: Medicare Part B provides additional optional medical insurance protection for covered services to persons age 65 or over, to certain disabled persons, and to individuals with chronic renal disease. Benefits are paid on the basis of a Medicare-set schedule of reasonable fees for covered services furnished by participating providers such as physicians, hospitals and home health agencies.

Eligibility Requirements: All persons who are eligible for hospital insurance benefits (**93.773**) are eligible for this coverage. You pay a monthly premium, approximately $45.50. Most persons entitled to hospital insurance (**93.773**) are enrolled automatically for supplementary medical insurance. But since the program is voluntary, you may decline coverage.

Financial Information: The beneficiary must meet an annual $100 deductible before benefits may begin. Thereafter, Medicare pays 80 percent of the fee schedule amount or the reasonable costs for covered services. Some items such as prescription drugs, most preventive health care, non-skilled care in a nursing home, most long-term care at home, dental care and hearing aids are not covered at all.

There are an estimated 37,905,000 enrollees.

Literature: "*Your Medicare Handbook*," SSA-79-10050, and other publications available free at any Social Security office.

Who To Contact: *Headquarters Office*: Ms. Carol Cronin, Director, Center for Beneficiary Services, Health Care Financing Administration, Room C5-19-07, 7500 Security Boulevard, Baltimore, MD 21244. (410) 786-3870. *Regional or Local Office*: Telephone or visit any Social Security Office.

Free Medicare
Qualified Medicare Beneficiary Program (QMB)

Description: Under this little-known program, certain low-income persons do not have to pay Medicare premiums, coinsurance or deductibles. By enrolling in this special program, it pays all or some of their Medicare fees for them.

See Chapter 1, page 33.

MEDICAID

Medicaid: Medical Coverage for the Poor
Medical Assistance Program—"Medicaid" (93.778)

Description: Under this program, financial assistance is provided to States to pay the medical expenses of welfare recipients, poor children, pregnant women, needy seniors, and other eligible recipients meeting certain income requirements.

Under Medicaid, States must provide:
- in- and out- patient hospital services
- rural health clinic services
- federally-qualified health center services

- other laboratory and x-ray services
- nursing facility services
- home health services for persons over 21 years old
- family planning services
- physicians' services
- early and periodic screening, diagnosis, and treatment for individuals under age 21
- pediatric or family nurse practitioner services, and nurse-midwife.

Eligibility Requirements: Persons in the following categories qualify:
- Low-income persons over age 65 or blind or disabled;
- Low-income children and pregnant women;
- Members of families with dependent children;
- Certain Medicare beneficiaries.

Financial Information: An estimated 34,300,000 recipients received assistance in the latest reported year.

Who To Contact: *Headquarters Office*: Jim Westmoreland, Director, Medicaid Bureau, Health Care Financing Administration, Rm. C4-25-02, 7500 Security Blvd., Baltimore, MD 21244. (410) 786-3870. *Application Procedure*: Individuals needing medical assistance may apply at any time directly to the State or local welfare agency.

How a Senior Can Get Medicaid—Even If You Own a Mansion

Description: To qualify for Medicaid, the government wants you to have almost no money. There are severe income and asset limitations. So what happens is that many people who worked hard all their lives and put away some savings for their retirement years wind up spending everything on medical costs — especially on nursing home care — before they can qualify for Medicaid.

If you are unmarried, you have to spend down (use up) your assets (savings and property) to certain Medicaid limits (generally around $2,000) and use a good chunk of your monthly retirement income before Medicaid benefits will start. For example, if a senior citizen goes into a nursing home, he or she will have to use up almost all her savings before qualifying for Medicaid. And then any income she receives (such as Social Security) will have to go to help pay her nursing-home bill, with Medicaid covering the rest.

If married, Medicaid decrees that you have to spend down half the assets, to no more the $72,660 left for the at-home spouse.

Either way, the net result is if a senior citizen isn't in the poor category going into a nursing home, it won't take long to get there.

How to Qualify: There are, however, a few hidden loopholes that can help you reduce this burden.

1. *Put money in your home*. Your home is probably your biggest asset. Medicaid won't touch your home as long as you or your spouse live there. Or, if you are single, and you intend to return home after your nursing home stay (and your doctor agrees). So putting money into your residence can protect a lot of savings.

   For example, you could pay off a mortgage; redecorate; build an addition; redo the kitchen and bathrooms; put on a new roof; add aluminum siding; adapt your home for easier handicapped living; even sell your home and buy a more expensive house. All these steps take money which would have to be spent down on nursing home costs and shelter it in your home.

2. *Put money into other exempt assets*. Instead of using your assets to pay down to qualify for Medicaid, put them into other exempt assets. These include a car; household goods and appliances; clothing and personal items; prepaid funeral costs; and burial plots for you and your spouse.

3. *Give your assets to your children*. You and your spouse can give away assets to get them out of your name for purposes of Medicaid qualification. However, you can't give all your money away and qualify right away. Generally, you have to

wait three to five years after disposing of your assets before qualifying.

Who To Contact: *Headquarters Office*: Jim Westmoreland, Director, Medicaid Bureau, Health Care Financing Administration, Rm. C4-25-02, 7500 Security Blvd., Baltimore, MD 21244. (410) 786-3870. *Application Procedure*: Each state has different income and asset limits, so you'll want to contact your local welfare or Medicaid office to get the exact figures for your state. Medicaid regulations are constantly being changed so you should also consult an attorney well versed in Senior Law, whether a private attorney if you cannot afford one or a Legal Assistance Agency (see Table 1k, Chapter 1).

ADDITIONAL RETIREMENT AND MEDICAL PROGRAMS

Longshore and Harbor Workers' Compensation (17.302)

Description: This program for longshoremen provides income replacement and supplement to provide compensation for disability or death resulting from injury, including occupational disease. It also provides benefits for the loss of sight or hearing, dismemberment, disfigurement etc., medical expenses (including hospital care); and funeral expenses up to $3,000. Benefits are paid by private insurance carriers or self-insured employers. Employers or their insurance carriers are required to begin compensation within 14 days of knowledge of the injury or death.

Eligibility Requirements: Longshoremen, harbor workers, and certain other employees—including their survivors—engaged in maritime employment on the navigable waters of the United States and adjoining pier and dock areas; employees engaged in activities on the Outer Continental Shelf; and others as specified. Puerto Rico is not covered.

Claims must be filed within one year after:
a) the injury or death (two years if injury is an occupational disease which does not immediately result in death or disability);
b) or the last compensation payment.

Financial Information: *Range and Average of Financial Assistance:*

1) *Disability Benefits*—two-thirds of average weekly wage;
2) *Death Benefits*—50 percent average wages of deceased to such widow or widower, plus $16\frac{2}{3}$ percent for each surviving child with two-thirds limit.

Benefits are limited to 200 percent of national average weekly wage.

For the latest reported year, approximately 17,000 longshore and harbor workers and specified other workers covered by this program, or their survivors, were receiving benefits.

Literature: *"Longshore and Harbor Workers' Compensation Act."* Copies may be obtained from the headquarters office below.

Who To Contact: *Headquarters Office*: Office of Workers' Compensation Programs, Division of Longshore and Harbor Workers' Compensation, Washington, DC 20210. (202) 219-8721. Contact: Joseph Olimpio. *Application Procedure*: Employee or his or her survivor files a written claim for compensation (Form LS-203 or LS-262) with the district office of the Office of Workers' Compensation Programs (see Table 6a.)

Coal Mine Workers' Compensation—Black Lung (17.307)

Description: Monthly cash benefits to coal miners who have become totally disabled due to black lung disease, and to widows and other surviving dependents of miners who have died of this disease. Employers or their insurance carriers are required to begin compensation within 30 days of the initial determination of eligibility.

Eligibility Requirements: Disabled coal miners (including some workers involved in coal transportation in and around mines and coal mine construction workers) must have worked in the Nation's coal mines or a coal preparation facility and become "totally disabled." The applicant may be able to work in areas other than coal mines and still be eligible for reduced benefits.

Financial Information: Payments are disbursed on a monthly basis as follows.

1) *Period of Assistance*. Miners with total disability—get payments till death; spouse—until death or remarriage; children—until age 18 or to age 23 if qualified as a student unless under a disability.

2) *Range and Average of Financial Assistance*. Basic monthly rate, $500 for claimant only. For three or more dependents, $1,001 maximum (this does not include medical services). Average monthly benefits payment, $472.46.

Some 6,600 claims a year are processed.

Literature: "*Black Lung Benefits*," Fact Sheet No. ESA 91-14.

Who To Contact: *Headquarters Office*: Division of Coal Mine Workers' Compensation, Office of Workers' Compensation Programs, Employment Standards Administration, Department of Labor, Washington, DC 20210. (202) 693-0046. Contact: James L. DeMarce, Director. *Application Procedure*: Telephone, write-in, or visit your local Social Security office, or Division of Coal Mine Workers' Compensation district office (Table 6b).

Special Benefits for Disabled Coal Miners
"Black Lung" (96.005)

Description: Monthly cash benefits to coal miners who have become disabled due to black lung disease or other chronic lung disease arising from coal mine employment; and, under prescribed circumstances, their widows, children, surviving divorced wife, parents, brothers and sisters

Eligibility Requirements: Disabled coal miners and their eligible dependents or survivors if the coal miner's death resulted from black lung or other chronic lung disease arising from coal mine employment.

Since 1973 no new applications have been accepted by the Social Security Administration (SSA) for this program except for applications from survivors of miners or widows who were receiving black lung benefits under this program when the miner or widow died.

Financial Information: Benefits payable to miners or widows are increased when there are dependents in the family. The basic black lung benefit is $500.50. Maximum, $1,001.00. An estimated 78,100 miners, widows and dependents receive monthly cash benefits under this program.

Who To Contact: Headquarters Office: Office of Public Inquiries, Room 4100, Annex, Social Security Administration, 6401 Security Boulevard, Baltimore, MD 21235. (410) 965-2736; Department of Labor, Employment Standards Administration, Division of Coal Mine Workers' Compensation, 200 Constitution Ave., NW., Washington, D.C. 20210, Phone: (202) 693-0047. *Regional or Local Office*: Telephone or visit any Social Security office.

Pensions and Benefits—for Railroad Workers
Railroad Retirement Act and Railroad Unemployment Insurance Act (57.001)

Description: This program covers direct payments of Railroad Social Security and Rail Industry Pensions to railroad workers and their beneficiaries and families. This includes payment of federal windfall benefits, supplemental annuities, permanent and occupational disability, and sickness and unemployment benefits.

Eligibility Requirements: Benefits are granted for:
1) workers who retire because of age or disability;
2) eligible spouses and divorced spouses of retired employees;
3) surviving widows, widowers, divorced spouses, children, and dependent parents of deceased employees;
4) unemployed workers;
5) workers who are sick or injured.

Under the **Railroad Retirement Act**, the worker must have had 10 or more years of railroad service in order to be eligible for employee, spouse and survivor benefits. For survivors to be eligible for benefits, the employee must also have been insured at death.

Under the **Railroad Unemployment Insurance Act,** an employee must have certain minimum earnings in railroad wages, and, if a new employee, must have worked for a railroad at least five months in a calendar year to be a qualified employee in the applicable benefit year.

Financial Information: *Range and Average of Financial Assistance*:
- Annuities—monthly maximum $2,885. Average $1,413;
- Disability—monthly maximum $2,845. Average $1,546;
- Employee supplemental annuities— monthly maximum $70. Average $42;
- Spouse benefits—monthly maximum $1,375. Average $555;
- Widows and widowers—monthly maximum $2,230. Average $865;
- Widowed mothers and fathers—monthly maximum $1,841. Average $1,078;
- Children—monthly maximum $1,639. Average $707;
- Unemployment and sickness—weekly $250.

In the latest reported year, $8.7 billion in benefits were paid to an estimated 849,000 retirees, beneficiaries and their families.

Literature: A series of free leaflets is available from the Office of Public Affairs shown below.

Who To Contact: *Headquarters Office*: Office of Public Affairs, Railroad Retirement Board, 844 North Rush Street, Chicago, IL 60611. (312) 751-4777. Contact: William Poulos. You can also call their toll-free Help Line (800) 808-0772. *Regional or Local Office*: Application for retirement, disability, survivor, unemployment or sickness benefits should be made to any office of the Railroad Retirement Board (Table 6c).

Prescription Drugs for Seniors Citizens

Description: Many of the States have special prescription plans for seniors citizens who need help paying for their medications. Most of these plans require the recipients to be over 65 years old and have a limited annual income. The plans require the recipient to pay just a small part of the cost of each medication, the plan paying the balance.

Some of the plans are described below.

New York State: Elderly Pharmaceutical Insurance Coverage (EPIC) is available for seniors with incomes under $18,500 if single, or $24,400 if married. There are two plans.
1. *Fee Plan*. You pay an annual fee of $10 to $240 (depending on income) to qualify right away; or
2. *Deductible Plan*. You pay no annual fee but you pay full price for your prescriptions until you spend an annual deductible amount (starting at $468).

At the drug store, those enrolled in the *Fee Plan* and those enrolled in the *Deductible Plan* who have met their annual deductible pay $3 for prescriptions costing up to $8; $5 for prescriptions costing $8 to $13; $7 for prescriptions costing $13 to $23; $10 for prescriptions costing $13 to $33; and $23 for each prescription costing over $33.

Who to Contact: EPIC, P.O. Box 15018, Albany, NY 12212. Telephone helpline: (800) 332-3742.

New Jersey: Pharmaceutical Assistance to the Aged and Disabled (PAAD) is available for seniors with incomes under $16,171 if single, or $19,828 if married. You pay $5 for each covered prescription. However, not all drugs are covered.

Who to Contact: PAAD Special Benefits Programs, CN715, Trenton, NJ 08625. (800) 792-9745.

Pennsylvania: Pharmaceutical Assistance for the Elderly (PACE Card) is available for seniors with incomes under $13,000 if single, or $16,200 if married. You pay $6 for each prescription.

Who to Contact: PACE Card, P.O. Box 8806, Harrisburg, PA 17105. (800) 225-7223.

Connecticut: Conn PACE is available for seniors with incomes under $13,800 if single, or $16,600 if married. You pay a $15 one-time registration fee and $12 for each prescription.

Who to Contact: Conn PACE, P.O. Box 5011, Hartford, CT 06102. (800) 423-5026.

Maine: The Elderly Low-Cost Drug Program is available for seniors over 62 years old or households where one person is 62 years old. Recipients must have incomes under $9,700 if single, or $12,100 if married or there are dependents.

You pay $2 or 20 percent of the price allowed by the Department of Human Services, whichever is greater, for each prescription.

Who to Contact: Elderly Low-Cost Drug Program, Bureau of Taxation, State Office Building, Augusta, ME 04333. (800) 773-7895.

Rhode Island: Rhode Island Pharmaceutical Assistance to the Elderly (RIPAE) is available for seniors with incomes under $13,860 if single, or $17,326 if married. You pay 40% of the cost of prescription drugs used to treat certain illnesses.

Who to Contact: Rhode Island Pharmaceutical Assistance to the Elderly, 160 Pine St., Providence, RI 02903. (401) 277-3330.

Vermont: The VScript program is available for seniors with incomes not over 175 percent of the federal poverty guidelines. There is a co-payment for each prescription, with the percentage amount set at the beginning of each fiscal year.

Who to Contact: VScript Program, Department of Social Welfare, Medicaid Division, 103 S. Main St., Waterbury, VT 05676. (800) 827-0589.

Delaware: A Delaware program is available for seniors with incomes under $11,300 if single, or $15,500 if married. You pay 20 percent of the cost of the prescription.

Who to Contact: Nemours Health Clinic, 915 N. DuPont Blvd., Milford, DE 19963. (800) 763-9326.

Illinois: The Pharmaceutical Assistance Program is available for seniors over 65, or for persons over 16 who are totally disabled, or for widows and widowers who turned 63 before spouse's death. Your income must be under $14,000.

Who to Contact: Pharmaceutical Assistance Program, Illinois Dept. of Revenue, P.O. Box 19021, Springfield, IL 62794. (800) 624-2459.

Further information: For information on whether your particular State has a subsidized prescription program as well as other special programs for seniors, contact your state's Agency On Aging (Table 6d.).

Health Insurance If Laid Off — "COBRA"

Description: A recently passed government program, "COBRA," provides that when you leave your job for almost any reason — including retirement, lay-off, job change, being fired, go on strike — your former employer must allow you to continue your personal or family medical coverage under the company's group plan while you look for a new insurance policy.

The coverage must last for at least 18 months, and you are guaranteed a premium no higher than 102 percent of the regular cost for participation in the health plan (including the employer's contribution).

The coverage isn't free but at least you'll be covered and at relatively low group rates. The purpose is to bridge the gap between policies when you leave a job. And you don't need proof of insurability — no matter what your health condition, "COBRA" must be made available. Even if you have preexisting conditions.

Eligibility Requirements: To qualify, your employer must have had an average of at least 20 employees in the past year, including part-timers; and must sponsor a group health plan.

You must have been participating in your company's health plan while you were working, even if you joined just before your job termination.

If you die or divorce, your spouse or dependent child may qualify for "COBRA" coverage.

Who To Contact: Your former employer's health insurance administrator.

Table 6a: OFFICE OF WORKERS' COMPENSATION PROGRAMS

REGIONAL OFFICES

Massachusetts
Kenneth Hamlett, Acting Regional
Director
U.S. Department of Labor,
ESA/OWCP
JFK Federal Building, Room E-260
Boston, MA 02203
(617) 565-2102

New York
Kenneth Hamlett, RD
U.S. Department of Labor,
ESA/OWCP
201 Varick Street, Room 740
New York, NY 10014
(212) 337-2033

Pennsylvania
R. David Lotz, RD
U.S. Department of Labor,
ESA/OWCP
3535 Market Street, Room 12300
Philadelphia, PA 19104
(215) 596-1180

Florida
Nancy Ricker, RD
U.S. Department of Labor,
ESA/OWCP
214 North Hogan Street, Suite 1026
Jacksonville, FL 32202
(904) 357-4777

Illinois
Deborah Sanford
U.S. Department of Labor,
ESA/OWCP
230 South Dearborn St., Room 800
Chicago, IL 60604
(312) 886-5883

Texas
Thomas Bouis
U.S. Department of Labor,
ESA/OWCP
525 South Griffin Street, Room 407
Dallas, TX 75202-5007
(214) 767-4713

Missouri
Charles O. Ketcham, Jr. RD

U.S. Department of Labor, ESA/OWCP
1100 Main Street, Suite 750
Kansas City, MO 64105
(816) 426-2195

Colorado
Robert Mansanares, RD
U.S. Department of Labor, ESA/OWCP
1801 California Street, Suite 915
Denver, CO 80202-2614
(303) 844-1223

California
Donna Onodera, RD
U.S. Department of Labor, ESA/OWCP
71 Stevenson Street, Suite 1705
San Francisco, CA 94105
(415) 975-4160

Washington
Thomas K. Morgan, RD
U.S. Department of Labor,
ESA/OWCP
1111 Third Avenue, Suite 615
Seattle, WA 98101-3212
(206) 553-5521

Table 6b: DIVISION OF COAL MINE WORKERS' COMPENSATION DISTRICT OFFICES

Pennsylvania ((Connecticut, Delaware, District of Columbia, Eastern Pennsylvania, Maine, Massachusetts, New Hampshire, New Jersey, New York, Rhode Island, Vermont)
ESA/OWCP/DCMWC
100 N. Wilkes-Barre Blvd.,
Room 300 A
Wilkes-Barre, PA 18702
(800) 347-3755

Western Pennsylvania and Maryland
ESA/OWCP/DCMWC
1225 South Main Street, Suite 405
Greensburg, PA 15601
(800) 347-3753

Central Pennsylvania and Virginia
U.S. Department of Labor
ESA/OWCP/DCMWC

319 Washington Street, 2nd Floor
Johnstown, PA 15901
(800) 347-3754

West Virginia
(Northern West Virginia)
ESA/OWCP/DCMWC
425 Juliana Street
Parkersburg, WV 26101
(800) 347-3751

(Southern West Virginia)
ESA/OWCP/DCMWC
Charleston Federal Center,
Suite 110
500 Quarrier Street
Charleston, West Virginia 25301
(800) 347-3749

Kentucky
ESA/OWCP/DCMWC
164 Main Street, Suite 508
Pikevílle, KY 41501

(800) 366-4599

Alabama, Florida, Georgia, Mississippi, North Carolina, South Carolina, Tennessee
ESA/OWCP/DCMWC
402 Campbell Way
Mt. Sterling, KY 40353
(800) 366-4628

Ohio (Illinois, Indiana, Michigan, Minnesota, Ohio, Wisconsin)
ESA/OWCP/DCMWC
1160 Dublin Road Suite 300
Columbus, OH 43215
(800) 347-3771

Colorado
(Western United States)
ESA/OWCP/DCMWC
1999 Broadway, Suite 690
Denver, CO 80201
(800) 366-4612

Table 6c: RAILROAD RETIREMENT BOARD DISTRICT OFFICES

Alabama
U.S. Railroad Retirement Board
Medical Forum Bldg.
950 22nd St North, Rm. 426
Birmingham, AL 35203-1134
Phone: (205) 731-0019

Arizona
U.S. Railroad Retirement Board
Financial Plaza, Room 4850
1201 S. Alma School Road
Mesa, AZ 85210-2097
Phone: (480) 610-5990)

Arkansas
U.S. Railroad Retirement Board
1200 Cherry Brook Dr., Ste. 500
Little Rock, AR 72211-4113
Phone:(501) 324-5241

California
U.S. Railroad Retirement Board
801 I St, Rm. 205
Sacramento, CA 95814
Phone: (916) 498-6654

Colorado
U.S. Railroad Retirement Board
721 19th St, Room 177
PO Box 8869
Denver, CO 80201-8869
Phone: (303) 844-4311

Florida
U.S. Railroad Retirement Board
Bennett Federal Building
400 W. Bay St, Rm. 315
Box 35026
Jacksonville, FL 32202-4412
Phone: (904) 232-2546

Georgia
U.S. Railroad Retirement Board
Peachtree Summit Bldg., Rm. 1702
401 W. Peachtree Street
Atlanta, GA 30308
Phone: (404) 331-2841

Illinois
U.S. Railroad Retirement Board
844 N Rush St., Ninth Floor
Chicago, IL 60611-2092
Phone: (312)751-4500

Indiana
U.S. Railroad Retirement Board

The Meridian Centre
50 S. Meridian, Suite 303
Indianapolis, IN 46204-3530
Phone: (317) 226-6111

Iowa
U.S. Railroad Retirement Board
Federal Building
210 Walnut ST, Room 921
Des Moines, IA 50309-2182
Phone: (515) 284-4344

Kansas
U.S. Railroad Retirement Board
1861 N. Rock Rd. Suite 390
Wichita, KS 67206-1264
Phone: (316) 687-5973

Kentucky
U.S. Railroad Retirement Board
Theatre Building
629 S. 4th Ave., Ste. 301, Box 3705
Louisville, KY 40201-3705
Phone: (502) 582-5208

Louisiana
U.S. Railroad Retirement Board
501 Magazine St. Rm. 1045
New Orleans, LA 70130-3394
Phone: (504) 589-2597

Maryland
U.S. Railroad Retirement Board
George H. Fallon Building
31 Hopkins Plaza, Suite 820
Baltimore, MD 21201-2825
Phone: (410) 962-2550

Massachusetts
U.S. Railroad Retirement Board
408 Atlantic Ave., Room 441
P. O. Box 2448
Boston, MA 02208-2448
Phone: (617) 223-8550

Michigan
U.S. Railroad Retirement Board
McNamara Federal Bldg.
477 W. Michigan Ave., Suite 1990
Detroit, MI 48226-2596
Phone: (313) 226-6221

Minnesota
U.S. Railroad Retirement Board
Federal Bldg.

515 W. First St., Rm. 125
Duluth, MN 55802-1392
Phone: (218) 720-5301

Missouri
U.S. Railroad Retirement Board
Federal Bldg.
601 E. 12th St., Rm. 113
Kansas City, MO 64106-2882
Phone: (816) 426-5884

Montana
U.S. Railroad Retirement Board
Judge Jameson Federal Bldg.
2900 Fourth Ave. N., Rm. 101
Billings, MT 59101-1266
Phone: (406) 247-7375

Nebraska
U.S. Railroad Retirement Board
Hruska Courthouse, Suite C125
111 S. 18 Plaza
PO Box 815
Omaha, NE 68101-0815
Phone: (402) 221-4641

New Jersey
U.S. Railroad Retirement Board
Veteran's Administration Bldg.
20 Washington Place, Rm. 516
Newark, NJ 07102-3110
Phone: (973) 645-3990

New Mexico
U.S. Railroad Retirement Board
300 San Mateo NE, Rm. 401
Albuquerque, NM 87108
Phone: (505) 346-6405

New York
U.S. Railroad Retirement Board
Leo W. O'Brien Fed. Bldg.
Clinton Ave. & Pearl St., Rm. 264
PO Box 529
Albany, NY 12201-0529
Phone: (518) 431-4004

North Carolina
U.S. Railroad Retirement Board
Quorum Business Park
7508 E. Independence Blvd.,
Suite 120
Charlotte, NC 28227-9409
Phone: (704) 344-6118

U.S. Railroad Retirement Board
USPO Building, Room 343
657 Second Ave. N., PO Box 383
Fargo, ND 58107-0383
Phone: (701) 239-5117

Ohio
U.S. Railroad Retirement Board
CBLD Center
36 East 7th St., Rm. 201
Cincinnati, OH 45202-4439
Phone: (513)684-3188

Oregon
U.S. Railroad Retirement Board
Green-Wyatt Fed. Bldg.
1220 SW 3rd Ave., Rm. 377
Portland, OR 97204-2807
Phone: (503) 326-2143

Pennsylvania
U.S. Railroad Retirement Board
1514 11th Ave., PO Box 990
Altoona, PA 16603-0990

Phone: (814) 946-3601
Tennessee
U.S. Railroad Retirement Board
233 Cumberland Bend Dr., Ste. 104
Nashville, TN 37228-1813
Phone: (615) 736-5131

Texas
U.S. Railroad Retirement Board
Leland Fed. Bldg.
1919 Smith, Ste. 845
Houston, TX 77002-8051
Phone: (713) 209-3045

Utah
U.S. Railroad Retirement Board
Bennett Fed. Bldg.
125 S. State, Rm. 1205
Salt Lake City, UT 84138-1102
Phone: (801) 524-5725

Virginia
U.S. Railroad Retirement Board
400 N. 8th St., Ste. 470

PO Box 10006
Richmond, VA 23240-0006
Phone: (804) 771-2997

Washington
U.S. Railroad Retirement Board
US Court House, Rm. 492
W 920 Riverside Ave.
Spokane, WA 99201-1081
Phone: (509) 353-2795

West Virginia
U.S. Railroad Retirement Board
New Federal Bldg., Rm. 112
640 4th Ave., PO Box 2153
Huntington, WV 25721-2153
Phone: (304) 529-5561

Wisconsin
U.S. Railroad Retirement Board
Reuss Federal Plaza, Ste. 1300
310 W. Wisconsin Ave.
Milwaukee, WI 53203-2211
Phone: (414) 297-3961

Table 6d: STATE AGENCIES ON AGING

Alabama
Alabama Commission on Aging
RSA Plaza, Suite 470
770 Washington Avenue
Montgomery, AL 36130
(334) 242-5743

Alaska
Alaska Commission on Aging
Division of Senior Services
Department of Administration
Juneau, AK 99811-0209
(907) 465-3250

Arizona
Aging and Adult Administration
Department of Economic Security
1789 West Jefferson Street - #950A
Phoenix, AZ 85007
(602) 542-4446

Arkansas
Division Aging and Adult Services
Arkansas Dept of Human Services
P.O. Box 1437, Slot S-530
1417 Donaghey Plaza South
Little Rock, AR 72203 - 1437
(501) 682-2441

California
California Department of Aging
1600 K Street
Sacramento, CA 95814
(916) 322-5290

Colorado
Aging and Adult Services
Department of Social Services
1575 Sherman Street, Ground Floor
Denver, CO 80203
(303) 866-2800

Connecticut
Community Services
Division of Elderly Services
25 Sigourney Street, 10th Floor
Hartford, CT 06106-5033
(860) 424-5298

Delaware
DE Division of Services for Aging
and Adults with Physical
Disabilities
Dept. of Health and Social Services
1901 North DuPont Highway
New Castle, DE 19720
(302) 577-4791

District Of Columbia
D.C. Office on Aging
441 Fourth Street, N.W., 9th Floor
Washington, DC 20001
(202) 724-5622

Florida
Department of Elder Affairs
4040 Esplanade Way, Suite 152
Tallahassee, FL 32399-7000
(850) 414-2000

Georgia
Division of Aging Services
Department of Human Resources
2 Peachtree Street N.E. 9th Floor
Atlanta, GA 30303
(404) 657-5258

Hawaii
Hawaii Executive Office on Aging
250 South Hotel Street, Suite 109
Honolulu, HI 96813
(808) 586-0100

Idaho
Idaho Commission on Aging
P.O. Box 83720
Boise, ID 83720-0007
(208) 334-3833

Illinois
Illinois Department on Aging
421 East Capitol Avenue, Suite 100
Springfield, IL 62701-1789
(217) 785-3356
Chicago Office: (312) 814-2630

Indiana
Bureau of Aging and In-Home Services
Division of Disability, Aging and
Rehabilitative Services
Family and Social Services Adm.
402 W. Washington Street, #W454
P.O. Box 7083
Indianapolis, IN 46207-7083
(317) 232-7020

Iowa
Iowa Department of Elder Affairs
Clemens Building, 3rd Floor
200 Tenth Street
Des Moines, IA 50309-3609
(515) 242-3333

Kansas
Department on Aging
503 S. Kansas Ave.
Topeka, KS 66603-3404
785-296-4986

Kentucky
KY Division of Aging Services
Cabinet for Human Resources
275 East Main Street
Frankfort, KY 40621
(502) 564-6930

Louisiana
Governor's Office of Elderly Affairs
P.O. Box 80374
Baton Rouge, LA 70898 - 0374
(225) 342-7100

Maine
Bureau of Elder and Adult Services
Department of Human Services
35 Anthony Avenue
State House - Station #11
Augusta, ME 04333
(207) 624-5335

Maryland
Maryland Office on Aging
301 West Preston Street, Rm. 1007
Baltimore, MD 21201-2374

(410) 767-1100

Massachusetts
MA Executive Office of Elder Affairs
One Ashburton Place, 5th Floor
Boston, MA 02108
(617) 727-7750

Michigan
Office of Services to the Aging
611 W. Ottawa, N. Ottawa Tower,
3rd Floor
P.O. Box 30676
Lansing, MI 48909-8176
(517) 373-8230

Minnesota
Minnesota Board on Aging
444 Lafayette Road
St. Paul, MN 55155-3843
(651) 296-2770

Mississippi
Division of Aging and Adult Services
750 State Street
Jackson, MS 39202
(601) 359-4925

Missouri
Division on Aging
Department of Social Services
P.O. Box 1337, 615 Howerton Ct.
Jefferson City, MO 65102-1337
(573) 751-3082

Montana
Senior and Long Term Care Division
Dept. of Public Health & Human Services
P.O. Box 4210, 111 Sanders, Rm. 211
Helena, MT 59620
(406) 444-4077

Nebraska
Dept. of Health and Human Services
Division on Aging
P.O. Box 95044
1343 M Street
Lincoln, NE 68509-5044
(402) 471-2307

Nevada
Nevada Division for Aging Services
Department of Human Resources
State Mail Room Complex
3416 Goni Road, Building D-132
Carson City, NV 89706
Phone: (775) 687-4210

New Hampshire
Division of Elderly and Adult Services
129 Pleasant Street, Annex Bldg. #1

Concord, NH 03301-3843
(603) 271-4680

New Jersey
Dept. of Health and Senior Services
Division of Senior Affairs
P.O Box 807
Trenton, New Jersey 08625-0807
(609) 943-3436; 1-800-792-8820

New Mexico
State Agency on Aging
228 East Palace Avenue, 1st Floor
Santa Fe, NM 87501
(505) 827-7640

New York
NYS Office for The Aging
2 Empire State Plaza
Albany, NY 12223-1251
1-800-342-9871

North Carolina
Division of Aging
2101 Mail Service Center
Raleigh, NC 27699-2101
(919) 733-3983

North Dakota
Department of Human Services
Aging Services Division
600 South 2n Street, Suite 1C
Bismarck, ND 58504
(701) 328-8910

North Mariana Islands
Commonwealth of the Northern
Mariana Islands Office on Aging
P.O. Box 2178
Saipan, MP 96950
(670) 233-1320/1321

Ohio
Ohio Department of Aging
50 West Broad Street - 9th Floor
Columbus, OH 43215-5928
(614) 466-5500

Oklahoma
Services for the Aging
Department of Human Services
Box 25352, 312 N.E. 28th Street
Oklahoma City, OK 73125
(405) 521-2281 or 521-2327

Oregon
Senior and Disabled Services Division
500 Summer St., N.E., 3rd Floor
Salem, OR 97301
(503) 945-5811

Pennsylvania

Pennsylvania Department of Aging
555 Walnut Street, 5th floor
Harrisburg, PA 17101-1919
(717) 783-1550

Puerto Rico
Governor's Office of Elderly Affairs
Call Box 50063
Old San Juan Station, PR 00902
(787) 721-5710 or 721-4560

Rhode Island
Department of Elderly Affairs
160 Pine Street
Providence, RI 02903-3708
(401) 222-2858

South Carolina
Office on Aging
SC Dept. of Health and Human Services
P.O. Box 8206
Columbia, SC 29202-8206
(803) 898-2501

South Dakota
Office of Adult Services and Aging
700 Governors Drive, Kneip Bldg.
Pierre, SD 57501-2291
(605) 773-3656

Tennessee

Commission on Aging
Andrew Jackson Building. 9th floor,
500 Deaderick Street,
Nashville, Tennessee 37243-0860
(615) 741-2056

Texas
Texas Department on Aging
4900 North Lamar, 4th Floor
Austin, TX 78751
(512) 424-6840
Utah
Division of Aging & Adult Services
Box 45500, 120 North 200 West
Salt Lake City, UT 84145-0500
(801) 538-3910

Vermont
VT Department of Aging and Disabilities
103 South Main Street, Waterbury Complex
Waterbury, VT 05671
(802) 241-2400

Virginia
Virginia Department for the Aging
1600 Forest Avenue, Suite 102
Richmond, VA 23229
(804) 662-9333

Virgin Islands
Senior Citizen Affairs
V.I. Department of Human Services

1303 Hospital Ground, Building A
Charlotte Amalie, VI 00802
(340) 774-0930

Washington
Aging and Adult Services Administration
Dept. of Social & Health Services
P.O. Box 45050
Olympia, WA 98504-5050
(360) 725-2310

West Virginia
WV Bureau of Senior Services
1900 Kanawha Boulevard East
Charleston, WV 25305-0160
(304) 558-3317

Wisconsin
Bureau of Aging and Long Term
Care Resources
1 West Wilson Street
Room 450
Madison, WI 53707-7850
(608) 266-2536

Wyoming
Office on Aging, Dept. of Health
6101 Yellowstone Road, Suite 259B
Cheyenne, WY 82002
(307) 777-7986

Chapter 7
SPECIAL BENEFITS FOR WOMEN, MINORITIES AND OTHER GROUPS

Uncle Sam has a raft of programs whose purpose is to help minorities, women, the disadvantaged and the disabled to be able to participate fully in the American system. These programs help increase opportunities for these groups — economically, educationally, with housing, health and more.

Programs for these groups are described throughout this book, in the pertinent chapters. In this chapter are other federal programs with special benefits for individuals in these groups.

PROGRAMS FOR MINORITIES

Money—for Needy Minority and Women Farmers
Outreach and Assistance Grants for Socially Disadvantaged Farmers and Ranchers (10.443)

Description: The purpose of this program is to assist socially disadvantaged farmers and ranchers to own and operate farms. The goal is to reverse the decline of small, limited resource farmers by providing educational, technical assistance, research and counseling services

Beneficiary Eligibility: Socially disadvantaged farmers and ranchers who are: Black, Women, American Indians, Alaskan Natives, Hispanics, Asians, and Pacific Islanders.

Financial Information: In the latest reported year, over 8,686 farmers and ranchers were assisted, for a total estimated $3,000,000.

Literature: FmHA Instruction 1943-C "*Farm Ownership, Soil, Water and Recreation,*" available from Farmers Home Administration State Offices (see Farm Service Agency offices, Table 2g, Chapter 2).

Who To Contact: *Headquarters Office*: Dept. of Agriculture, UDSA Office of Outreach, 1400 Independence Ave., SW, AG Stop 1710, Washington, DC 20250. (202) 720-6390, *Regional or Local Office*: Table 2g, Chapter 2.

Free Job Training for Displaced Homemakers. Single Parents, Minorities

Employment Services and Job Training—Pilot and Demonstration Programs (17.249)

Description: This program funds pilot projects that offer job training, related services, and job opportunities for members of groups with particular disadvantages in the general labor market or in certain segments of the labor market.

See Chapter 1, page 24.

Free Help for Minority Businesses

Minority Business Resource Development (11.802)

DESCRIPTION: This program promotes the growth of minority businesses by identifying and developing private capital sources, expanding business information and business services through trade associations, mobilizing the resources of federal, State and local government agencies, and assist minorities in entering new and growing markets.

See Chapter 2, page 63.

Money—for Minority Students in Colorado to Study Science

Colorado Independent Education and Science Projects and Programs (11.449)

Description: This is a program of incentive awards to students, and special tutors in math and science, in order to increase the number of minority students enrolling in college and majoring in math, science and engineering from the St. Vrain and Boulder Valley School districts in Colorado. It is administered by the CMEA/MESA (Colorado Minority Engineering Association/Mathematics, Engineering, Science Achievement) in Boulder.

Beneficiary Eligibility: Minority elementary, junior high school, and high school students in the above school districts.

Financial Information: Not applicable.

Who To Contact: *Headquarters Office*: None. *Regional or Local Office*: NOAA/Environmental Research Laboratories, R/EX-4, 325 Broadway, Boulder CO 80303. Contact: Tony Tafoya, Program Officer for this award. (303) 497-6731.

Free Help for Minorities to Start a Small Business

Minority Business Development Centers (11.800)

DESCRIPTION: Free business development services to minority firms and individuals interested in entering, expanding or improving their efforts in the marketplace.

See Chapter 2, page 63.

Money for Minority Transportation-Related Businesses

Human Resource Programs (20.511)

Description: Cash grants so that minorities and women can participate fully in public transportation projects and activities.

See Chapter 2, page 70.

4-Year Scholarships for Minority Undergraduates

Higher Education Multicultural Scholars Program (10.220)

Description: This program gives money to selected colleges and universities to provide four-year undergraduate scholarships to minority students pursuing bachelors degrees in the food and agricultural sciences. The purpose of the scholarships is to increase minority representation in the fields of agriculture, agriscience, agri-business, natural resources, forestry, veterinary medicine, home economics, and disciplines closely allied to the food and agricultural system.

Beneficiary Eligibility: Students eligible to receive scholarships under this program must be enrolled or accepted as a full-time bachelor degree candidate, and must be a member of a minority group traditionally under-represented in food and agricultural scientific and professional fields. Such groups include:

- African-Americans
- Hispanics
- Asians
- Native-Americans
- Alaskan Natives
- Pacific Islanders.

Financial Information: $970,000 was awarded last year for 102 four-year scholarships.

Literature: Program Announcement and Application Kit for the Food and Agricultural Sciences All-Americans/Undergraduate Scholars Program.

Who to Contact: *Headquarters Office*: Grant Programs Manager, Education Programs, CSREES, Department of Agriculture, Room 3912, South Building, Washington, DC 20250-2251. (202) 720-7854. *Regional or Local Office*: None. Scholarship recipients are selected by the individual colleges, and students must apply for the scholarships through procedures established by the individual institutions.

Student Training and Internships

Hispanic Serving Institutions—Student Training and Education (20.906)

Description: Financial assistance is provided to Hispanic-serving educational institutions to:

- Implement programs that attract minority students into transportation-related careers by providing student training and internships in transportation-related careers;
- Develop programs to promote and assist minority entrepreneurs to compete in transportation-related contracts and projects

Beneficiary Eligibility: Students meeting eligibility requirements at Hispanic-serving colleges.

Financial Information: Different Hispanic-serving Institutions participate each year.

Who to Contact: *Headquarters Office*: Department of Transportation, Office of Small and Disadvantaged Business Utilization, S-40, 400 Seventh Street, SW., Room 9414, Washington, DC 20590. Att: Minority Educational Executive, phone: (800) 532-1169, or (202) 366-2852. *Regional or Local Office*: Not applicable. *Hispanic Serving Institutions*: See Table 7c.

Money—for Women and Minority Businesses

Women's & Minorities Prequalification Loan Program: Specialized 7(a)

Description: If you are a woman or minority who owns or wants to start a business, the Small Business Administration has this special program to help you. Intermediary lenders assist you in developing your loan application package. On approval, the SBA provides a letter of pre-qualification you can take to a lender, stating the agency's intent to guarantee the loan. The intermediary will then help you locate a lender offering the most competitive rates.

The women's program uses only non-profit organizations as intermediaries; the minority program uses for-profit intermediaries as well.

Eligibility: Businesses must meet the following qualifications:

- Be at least 51 percent owned, operated and managed by people of ethnic or racial minorities, or by women.
- Have average annual sales under $5 million.
- Employ less than 100 persons.

Financial Information: Generally, the maximum loan is $250,000.

Literature: "*SBA Business Loans from the SBA.*"

Who To Contact: *Headquarters Office*: Director, Loan Policy and Procedures Branch, Small

Business Administration, 409 Third Street, SW., Washington, DC 20416. (202) 205-6570. *Regional or Local Office*: Initial contact should be with the SBA district offices listed in Table 2a, Chapter 2.

Help for Minority Veterans

Description: The Veterans Administration has a special program called the *Center for Minority Veterans* that promotes the use of existing VA programs, benefits and services by minority veterans, and proposes new ways to meet the needs of minority veterans.

Eligibility: Five distinct minority veteran groups: African Americans, Hispanic Americans, Asian Americans, Native Americans and Pacific Islanders.

Who to Contact: *Headquarters Office*: VA Center for Minority Veterans, Dept. of Veterans Affairs, 810 Vermont Ave., NW, Washington, DC 20420; (202) 273-6708. *Regional or Local Office*: There are over 300 Minority Veterans Program Coordinators. They are located at almost every VA facility (see Table 5a, Chapter 5).

PROGRAMS FOR WOMEN

Free Job Training for Women
Vocational Education—Basic Grants to States (84.048)

DESCRIPTION: This program gives money to the States to provide vocational education and training to single parents, displaced homemakers and single pregnant women. It funds vocational education programs at the secondary, post-secondary, and adult levels.

Beneficiary Eligibility: A wide range of individuals pursuing vocational education and training.

Financial Information: About $1.1 billion dollars was spent in the latest reported year.

Who to Contact: *Headquarters Office*: Division of Vocational-Technical Education, Office of Vocational and Adult Ed., U.S. Dept. of Education, 400 Maryland Ave., SW, Wash., DC 20202-7323. Contact: Maurice James. (202) 205-9441. *Regional or Local Office*: Not applicable.

Women's Bureau—Free Employment Assistance
Women's Special Employment Assistance (17.700)

Description: The Women's Bureau in the Department of Labor provides advisory services and counseling concerning the employment of women. It promotes training and employment opportunities for women. And promotes women's entry into better paying jobs, especially in new technology and nontraditional occupations.

The Bureau has an Internet website, with links designed especially for children, parents, teachers. Through the Women's Bureau Clearinghouse, as well as the Internet, you can access basic information and resources on specific topics such as dependent care, alternative work schedules, flexible benefit plans, and worker's rights, and many Bureau publications related to work and family.

Beneficiary Eligibility: Individuals (particularly women).

Financial Information: *Range and Average of Financial Assistance*: Not applicable.

Literature: Facts sheets, including "*Black Women in the Labor Force*," and "*Women of Hispanic Origin in the Labor Force*." Other brochures in English and Spanish on such topics as Sexual Harassment, Pregnancy Discrimination, and the Family and Medical Leave Act.

Who to Contact: *Headquarters Office*: Director, Women's Bureau, Office of the Secretary, Dept. of Labor, Washington, DC 20210. (202) 693-6710. Contact: Office of Administrative Management, Women's Bureau, Room S3305, Office of the Secretary, Department of Labor, Washington, DC 20210. (202) 693-6727. The Internet address is www.dol.gov/do/wb/welcome. *Regional or Local Office*: Contact the nearest Department of Labor, Women's Bureau regional office in Table 7a.

Money–Owned Businesses from Special Development Organizations
Women's Business Ownership Assistance (59.043)

Description: This program establishes and funds 61 local nonprofit economic development centers to assist small business concerns owned and controlled by women.

See Chapter 2, page 61.

Help for Women Veterans

Description: The Veterans Administration has a special program called the *Center for Women Veterans* that promotes the use of existing VA programs, benefits and services by women veterans and sees that they receive benefits on a par with male veterans.

Eligibility: Women veterans.

Who to Contact: *Headquarters Office*: VA Center for Women Veterans, Dept. of Veterans Affairs, 810 Vermont Ave., NW, Washington, DC 20420. *Regional or Local Office*: There are full-time women veterans coordinators at various VA medical centers. See Table 5a.

PROGRAMS FOR NATIVE AMERICANS

Money—for Businesses in Rural Areas
Business and Industrial Loans (10.768)

Description: Rural businesses, Indian tribes, and individuals in rural areas are eligible for direct loans and guaranteed/insured loans to improve, develop, or finance their business.

See Chapter 2, page 67.

Money—to Acquire Land on Indian Reservations
Indian Tribes and Tribal Corporation Loans (10.421)

Description: Direct loans to enable Indian tribes to acquire land within tribal reservations and Alaskan Communities. Loan funds may be used to acquire land for the use of the tribe or its members for purposes such as rounding out farming and ranching units or elimination of fractional heirships. Funds may also be used for incidental costs connected with land purchase such as appraisals, title clearance, legal services, land surveys, and loan closing.

Eligibility Requirements: Federally recognized American Indian Tribes or tribal corporations or Communities in Alaska incorporated by the Secretary of Interior

Financial Information: Loans totaled over $3.2 million in the latest reported year.

Literature: "*FmHA Credit for American Indians*."

Who To Contact: *Headquarters Office*: Department of Agriculture, Farm Service Agency, Director, Loan Making Division, Ag Box 0523, Washington, DC 20250. (202) 720-4572. *Regional or Local Office*: Contact the appropriate FSA State office listed in Table 2g, Chapter 2.

Money—for Native Americans to Attend Graduate School
Indian Graduate Student Scholarships—"Special Higher Education Scholarships" (15.059)

Description: Scholarships for Indian students to get a graduate degree..

Eligibility Requirements: Indian students who are members of Federally Recognized Indian Tribes, who have been admitted to a graduate program and have unmet financial need.

Financial Information: Annually, about 325 Indian students receive support to help finance graduate studies. Law, health professions, and natural resources are the most often selected areas of concentration.

Who To Contact: *Headquarters Office*: American Indian Graduate Center, 4520 Montgomery Boulevard, Suite 1-B, Albuquerque, NM, 87109. (505) 881-4584. *Regional or Local Office*: None. *Application Procedure*: Application forms may be obtained from the Bureau of Indian Affairs agency or area education office listed in Table 7d, Chapter 7.

Free Job Training for Native Americans

Indian Vocational Training—United Tribes Technical College (15.060)

Description: This program provides vocational training and financial aid to individual American Indians through the United Tribes Technical College, located in Bismarck, North Dakota.

Beneficiary Eligibility: Individual American Indians who are members of a Federally Recognized Indian Tribe and reside on or near an Indian reservation under the jurisdiction of the Bureau of Indian Affairs.

You must submit a certificate signed by a Bureau Agency Superintendent or an authorized Tribal representative that indicates the applicant is an enrolled member or registered with a Federally Recognized Indian Tribe.

Financial Information: The United Tribes Technical College admits approximately 160 new students each year. Total enrollment is approximately 337. *Range and Average of Financial Assistance*: $500-$3,000; $2,500 average.

Who To Contact: *Headquarters Office*: Office of Economic Development, Division of Job Placement and Training, Bureau of Indian Affairs, 1849 C Street, NW, MS-4640 MIB, Wash., DC 20240. (202) 208-2671. Contact: Deano Poleahla. *Regiona/Local Office*: You can get application forms directly from the United Tribes Technical College or from Bureau of Indian Affairs Agency or Area Offices listed in Table 2i. *For Direct Contact*: United Tribes Technical College, 3315 University Dr., Bismarck, North Dakota 58504. Contact: David Gipp. (701) 255-3285, ext. 334.

Child Care for Needy Native American Children

Indian Social Services—Child Welfare Assistance

Description: Funds to enable local agencies to provide foster home care and appropriate institutional (non-medical) care for dependent, neglected, and handicapped Indian children.

Eligibility Requirements: Dependent, neglected, and handicapped Indian children in need of protection whose families live on or near Indian reservations or in Bureau of Indian Affairs service area jurisdictions in Alaska and Oklahoma, and who are not eligible for similar Federal, State or county funded programs.

Financial Information: Child welfare assistance was provided to a monthly average of 3,000 children during the latest reported year. $11.7 million is budgeted this year.

Who To Contact: *Headquarters Office*: Division of Social Services, Office of Tribal Services, Bureau of Indian Affairs, MS-4603, 1849 C Street, NW, Washington, DC 20240. Contact: Larry Blair. (202) 208-2721. *Regional or Local Office*: Information can be secured from the Agency Superintendents, and from Area Directors. (See Table 2i, Chapter 2.) Applications for child welfare assistance are made may be made by a parent, guardian or person having custody of the child, or by court referral, at the local agency, area, or tribal level.

$5,100 a Year—for Job Training

Indian Employment Assistance (15.108)

Description: Financial aid to assist individual Indians to obtain a marketable skill through vocational training and to assist those who have a job skill to find permanent employment. The grants are for subsistence, tuition and related training costs, and supportive services. Individuals may not receive more than 24 months of full-time training, except for Registered Nursing students who may receive 36 months of training.

Beneficiary Eligibility: Members of Federally Recognized Indian Tribes who are unemployed, underemployed, or in need of training to obtain reasonable and satisfactory employment.

Applicants must need financial assistance, and reside on or near an Indian reservation under the jurisdiction of the Bureau of Indian Affairs.

Financial Information: 1500 individuals receive assistance annually. *Range and Average of Financial Assistance*: $200 to $10,000; $5,100.

Who To Contact: *Headquarters Office*: Office of Economic Development, Division of Job Placement and Training, Bureau of Indian Affairs, 1849 C Street NW, MS: 4640 MIB, Washington, DC 20240. (202) 208-5819. Contact: Terry Parks. *Regional or Local Office*: Individual American Indian applicants should apply for program services on Bureau of Indian Affairs Form BIA-8205 at their local Bureau of Indian Affairs agency office as listed in Table 2i or with the Tribal Government administering the program.

Cash Payments—to Needy Native Americans
Indian Social Services—General Assistance (15.113)

Description: Needy Indians can receive financial assistance. This program provides such assistance for basic needs to needy eligible Indians who reside on or near reservations, including those Indians living under Bureau of Indian Affairs service area jurisdictions, when such assistance is not available from State or local public agencies. The assistance consists of cash payments for food, clothing, shelter, etc.

The program also pays monthly assistance for:
- non-medical institutional or custodial care of adults who are not eligible for care from Indian Health Services, Social Security, or any other county, State or Federal program;
- burial expenses of indigent Indians;
- emergency assistance to prevent hardship caused by fire, flood or acts of nature.

Eligibility Requirements: You must be a member of a federally recognized Indian Tribe, living on or near federally recognized Indian reservations and in need of financial assistance.

Financial Information: General assistance is provided to a monthly average of 41,400 persons, ranging from several dollars monthly to several hundred dollars monthly depending upon family size and needs.

Who To Contact: *Headquarters Office*: Office of Tribal Services, Human Services, Bureau of Indian Affairs, MS 4660 MIB, 1849 C St., NW., Washington, DC 20245. Contact: Larry R. Blair. Phone: (202) 208- 2479. *Regional or Local Office*: Information can be secured from the Agency Superintendents and from Area Directors (see Table 7e for addresses). Applications for general assistance are made at the local agency or tribal level.

Money—for Native Americans to Go to College
Indian Education—Higher Education Grant Program (15.114)

Description: This program gives financial aid to eligible Indian students so they can attend accredited institutions of higher education. The aid augments any campus-based financial aid programs or any other scholarships you receive.

Beneficiary Eligibility: You must be a member of a Federally Recognized Indian Tribe, enrolled or accepted for enrollment in an accredited college, and have financial need as determined by the institution's financial aid office. You have to submit a certificate of Indian ancestry, college financial aid package, statement of acceptance by college and a Bureau of Indian Affairs grant application.

Financial Information: In the latest reported year, an estimated 9,800 students received assistance. *Range and Average of Financial Assistance*: $300 to $5,000; $3,000 average.

Who To Contact: *Headquarters Office*: Office of Indian Education Programs, Bureau of Indian Affairs, Room MS 3512-MIB, 1849 C Street, NW, Washington, DC 20240. Contact: Gary Martin. (202) 208-3478. *Regional or Local Office*: See Education Line Officers' addresses in Table 7d.

Money—to Native Americans for Business Development

Indian Loans—Economic Development (15.124)

Description: Indian Tribal Governments, Native American Organizations, and individual American Indians are eligible to receive guaranteed and insured loans to promote business development initiatives on or near Federally Recognized Indian Reservations.

See Chapter 2, page 69.

Money—for Needy Native Americans to Build Houses

Indian Housing Assistance (15.141)

Description: The goal of this program is to help eliminate substandard Indian housing through renovations, repairs, or additions to existing homes. And, where no other program will meet the need (i.e., limited income does not qualify applicant for other programs; or extremely isolated areas or reservations where only a very small number of homes are needed), the Bureau will build an entire house.

Applicant Eligibility: Individual Members of American Indian tribes in need of housing assistance who are unable to obtain assistance from any other source, and meet certain eligibility criteria.

Financial Information: In the latest reported year, 654 units were repaired or renovated and 195 units were constructed. *Range and Average of Financial Assistance*: $35,000 maximum for repairs; $2,500 maximum for temporary repairs; $41,100 average for new standard housing.

The average cost for repairs is approximately $8,000. Average new housing construction is approximately $36,000 ($49,000 in Alaska).

Literature: *"Housing Improvement Program."*

Who To Contact:
Headquarters Office: Office of Tribal Services, Human Services, Bureau of Indian Affairs, MS 4660 MIB, 1849 C St., NW., Washington, DC 20240. Contact: June Henkel.

Phone: (202) 208-3667.
Regional or Local Office: Indians should submit written applications to the local tribal servicing housing office, or nearest Bureau of Indian Affairs agency or area office listed in Table 2i.

$185 a Week—for Ironworker Job Training

Ironworker Training Program (15.146)

Description: Ironworker vocational training, apprenticeships, and job placement to eligible American Indians who reside on or near an Indian reservation.

Beneficiary Eligibility: American Indian members of a Federally Recognized Indian Tribal Government who are at least 20 years old, have a high school diploma or equivalency certificate, are in good physical health, and reside on or near an Indian reservation under the jurisdiction of the Bureau of Indian Affairs.

Financial Information: In the latest reported year, 120 individuals participated in this program. Students get $185 a week for the duration of the program for room, board and miscellaneous expenses. Work clothes, tools are also provided.

Who To Contact: *Headquarters Office*: Office of Economic Development, Division of Job Placement and Training, Bureau of Indian Affairs, 1849 C Street, N.W., MS-4640 MIB, Washington, DC 20240. Contact: Terry Parks. (202) 208-5819.
Regional or Local Office: Applicants should apply for program services on Bureau of Indian Affairs Form BIA-8205 at the nearest Bureau of Indian Affairs office (listed in Table 2i) or tribal government office. *For Direct Contact*: Robert Mitacek, Director, National Ironworkers Training Program for American Indians, 1819 Beach St., Broadview, Illinois 60153. (708) 345-2344.

Free Help for Native Americans to Start a Small Business
Native American Program (11.801)

DESCRIPTION: Uncle Sam funds eight Native American Business Development Centers that provide business development service to Native Americans interested in entering, expanding or improving their efforts in the marketplace.

See Chapter 2, page 63.

Money—for Native Americans to Buy Homes
Indian Community Development Block Grant Program (14.862)

Description: Indian Community Development Block Grants assist Indian Tribes and Alaskan Native Villages in the development of viable Indian communities by providing grants to rehabilitate housing and expand job opportunities by supporting the economic development of their communities. Activities which are eligible for funding include direct assistance to facilitate homeownership among low and moderate income persons,

Beneficiary Eligibility: The principal beneficiaries of ICDBG funds are low and moderate income persons who are members of any eligible Indian tribe, band, group, or nation, including Alaskan Indians, Aleuts, and Eskimos, and any Alaskan Native Village.

Financial Information: In the latest reported year, $70,280,515 was budgeted.

Who To Contact: *Headquarters Office*: Office of Native American Programs, U.S. Department of Housing and Urban Development, Suite 3990. PO Box 90, 1999 North Broadway, Denver, Colorado 80202. (303)675-1600. *Regional or Local Office:* Contact appropriate HUD Office of Native American Programs Field Office listed in Table 7e.

SUPPORT FOR DISABLED PEOPLE

Free Support to Help the Disabled Be Employed
Supported Employment Services for Individuals with Severe Disabilities (84.187)

Description: This program helps severely disabled persons support themselves by funding special services to help the disabled make the transition to employment. Among the supported employment services provided are:
- skilled job trainers who accompany the worker for intensive on-the-job training
- systematic training
- job development
- follow-up services and other services needed to support an individual in employment

Beneficiary Eligibility: Severely disabled individuals whose ability to engage in a training program leading to supported employment has been determined by evaluating rehabilitation potential. In addition, individuals must need extended services in order to perform competitive work and have the ability to work in a supported employment setting.

Financial Information: In the latest reported year, $38,152,000 was appropriated.

Literature: *"Supported Employment Services for Individuals with the most Severe Disabilities."*

Who to Contact: *Headquarters Office*: Office of Program Operations, Rehabilitation Services Administration, Office of the Assistant Secretary for Special Education and Rehabilitative Services, Department of Education, 400 Maryland Ave., SW., Washington, DC 20202-2574. Contact: RoseAnn Ashby. Phone: (202) 205-8719. *Regional or Local Office*: Department of Education Regional Offices. See Table 4a, Chapter 4, for a list of Regional Offices.

Government Jobs for Disabled Persons

Federal Employment for Individuals With Disabilities (27.005)

Description: The Federal Government provides employment opportunities in government agencies to persons with physical, cognitive, or mental disabilities in positions for which they qualify. Some of these jobs come with reasonable accommodations including readers, interpreters, and other personal assistants. Hiring is carried out by individual Federal agencies.

Eligibility Requirements: Persons with physical, cognitive or mental disabilities, including disabled veterans.

Financial Information: In the latest reported year, 11,847 disabled persons with disabilities were hired as full time permanent employees, bringing the total count of Federal employees with targeted and non-targeted disabilities to 127,076.

Who to Contact: *Headquarters Office*: Diversity Office, Employment Service, Office of Personnel Management, 1900 E Street, NW., Room 2445, Washington, DC 20415. (202) 606-1059. Contact: Armando E. Rodriquez, Director. *Regional or Local Office*: Information may be obtained from the Personnel Office in Federal agencies of interest. Or contact your nearest Federal Employment Service Center in Table 7b.

Free Job Placement Services for Disabled Persons and Others

Employment Service (17.207)

Description: The goal of this program is to place persons in employment by providing a variety of free placement-related services to job seekers. For example, it maintains a nationwide computerized interstate job openings. Also available may be job search training or assistance, job counseling and testing services to job seekers. Handicapped workers are entitled to special employment services.

See Chapter 1, page 21.

Supported Job Programs for Disabled Persons

Rehabilitation Services—Service Projects (84.128)

Description: This program provides grants to State vocational rehabilitation agencies and public nonprofit organizations for special projects to improve services to individuals with disabilities. This includes funding for supported employment services for individuals with the most severe disabilities through statewide, community-based, and technical assistance projects.

Beneficiary Eligibility: Individuals with the most severe disabilities.

Financial Information: Not applicable.

Who to Contact: *Headquarters Office*: Rehabilitation Services Administration, Department of Education, Switzer Bldg., 330 C Street, SW., Washington, DC 20202. Contact: Mary Chambers. Phone: (202) 205-8435. *Regional or Local Office*: State Vocational Rehabilitation Agencies or the Dept of Education Rehabilitative Service regional offices (Table 2m, Chapter 2).

Free Job Training for Disabled Persons

Rehabilitation Services—Vocational Rehabilitation Grants to States (84.126)

Description: Under this program the States receive funds to provide vocational rehabilitation services and job training programs to individuals with disabilities so they may prepare for competitive employment. Services include:

- assessment, counseling, vocational and other training
- job placement
- reader services for the blind, interpreter services for the deaf, prosthetic and orthotic devices
- medical and related services
- transportation to secure vocational rehabilitation services
- maintenance during rehabilitation
- other goods and services necessary for a

disabled person to become employed

In addition, services are provided to families of disabled individuals when such services will contribute substantially to the rehabilitation of such individuals who are being provided vocational rehabilitation services.

Beneficiary Eligibility: Eligibility for vocational rehabilitation services is based on the presence of a physical and/or mental impairment which results in a substantial impediment to employment, and the need for vocational rehabilitation services that may be expected to benefit the individual in terms of an employment outcome.

Financial Information: $2.4 billion dollars is budgeted for this year. To date, 203,035 persons have obtained employment as a result of this program.

Who to Contact: *Headquarters Office*: Office of Program Operations, Rehabilitation Services Administration, Office of Special Education and Rehabilitative Services, Department of Education, 400 Maryland Ave., SW., Washington, DC 20202. Contact: RoseAnn Ashby. Phone: (202) 205-8719. *Regional/Local Office*: See Table 2m, Chapter 2.

Books for the Blind and Physically Handicapped
(42.001)

Description: This program provides library service to the blind and physically handicapped. It provides books on cassette, disc, in Braille, and talking book and recorded cassette machines. There are 57 regional libraries and 83 subregional libraries in the United States with a collection of approximately 253,000 titles in recorded and Braille formats and 30,000 music scores, textbooks, and instructional materials in Braille, large type and recorded formats.

Beneficiary Eligibility: Anyone who is unable to read or use standard printed materials as a result of temporary or permanent visual or physical limitations may receive service.

Annual Information: In the latest reported year, more than 23 million recorded and Braille books

and magazines were circulated to a readership of 780,000

Literature: "*Reading is for Everyone.*"

Who to Contact: *Headquarters Office*: Frank Kurt Cylke, Director, National Library Service for the Blind and Physically Handicapped, Library of Congress, 1291 Taylor Street, NW., Washington DC 20542. (202) 707-5100. *Regional or Local Office*: Fifty-seven regional and 83 subregional libraries in the United States (see Table 7f). Each State has an agency distributing talking book machines. Local public libraries have information available. Otherwise contact the headquarters office listed above.

Schools for the Deaf: Gallaudet University

Description: Gallaudet University, a government chartered institution in Washington, D.C., is the nation's preeminent university for deaf persons. It has both undergraduate and graduate divisions. Admission to the 1344-student undergraduate division is competitive, and costs about $13,000 a year for tuition, room and board. However, about 80 percent of the students receive financial assistance.

Gallaudet has partnerships with five other colleges around the nation to bring continuing education opportunities to deaf and hard of hearing people and their families.

In addition, in cooperation with the U.S. Department of Education, Gallaudet operates a model secondary school for the deaf for students from Washington, DC, Maryland, West Virginia, Pennsylvania, Delaware and Virginia. It also operates the Kendall Elementary Demonstration School.

The federal government also supports the National Technical Institute for the Deaf, in Rochester, NY, a technical college for deaf students from around the country.

Beneficiary Eligibility: Deaf and hard of hearing students and their families.

Literature: "*Partners in Education*," an article written by Dr. James Fernandes, Director of University Outreach, published in the Spring 1996 issue of Gallaudet Today.

Who to Contact:

Gallaudet University, 800 Florida Ave., NE, Washington, DC 20002-3695; Telephone 202-651-5000 (TTy/Voice). It's outreach program and local partners are:

- *Gallaudet University*, Distance Education Program, College for Continuing Education, 800 Florida Avenue, NE, Washington, DC 20002-3695, (202) 651-6060 (TTY/Voice), serving Mid-Atlantic states DE, DC, MD, NJ, PA, VA, WV, PR, VI

- *Flagler College*, P.O. Box 1027, St. Augustine, FL 32085-1027, (904) 829-6581 (Voice), (904) 829-2424 (TTY/FAX), serving the South Eastern States AL, FL, GA, KY, LA, MS, NC, SC, TN

- *Johnson County Community College*, 12345 College Boulevard, Overland Park,

KS 66210-1299, (913) 469-3872 (TTY/Voice), serving the Mid-Western States AR, IL, IA, KS, MI, MN, MO, NE, ND, OH, OK, SD, TX, WI

- *Kapiolani Community College*, 4303 Diamond Head Road, Honolulu, HI 96816-4496, (808) 734-9210 (TTY/Voice), serving Hawaii & Pacific Island Region including U.S. Territories

- *Northern Essex Community* College, 100 Elliot Way, Haverhill, MA 01830, (978) 556-3701 (TTY/Voice), serving North Eastern States CT, MA, ME, NH, NY, RI, VT

- *Ohlone College*, 43600 Mission Boulevard, Fremont, CA 94539, (510) 659-6267 (TTY/Voice), serving Western States AK, AZ, CA, CO, ID, MT, NV, NM, OR, UT, WA, WY

You can contact the *National Technical Institute for the Deaf* at National Technical Institute for the Deaf, Office of Career Opportunities, 1 Lamb Memorial Drive, Rochester, NY 14623

Table 7a: WOMEN'S BUREAU, DEPARTMENT OF LABOR

REGIONAL OFFICES

Region I
(Connecticut, Maine, Massachusetts, New Hampshire, Rhode Island,Vermont)
Jacqueline Cooke,
Regional Administrator
J.F.K. Federal Building
Government Center Room E-270
Boston, MA 02203
(617) 565-1988

Region II
(New Jersey, New York, Puerto Rico, Virgin Islands)
Mary C. Murphree, Regional Adm.
201 Varick Street, Room 708
New York, NY 10014

(212) 337-2389

Region III
(Delaware, District of Columbia, Maryland, Pennsylvania, Virginia, West Virginia)
Cornelia Moore, Regional Admin.
The Curtis Center, Suite 880
West 170 S. Independence Mall
West Philadelphia, PA 19106-3318
 (215) 861 - 4860

Region IV
(Alabama, Florida, Georgia, Kentucky, Mississippi, North Carolina, South Carolina, Tennessee)
Ms. Delores L. Crockett,

Regional Administrator
Atlanta Federal Center, Suite 7T95
61 Forsyth Street, SW
Atlanta, GA 30303
(404) 562-2336

Region V
(Illinois, Indiana, Michigan, Minnesota, Ohio, Wisconsin)
Nancy S. Chen, Regional Admin.
230 South Dearborn St., Room 1022
Chicago, IL 60604
(312) 353-6985

Region VI
(Arkansas, Louisiana, New Mexico, Oklahoma, Texas)
Beverly Lyle, Regional Admin.
525 Griffin Street, Suite 735

Dallas, TX 75202
(214) 767-5418

Region VII
(Iowa, Kansas, Missouri, Nebraska)
Rose A. Kemp, Regional Admin.
Center City Square Building
1100 Main Street, Suite 845
Kansas City, MO 64105
(800) 252-4706

Region VIII
(Colorado, Montana, North Dakota, South Dakota, Utah, Wyoming)
Frances Jefferson, Reg. Admin.
1999 Broadway, Suite 1620
P.O. Box 46550
Denver, CO 80201-6550
(303) 844-1286

Region IX
(Arizona, California, Hawaii, Nevada)

Jenny Erwin, Regional Admin.
71 Stevenson Street, Room 927
San Francisco, CA 94105
(415) 975-4750

Region X
(Alaska, Idaho, Oregon, Washington)
Karen Furia, Regional Administrator
1111 Third Avenue, Room 925
Seattle, WA 98101-3211
(206) 553-1534

Table 7b: FEDERAL EMPLOYMENT SERVICE CENTER NETWORK

ATLANTA Service Center
Ms. Jacqueline Y. Moses
75 Spring Street, SW, Suite 1000
Altanta, GA 30303
(404) 331-3455

NORFOLK Service Center
Mr. F. Alan Nelson
200 Granby St., Room 500
Norfolk, VA 23510-1886
(757) 441-3373

CHICAGO Service Center
Ms. Vera Garcia
230 South Dearborn St., DPN 30-3
Chicago, IL 60604
(312) 353-6234

PHILADELPHIA Service Center
Mr. Joe Stix
600 Arch St., Room 3400
Philadelphia, PA 19106
(215) 861-3031

DAYTON Service Center
Mr. Michael Pajari
200 West 2nd St., Room 507
Dayton, OH 45402
(937) 225-2576

RALEIGH Service Center
Mr. Allan N. Goldberg
4407 Bland Rd., Suite 200
Raleigh, NC 27609-6296

(919) 790-2817

DENVER Service Center
Mr. Phong Ngo
12345 Alameda Pkwy
Denver, CO 80225
(303) 236-8550

SAN ANTONIO Service Center
Mr. Miguel Hernandez
8610 Broadway, Room 305
San Antonio, TX 78217
(210) 805-2423

DETROIT Service Center
Mr. David Nason
477 Michigan Ave., Room 594
Detroit, MI 48226
(313) 226-6950

SAN FRANCISCO Service Center
Ms. Linda Petersen
120 Howard St., Room 735
San Francisco, CA 94105
(415) 281-7094

HONOLULU Service Center
Mr. Paul Miller
300 Ala Moana Blvd., Box 50028
Honolulu, HI 96850
(808) 541-2795

SAN JUAN Service Center
Mr. Luis Rodriguez

Torre de Plaza las Americas
525 F.D. Roosevelt Ave., Ste. 1114
San Juan, PR 00918
(787) 766-5259

HUNTSVILLE Service Center
Ms. Carol Y. Toney
150 West Park Loop
Huntsville, AL 35806-1762
(256) 837-1271

SEATTLE Service Center
Ms. Mary Alice Kline
700 5th Ave., Suite 5950
Seattle, WA 98104-5012
(206) 553-0870

KANSAS CITY Service Center
Mr. James D. Witkop
601 East 12th St., Room 131
Kansas City, MO 64106
(816) 426-5705

TWIN CITIES Service Center
Ms. Diane Granos
One Federal Dr., Room 266
Fort Snelling, MN 55111-4007
(612) 725-3437

WASHINGTON DC Service Center
Ms. Pam T. Shivery
1900 E St., NW, Room 2469
Washington, DC 20415
(202) 606-2575

Table 7c: HISPANIC SERVING INSTITUTIONS

Arizona
South Mountain Community.
College
President: John Cordova
(602) 243-8000

California
California State Univ.—Bakersfield
President: Tomas Arciniega
(661) 664-2011

California State U. — Los Angeles
President: James M. Rosser
(323) 343-3000

East Los Angeles College
President: Dr. Ernest Moreno
(323) 265-8650

Hartnell College
President: Dr. Edward J. Valeau
(831) 755-6700

Imperial Valley College
President: Gilbert Dominguez
(760) 352-8320

Mount St. Mary's College
President: Dr. Karen Kennelly
(310) 954-4000

Rio Hondo College
President: Dr. Jesus Carreon
(562) 692-0921

San Bernardino Valley College
President: Sharon Caballero
(909) 888-6511

Colorado
Community College of Denver
President: Byron McClenney
(303) 289-2243

Pueblo Community College
President: Dr. Joe May
(719) 549-3200

Florida
Barry University
President: Jeanne O'Laughlin
(305) 899-3000

Florida International University
President: Modesto A. Maidique
(305) 348-2000

Miami-Dade Community College
President: Dr. Eduardo J. Padron
(305) 237-3221

St. Thomas University
President: Dr. Richard Greene
(305) 625-6000

Illinois
MacCormac College
President: John H. Allen
(630) 941-1200

St. Augustine College
President: Dr. Bernard W. Franklin
(312) 878-8756

New Jersey
Hudson Cty. Community College
President: Dr. Glen Gabert
(201) 714-2127

New Mexico
College of Santa Fe
President: James Fries
(505) 473-6133

New Mexico Highlands University
President (Interim): Selimo Rael
(505) 425-7511

NM State Univ. — Main Campus
President: J.Michael Orenduff
(505) 646-0111

Northern NM Community College
President: Dr. Sigfredo Maestas
(505) 747-2100

Santa Fe Community College
President: Leonardo De La Garza
(505) 471-8200

Univ. of NM — Main Campus
President: Richard E. Peck
(505) 277-0111

Univ. of NM — Valencia Campus
President: Richard E. Peck
(505) 925-8500

Western New Mexico University
President: John E. Counts
(505) 538-6011

New York
Boricua College

President: Victor G. Alicea
(212) 694-1000

Herbert H. Lehman College
President: Ricardo R. Fernandez
877-Lehman-1

Hostos Community College, CUNY
President: Dr. Isaura Santiago
(718) 518-6633

John Jay College of Criminal Justice
President: Gerald W. Lynch
(212) 237-8000

Mercy College
President: Jay Sexter
(800) Mercy-NY

Puerto Rico
American University of Puerto Rico
President: Juan B. Nazario-Negron
(787) 798-2040

Inter American University of Puerto
Rico — San German Campus
President: Dr. Agnes Mojica
(787) 264-1912

Pontifical Catholic Univ. of PR
Pres.: Mgr. Lorenzo Albacete Cintron
(787) 841-2000

Universidad Del Turabo
Chancellor: Dr. Dennis Alicea
(787) 751-0178

Universidad Metropolitana
Chancellor: Dr. Rene La Barca
(787) 751-0178

Universidad Politecnica de PR
President: Ernesto Vazquez-Barquet
(787) 622-8000

University of Puerto Rico —
Aguadilla Regional College
President: Dr. Nelson Mercado
(787) 890-2681

University of Puerto Rico —
Arecibo Technological University
Chancellor: Ivette Ramos Buonomo
(809) 878-2830

University of Puerto Rico —
Bayamon Technical University
Chancellor: Ivette Ramos Buonomo

(809) 786-2885

University of Puerto Rico —
Carolina Regional College
Chancellor: Ivette Ramos Buonomo
(809) 757-2000

University of Puerto Rico —
Cayey University College
Chancellor: Margarita Benitez
(787) 738-2161

University of Puerto Rico —
Central Administration
President: Jose M. Saldana
(809) 250-0000

University of Puerto Rico —
Humacao University College
Chancellor: Dr. Roberto Corletto
(787) 850-0000

University of Puerto Rico —
La Montana Regional College
Chancellor: Ivette Ramos Buonomo
(809) 894-2828

University of Puerto Rico —
Mayaguez Campus
Chancellor: Stuart J. Ramos
(787) 832-4040

University of Puerto Rico —
Medical Science Campus
Chancellor: Dr. Manuel Marina
(809) 753-5353

University of Puerto Rico —
Ponce Technical University College
Chancellor: Ivette Ramos Buonomo

(809) 844-8181

University of Puerto Rico —
Regional Colleges Administration
Chancellor: Ivette Ramos Buonomo
(809) 766-2157

University of Puerto Rico —
Rio Piedras Campus
Chancel.: Dr.Efrain Gonzales Tejera
(809) 764-0000

University of the Sacred Heart
President: Jose A. Morales
(787) 728-1515

Texas
Del Mar College
President: Terry L. Dicianna
(361) 698-1200

El Paso Community College
President: Dr. Adriana D. Barrera
(915) 831-2000

Laredo Community College
President: Ramon H. Dovalina
(956) 722-0521

Our Lady of the Lake University of
San Antonio
Pres: Sister Elizabeth Anne Sueltenfuss
(210) 434-6711

Palo Alto College
Pres. (Interim): Dr. Ernest Martinez
(210) 921-5000

San Antonio College
President (Interim): Vern Loland
(210) 733-2000

St. Mary's Univ. of San Antonio
President: Dr. John J. Moder
(800) FOR-STMU

Sul Ross State University
President: R. Victor Morgan
(915) 837-8011

Texas A & M International Univ.
President: J. Charles Jennett
(956) 326-2001

Texas A & M Univ., Corpus Christi
President: Robert R. Furgason
(361) 825-5700

Texas A & M Univ. at Kingsville
President: Dr. Manuel Ibanez
(361) 593-2111

University of Texas—Pan American
President: Dr. Miguel A Nevarez
(956) 381-2011

University of Texas at El Paso
President: Dr. Diana Natalicio
(915) 747-5000

University of Texas at San Antonio
Pres.: Dr. Samuel A. Kirkpatrick
(210) 458-4011

University of the Incarnate Word
President: Dr. Louis Agnese
(210) 829-6005

Table 7d: # BUREAU OF INDIAN AFFAIRS, EDUCATION LINE OFFICES

Arizona
Chinle Agency-Education
PO Box 6003
Chinle, AZ 86503
(928) 674-5131

Ft. Apache Agency-Education
Highway 73 and Elm Street
PO Box 560
White River, AZ 85941
(928) 338-5442

Fort Definace Agency-Education

Building 38, Blue Canyon Highway
PO Box 110
Fort Defiance, AZ 86504
(928) 729-7251

Hopi Agency-Education
Highway 264, P.O. Box 568
Keams Canyon, AZ 86034
(928) 738-2262

Papago Agency-Education
HC 01, Box 8600
Sells, AZ 85634

(928) 361-3510

Pima Agency-Education
PO Box 10
400 North 5th Street
Phoenix, AZ 85001
(602) 379-3944

Western Navajo Agency-Education
Highway 160 and Warrior Drive
Building 407, P.O. Box 746
Tuba City, AZ 86045
(520) 283-2218

California
Northern California Agency
P.O. Box 494879
Redding, CA 96049
(916) 246-5141

Sacramento Area Education Office
2800 Cottage Way
Sacramento, CA 95825
(916) 978-6057

Michigan
Michigan Agency
2901.5 I-75 Business Spur
Sault Ste. Marie, MI 49783
(906) 632-6809

Minnesota
Minneapolis Area Education Office
One Federal Drive
Room 550
Ft. Snelling, MN 55111
(612) 713-4400

Montana
Billings Area Education Office
316 North 26th Street
Billings, MT 59101-1397
(406) 247-7953

New Mexico
Eastern Navajo Agency-Education
1 Main Street, P.O. Box 328
Crownpoint, NM 87313
(505) 786-6150

Laguna Agency
PO Box 1448
Laguna, NM 87026
(505) 552-6001

New Mexico
Northern Pueblos Agency-Education
PO Box 426
Fairview Station
Espanola, NM 87533

(505) 753-1466

Shiprock Agency-Education
Highway 666N, P.O. Box 3239
Shiprock, NM 87420-3239
(505) 368-3400

Southern Pueblos Agency-Education
1000 Indian School Road NW
P.O. Box 1667
Albuquerque, NM 87103
(505) 346-2431

North Dakota
Standing Rock Agency-Education
Main Street off Highway 106
Agency Avenue , P.O. Box E
Fort Yates, ND 58538
(701) 854-3497

Southwestern Indian Polytechnic Inst.
9169 Coors Rd. NW, P.O.Box 101046
Alburquerque, NM 87184
(505) 897-5347

Turtle Mountain Agency-Education
School Street, P.O. Box 30
Belcourt, ND 58316
(701) 477-3463

Oklahoma
Chickasaw Agency
P.O. Box 2248
Ada, OK 74821
(405) 436-0784

Oklahoma Education Office
4149 Highline Boulevard, Suite 380
Oklahoma City, OK 73108
(405) 605-6061

Oregon
Portland Area Education Office
911 North East 11 Avenue
Portland, OR 97232-4169
(503) 872-2743

Siletz Agency
PO Box 569
Siletz, OR 97380
(541) 444-2679

South Dakota
Cheyenne River Agency-Education
100 North Main, P.O. Box 2020
Eagle Butte, SD 51625
(605) 964-8722

Crow Creek/Lower Brule Agencies-
Education
140 Education Ave., PO Box 139
Fort Thompson, SD 57339
(605) 245-2398

Pine Ridge Agency-Education
101 Main Street, P.O. Box 333
Pine Ridge, SD 57770
(605) 867-1306

Rosebud Agency-Education
1001 Avenue D, P.O. Box 669
Mission, SD 57555
(605) 856-4478

Virginia
Eastern States Agency-Education
3701 North Fairfax Drive, Suite 260
Arlington, VA 22203
(703) 235-3003

Washington
Office of Self-Governance
Northwest Field Office
500 West 12th Street, Room 170
Vancouver, WA 98660

Olympic Peninsula Agency
P.O. Box 120
Hoquaim, WA 98550
(360) 533-9100

Table 7e: OFFICE OF NATIVE AMERICAN PROGRAMS FIELD OFFICES

Idaho, Oregon, and Washington
Administrator, Office of Northwest
Native American Programs
Seattle Federal Office Building
909 First Avenue, Suite 300
Seattle, WA 98104-1000

(206) 220-5270

**Arizona, California, Nevada, and
New Mexico**
Adm. Office of Southwest Native

American Programs
One North Central Avenue,
Suite 600
Phoenix, AZ 85004-2361
(602) 379-7200

Colorado, Montana, Nebraska, the Dakotas, Utah, and Wyoming
Adm. Office of Northern Plains
Native American Programs
First Interstate Tower North
633 17th Street
Denver, CO 80202-3607
(303) 672-5465

Oklahoma

Adm. Southern Plains Office of
Native American Programs
500 West Main Street, Suite 400
Oklahoma City, OK 73102-2233
(405) 553-7520

All States east of the Mississippi River and Iowa
Adm. Office of Eastern/Woodlands
Native American Programs

77 W. Jackson Boulevard, Rm 2404
Chicago, IL 60604-3507
(312) 353-8936

Alaska
Adm. Office of Alaska Native
American Programs
949 E. 36th Avenue, Suite 401
Anchorage, AK 99508-4399
(907) 271-4644

Table 7f: # REGIONAL AND SUBREGIONAL LIBRARIES FOR THE BLIND AND PHYSICALLY HANDICAPPED

ALABAMA
Regional Library
Alabama Regional Library for the Blind
and Physically Handicapped
Alabama Public Library Service
6030 Monticello Drive
Montgomery, AL 36130
(334) 213-3906

Subregional Libraries
Library for the Blind and Handicapped
Public Library of Anniston and Calhoun
PO Box 308
Anniston, AL 36201
(205) 237-8501

Department for the Blind and Physically
Handicapped
Houston-Love Memorial Library
PO Box 1369
Dothan, AL 36302
(334) 793-9767

Huntsville Subregional Library for
Blind and Physically Handicapped
PO Box 443
Huntsville, AL 35804
(205) 532-5980

Library and Resource Center for the
Blind and Physically Handicapped
Alabama Institute for Deaf & Blind
705 South Street, PO Box 698
Talladega, AL 35161
(205) 761-3561

Tuscaloosa Subregional Library for the
Blind & Physically Handicapped
Tuscaloosa Public Library
1801 River Road
Tuscaloosa, AL 35401
(205) 345-3994

ALASKA
Regional Library
Alaska State Library
Talking Book Center
344 West Third Avenue, Suite 125
Anchorage, AK 99501
(907) 269-6575

ARIZONA
Regional Library
AZ State Braille & Talking Book Library
1030 North 32nd Street
Phoenix, AZ 85008
(602) 255-5578

ARKANSAS
Regional Library
Library for the Blind and Physically
Handicapped
One Capitol Mall
Little Rock, AR 72201-1081
(501) 682-1155

Subregional Libraries
Library for the Blind and Handicapped,
Northwest Ozarks Regional Library
217 East Dickson Street
Fayetteville, AR 72701
(501) 442-6253

Fort Smith Public Library for the Blind
and Handicapped
61 South Eighth Street
Fort Smith, AR 72901
(501) 783-0229

Library for the Blind and Handicapped,
Southwest CLOC Regional Library
PO Box 668
Magnolia, AR 71754
(870) 234-0399

CALIFORNIA (Southern)
Regional Library
Braille Institute Library Services
741 North Vermont Avenue
Los Angeles, CA 90029-3594
Phone: (323) 663-1111, ext. 500

CALIFORNIA (Northern)
Regional Library
Braille and Talking Book Library
California State Library
PO Box 942837
Sacramento, CA 94237-0001
(916) 654-0640

Subregional Libraries
Talking Book Library for the Blind
Fresno County Public Library
770 North San Pablo
Ted Wills Community Center
Fresno, CA 93728-3640
(559) 488-3217

S.F. Public Library, Library for the
Blind and Print Handicapped
100 Larkin Street
San Francisco, CA 94102
(415) 557-4253

COLORADO
Regional Library
Colorado Talking Book Library
180 Sheridan Boulevard
Denver, CO 80226-8097
(303) 727-9277

CONNECTICUT
Regional Library
CT State Library, Library for the Blind
and Physically Handicapped
198 West Street
Rocky Hill, CT 06067
(860) 566-2151

DELAWARE
Regional Library
DE Division of Libraries, Library for
the Blind and Physically Handicapped
43 South DuPont Highway
Dover, DE 19901
(302) 739-4748

DISTRICT OF COLUMBIA
Regional Library
District of Columbia Regional Library
for the Blind & Physically Handicapped
901 G Street NW, Room 215
Washington, DC 20001
(202) 727-2142

FLORIDA
Regional Library
Florida Bureau of Braille and Talking
Book Library Services
420 Platt Street
Daytona Beach, FL 32114-2804
(386) 239-6000

Subregional Libraries
Talking Book Service
South Manatee Branch Library
6081 26th Street West
Bradenton, FL 34207
(941) 742-5914

Brevard County Library System
Talking Books Library
308 Forrest Avenue
Cocoa, FL 32922-7781
(321) 633-1810

Broward County Talking Book Library
100 South Andrews Avenue
Ft. Lauderdale, FL 33301
(954) 357-7555

Talking Book Library
Jacksonville Public Libraries
1755 Edgewood Ave., West, Suite 1
Jacksonville, FL 32208-7206
(904) 765-5588

Pinellas Talking Book Library for the
Blind & Physically Handicapped
1330 Cleveland St.
Clearwater FL, 33755
(727) 441-9958

Talking Book Library of Dade and
Monroe Counties, Public Library System
150 NE 79th Street
Miami, FL 33138-4890
(305) 751-8687

Lee County Talking Books Library
13240 North Cleveland Ave., #5-6
North Ft. Myers, FL 33903-4855
(941) 995-2665

Orange County Library System
Audio-Visual Department
Talking Book Section
101 East Central Boulevard
Orlando, FL 32801
Phone: (407) 835-7464

West Florida Regional Library
Subregional Talking Book Library
200 West Gregory Street
Pensacola, FL 32501
(850) 436-5065

Talking Books
Palm Beach County Library Annex
7950 Central Industrial Dr., Ste. 104
Riviera Beach, FL 33404-9947
(561) 845-4600

Hillsborough County Talking Book
Library
Tampa-Hillsborough Public Library
900 Ashley Drive North
Tampa, FL 33602-3704
(813) 273-3609

GEORGIA
Regional Library
Georgia Library for the Blind and
Physically Handicapped
1150 Murphy Avenue SW
Atlanta, GA 30310
(404) 756-4619

Subregional Libraries
Albany Library for the Blind and
Handicapped
Dougherty County Public Library
300 Pine Avenue
Albany, GA 31701
(912) 430-3220

Athens Talking Book Center
Athens-Clarke County Regional Library
2025 Baxter Street
Athens, GA 30606
(706) 613-3655

Talking Book Center, Augusta-
Richmond County Public Library
425 Ninth Street
Augusta, GA 30901
(706) 821-2625

Bainbridge Subregional Library for the
Blind and Physically Handicapped

Southwest Georgia Regional Library
301 South Monroe Street
Bainbridge, GA 31717
(912) 248-2680

Talking Book Center, Brunswick-Glynn
County Regional Library
606 O Street
Brunswick, GA 31520
(912) 267-1212

Subregional Library for the Blind and
Physically Handicapped
Talking Book Center
1120 Bradley Drive
Columbus, GA 31906-2800
(706) 649-0780, ext. 123

Oconee Regional Library, Library for
the Blind and Physically Handicapped
801 Bellevue Avenue
PO Box 100
Dublin, GA 31040
(478) 275-5382

Hall County Library, Library for the
Blind and Physically Handicapped
127 North Main Street
Gainesville, GA 30505
(770) 535-5738

LaFayette Subregional Library for the
Blind and Physically Handicapped
305 South Duke Street
LaFayette, GA 30728
(706) 638-2992

Macon Subregional Library for the
Blind and Physically Handicapped
Washington Memorial Library
1180 Washington Avenue
Macon, GA 31201-1790
(912) 744-0877

Rome Subregional Library for the Blind
and Physically Handicapped
Sara Hightower Regional Library
205 Riverside Parkway NE
Rome, GA 30161-2911
(706) 236-4618

Subregional Library for the Blind and
Physically Handicapped
CEL Regional Library
2708 Mechanics
Savannah, GA 31404
(912) 354-5864

Subregional Library for the Blind and
Physically Handicapped
South Georgia Regional Library
300 Woodrow Wilson Drive

Valdosta, GA 31602-2592
(912) 333-7658

GUAM (see Hawaii)

HAWAII
Regional Library
Hawaii State Library, Library for the
Blind and Physically Handicapped
402 Kapahulu Avenue
Honolulu, HI 96815
(808) 733-8444

Subregional Library
Guam Public Library for the Blind and
Physically Handicapped
Nieves M. Flores Memorial Library
254 Martyr Street
Agana, GU 96910
(671) 475-4753 and (671) 475-4754

IDAHO
Regional Library
Idaho State Talking Book Library
325 West State Street
Boise, ID 83702
(208) 334-2117

ILLINOIS
Regional Library
Illinois State Library
Talking Book and Braille Service
300 South Second Street
Springfield, IL 62701

Subregional Libraries
Southern Illinois Talking Book Center
c/o Shawnee Library System
607 Greenbriar Road
Carterville, IL 62918-1600
(618) 985-8375

Harold Washington Library Center
Talking Book Center
400 S. State St, Room 5N7
Chicago, IL 60605
(312) 747-4100

Talking Book Center of NW Illinois
PO Box 125
Coal Valley, IL 61240
(309) 799-3137

Voices of Vision Talking Book Center
DuPage Library System
127 South First Street
Geneva, IL 60134
(630) 208-0398

Mid-Illinois Talking Book Center
Alliance Library System
845 Brenkman Drive

Pekin, IL 61554
(309) 353-4110

Mid-Illinois Talking Book Center
Alliance Library System
515 York
Quincy, IL 62301
(217) 224-6619

INDIANA
Regional Library
Indiana State Library
Special Services Division
140 North Senate Avenue
Indianapolis, IN 46204
(317) 232-7763

Subregional Libraries
Bartholomew County Public Library
536 Fifth Street
Columbus, IN 47201
(812) 379-1277

Blind and Physically Handicapped
Services, Elkhart Public Library
300 South Second
Elkhart, IN 46516-3184
(219) 522-2665, ext. 52

Talking Books Service, Evansville-
Vanderburgh County Public Library
22 SE Fifth Street
Evansville, IN 47708-1694
(812) 428-8235

Northwest Indiana Subregional Library
for the Blind and Physically Handicapped, Lake County Public Library
1919 West 81st Avenue
Merrillville, IN 46410-5382
(219) 769-3541, ext. 323 or 390

IOWA
Regional Library
Library for the Blind and Physically
Handicapped
Iowa Department for the Blind
524 Fourth Street
Des Moines, IA 50309-2364
(515) 281-1333

KANSAS
Regional Library
Kansas State Library
Kansas Talking Book Service
ESU Memorial Union
1200 Commercial
Emporia, KS 66801
(620) 343-7124

Subregional Libraries

Talking Book Service
CKLS Headquarters
1409 Williams
Great Bend, KS 67530
(620) 792-2393

South Central Kansas Library System
Talking Book Subregional
901 North Main
Hutchinson, KS 67501
(620) 663-5441, ext. 129

Talking Book Service
Manhattan Public Library
North Central Kansas Libraries System
629 Poyntz Avenue
Manhattan, KS 66502-6086
(785) 776-4741

Talking Books
Northwest Kansas Library System
2 Washington Square, PO Box 446
Norton, KS 67654-0446
(785) 877-5148

Talking Books, Topeka and Shawnee
County Public Library
1515 SW 10th Avenue
Topeka, KS 66604
(785) 580-4531

Wichita Library, Talking Books Section
223 South Main
Wichita, KS 67202
(316) 261-8500

KENTUCKY
Regional Library
Kentucky Library for the Blind and
Physically Handicapped
300 Coffee Tree Road
PO Box 818
Frankfort, KY 40602
(502) 564-8300

Subregional Libraries
Northern KY Talking Book Library
502 Scott Street
Covington, KY 41011
(859) 491-7610

Talking Book Library
Louisville Free Public Library
301 West York Street
Louisville, KY 40203
(502) 574-1625

LOUISIANA
Regional Library
Louisiana State Library, Section for the
Blind and Physically Handicapped
701 North Fourth Street

Baton Rouge, LA 70802
(225) 342-4944 and (225) 342-4943

MAINE
Regional Library
Library Services for the Blind and
Physically Handicapped
Maine State Library
64 State House Station
Augusta, ME 04333-0064
(207) 287-5650

MARYLAND
Regional Library
Maryland State Library for the Blind
and Physically Handicapped
415 Park Avenue
Baltimore, MD 21201-3603
(410) 230-2424

Subregional Library
Special Needs Library, Montgomery
County Department of Public Libraries
6400 Democracy Boulevard
Bethesda, MD 20817
(301) 897-2212

MASSACHUSETTS
Regional Library
Braille and Talking Book Library
Perkins School for the Blind
175 North Beacon Street
Watertown, MA 02472
(617) 972-7240

Subregional Library
Talking Book Library
Worcester Public Library
3 Salem Square
Worcester, MA 01608-2074
(508) 799-1621

MICHIGAN (Except Wayne County)
Regional Library
Library of Michigan, Service for the
Blind and Physically Handicapped
PO Box 30007
Lansing, MI 48909
(517) 373-5614

Subregional Libraries
Northland Library Cooperative
316 East Chisholm Street
Alpena, MI 49707
(517) 356-1622

Washtenaw County Library for the
Blind and Physically Handicapped
PO Box 8645
Ann Arbor, MI 48107-8645
(734) 971-6059

Macomb Library for the Blind and
Physically Handicapped
16480 Hall Road
Clinton Township, MI 48038-1132
(810) 286-1580

Talking Book Center
Mideastern Michigan Library for the
Blind and Physically Handicapped
G-4195 West Pasadena Avenue
Flint, MI 48504
(810) 732-1120

Kent District Library for the Blind and
Physically Handicapped
3350 Michael Street, SW
Wyoming, MI 49509
(616) 647-3980

Upper Peninsula Library for the Blind
and Physically Handicapped
1615 Presque Isle Avenue
Marquette, MI 49855
(906) 228-7697

Muskegon County Library for the Blind
and Physically Handicapped
97 East Apple Ave.
Muskegon, MI 49442
(231) 724-6257

Oakland County Library for the Blind
and Physically Handicapped
1200 North Telegraph, Dept. 482
Pontiac, MI 48341-0482
(248) 858-5050

St. Clair County Library System, Blind
and Physically Handicapped Library
210 McMorran Boulevard
Port Huron, MI 48060
(810) 982-3600

Grand Traverse Area Library for the
Blind and Physically Handicapped
610 Woodmere Ave.
Traverse City, MI 49686
(231) 932-8558

MICHIGAN (Wayne County Only)
Regional Library
Wayne County Regional Library for the
Blind and Physically Handicapped
30555 Michigan Avenue
Westland, MI 48186
(734) 727-7300
In-Wats: 888-968-2737

Subregional Library
Downtown Detroit Subregional Library
for the Blind & Physically Handicapped

3666 Grand River
Detroit, MI 48208
(313) 833-5494

MINNESOTA
Regional Library
Minnesota Library for the Blind and
Physically Handicapped
388 SE 6th Ave.
Faribault, MN 55021
(507) 333-4828

MISSISSIPPI
Regional Library
Mississippi Library
Talking Book and Braille Services
1221 Ellis Ave.
Jackson, MS 39209
(601) 961-4111

MISSOURI
Regional Library
Wolfner Library for the Blind and
Physically Handicapped
PO Box 387
Jefferson City, MO 65102-0387
(573) 751-8720

MONTANA
Regional Library
Montana Talking Book Library
1515 East Sixth Avenue
Helena, MT 59620
(406) 444-2064

NEBRASKA
Regional Library
Nebraska Library
Talking Book and Braille Service
1200 N Street, Suite 120
Lincoln, NE 68508-2023
(402) 471-4038

NEVADA
Regional Library
Nevada State Library and Archives
Regional Library for the Blind and
Physically Handicapped
100 North Stewart Street
Carson City, NV 89701
(775) 684-3354

Subregional Library
Subregional Library for the Blind and
Handicapped, Las Vegas-Clark County
1401 East Flamingo Road
Las Vegas, NV 89119
(702) 733-1925

NEW HAMPSHIRE
Regional Library

New Hampshire State Library, Library
Services to Persons with Disabilities
117 Pleasant Street
Concord, NH 03301-3852
(603) 271-3429

NEW JERSEY
Regional Library
New Jersey Library for the Blind and
Handicapped
PO Box 501
Trenton, NJ 08625-0501
(609) 530-4000

NEW MEXICO
Regional Library
New Mexico State Library
Talking Book Library
1209 Camino Carlos Rey
Santa Fe, NM 87501
(505) 476-9770

**NEW YORK (Except New York City
and Long Island)**
Regional Library
NYS Talking Book and Braille Library
Cultural Education Center
Empire State Plaza
Albany, NY 12230
(518) 474-5935

**NEW YORK (New York City and
Long Island)**
Regional Library
Andrew Heiskell Library for the Blind
and Physically Handicapped
The New York Public Library
40 West 20th Street
New York, NY 10011-4211
(212) 206-5400

Subregional Libraries
Talking Books Plus, Outreach Services
Suffolk Cooperative Library System
627 North Sunrise Service Road
Bellport, NY 11713
(631) 286-1600

Talking Books
Nassau Library System
900 Jerusalem Avenue
Uniondale, NY 11553
(516) 292-8920

NORTH CAROLINA
Regional Library
North Carolina Library for the Blind
and Physically Handicapped
State Library of North Carolina
Department of Cultural Resources
1811 Capital Boulevard
Raleigh, NC 27635

(919) 733-4376

NORTH DAKOTA
Regional Library
North Dakota State Library
Talking Book Services
604 East Blvd., Dept. 250
Bismarck, ND 58505-0800
(701) 328-1408

OHIO (Southern)
Regional Library
The Public Library of Cincinnati and
Hamilton County, Library for the Blind
and Physically Handicapped
800 Vine Street, Library Square
Cincinnati, OH 45202-2071
(513) 369-6999

OHIO (Northern)
Regional Library
Library for the Blind and Physically
Handicapped, Cleveland Public Library
17121 Lake Shore Boulevard
Cleveland, OH 44110-4006
(216) 623-2911

OKLAHOMA
Regional Library
Oklahoma Library for the Blind and
Physically Handicapped
300 NE 18th Street
Oklahoma City, OK 73105
(405) 521-3514

OREGON
Regional Library
Oregon State Library
Talking Book and Braille Services
250 Winter Street NE
Salem, OR 97310-3950
(503) 378-3849

PENNSYLVANIA (Eastern)
Regional Library
Library for the Blind and Physically
Handicapped
Free Library of Philadelphia
919 Walnut Street
Philadelphia, PA 19107
(215) 683-3213

PENNSYLVANIA (Western)
Regional Library
Library for the Blind and Physically
Handicapped
The Carnegie Library of Pittsburgh
The Leonard C. Staisey Building
4724 Baum Boulevard
Pittsburgh, PA 15213-1389
(412) 687-2440

PUERTO RICO
Regional Library
Puerto Rico Regional Library for the
Blind and Physically Handicapped
520 Ponce de Leon Avenue, Suite 2
San Juan, PR 00901
(787) 723-2519

RHODE ISLAND
Regional Library
Talking Books Plus
Rhode Island Regional Library for the
Blind and Physically Handicapped
One Capitol Hill
Providence, RI 02908
(401) 222-5800

SOUTH CAROLINA
Regional Library
South Carolina State Library, Dept. for
the Blind and Physically Handicapped
PO Box 821
Columbia, SC 29202-0821
(803) 734-4611

SOUTH DAKOTA
Regional Library
South Dakota Braille and Talking Book
Library
State Library Building
800 Governors Drive
Pierre, SD 57501-2294
(605) 773-3131

TENNESSEE
Regional Library
Tennessee Library for the Blind and
Physically Handicapped
Tennessee State Library and Archives
403 Seventh Avenue North
Nashville, TN 37243-0313
(615) 741-3915

TEXAS
Regional Library
Texas State Library
Talking Book Program
PO Box 12927
Austin, TX 78711-2927
(512) 463-5458

UTAH
Regional Library
Utah State Library Div., Program for
the Blind and Physically Handicapped
250 North 1950 West, Ste. A
Salt Lake City, UT 84116
(801) 715-6789

VERMONT
Regional Library

Vermont Department of Libraries
Special Services Unit
578 Paine Turnpike North
Berlin, VT 05602
(802) 828-3273

VIRGIN ISLANDS
Regional Library
Virgin Islands Library for the Visually
and Physically Handicapped
3012 Golden Rock
Christiansted, St. Croix, VI 00820
(340) 772-2250

VIRGINIA
Regional Library
Library and Resource Center, Virginia
Dept. for the Visually Handicapped
395 Azalea Avenue
Richmond, VA 23227-3633
(804) 371-3661

Subregional Libraries
Access Services-Talking Books
Fairfax County Public Library
12000 Govt. Ctr. Parkway
Fairfax, VA 22035-0012
(703) 324-8380

Alexandria Library
Talking Book Service
5005 Duke Street
Alexandria, VA 22304
(703) 823-6152

Talking Book Service
Arlington County Dept. of Libraries
1015 North Quincy Street
Arlington, VA 22201
(703) 228-6333

Fredericksburg Area Subregional
Library
Central Rappahannock Regional Library
1201 Caroline Street
Fredericksburg, VA 22401
(540) 372-1144

Hampton Subregional Library for the
Blind and Physically Handicapped

4207 Victoria Boulevard
Hampton, VA 23669
(757) 727-1900

Library for the Blind and Physically
Handicapped
Newport News Public Library System
110 Main Street
Newport News, VA 23601
(757) 591-4858

Roanoke City Public Library Outreach
Services, Melrose-Outreach Branch
2607 Salem Turnpike NW
Roanoke, VA 24017-5397
(540) 853-2648

Talking Book Center
Staunton Public Library
1 Churchville Avenue
Staunton, VA 24401
(540) 885-6215

Special Services Library
Virginia Beach Public Library
930 Independence Boulevard
Virginia Beach, VA 23455
(757) 464-9175

WASHINGTON
Regional Library
WA Talking Book and Braille Library
2021 9th Avenue
Seattle, WA 98121-2783
(206) 615-0400

WEST VIRGINIA
Regional Library
WV Library, Services for the Blind and
Physically Handicapped
1900 Kanawha Boulevard East
Charleston, WV 25305
(304) 558-4061

Subregional Libraries
Services for Blind and Physically
Handicapped
Kanawha County Public Library
123 Capitol Street
Charleston, WV 25301

(304) 343-4646, ext. 264

Services for the Blind and Physically
Handicapped
Cabell County Public Library
455 Ninth Street Plaza
Huntington, WV 25701
(304) 528-5700

Services for the Blind and Physically
Handicapped, Parkersburg and Wood
County Public Library
3100 Emerson Avenue
Parkersburg, WV 26104-2414
(304) 420-4587

WV School for the Blind Library
301 East Main Street
Romney, WV 26757
(304) 822-4894

Ohio County Public Library, Services
for the Blind & Physically Handicapped
52 16th Street
Wheeling, WV 26003-3696
(304) 232-0244

WISCONSIN
Regional Library
Wisconsin Regional Library for the
Blind and Physically Handicapped
813 West Wells Street
Milwaukee, WI 53233-1436
(414) 286-3045

WYOMING
Eligible readers of Wyoming receive
library service from the regional library
in Salt Lake City, Utah.

U.S. citizens residing in foreign
countries receive library service from:
Network Services Section, National
Library Service for the Blind and
Physically Handicapped
Library of Congress
Washington, DC 20542
(202) 707-9261

APPENDIX A

SOURCES OF ADDITIONAL INFORMATION

The information revealed in this book is the result of countless hours of research. It is as up-to-date as possible. You have to realize, however, that programs, addresses, and telephone numbers change. If you find you cannot contact an agency because of such changes, or you want additional information about Federal programs and services, or if you are not certain about which agencies to contact for information, you can get current information by using the sources of the Federal Government itself. Uncle Sam has two principal services that help you get the information you need.

Federal Information Center Program (FIC)

The Federal Information Center Program will assist you if you have questions about Federal agencies, services, and programs, but do not know where to turn for an answer. FIC information specialists either answer your questions directly, or perform the necessary research to locate and refer you to the expert best able to help.

Residents of the metropolitan areas listed below may call the FIC toll-free on (800) 688-9889 workdays between 9 a.m. and 5 p.m., except as noted. Callers from outside the areas listed below should reach the FIC by dialing (301) 722-9000.

FIC LOCATIONS

Alabama
Birmingham
Mobile

Alaska (8 a.m. - 4 p.m.)
Anchorage

Arizona
Phoenix

Arkansas
Little Rock

California
Los Angeles
Sacramento
San Diego
San Francisco
Santa Ana

Colorado
Colorado Springs
Denver
Pueblo

Connecticut
Hartford
New Haven

Delaware
Wilmington

Florida
Ft. Lauderdale
Jacksonville
Miami
Orlando
St. Petersburg
Tampa
West Palm Beach

Georgia
Atlanta

Hawaii
Honolulu (7 AM- 3 PM)

Idaho
Boise

Illinois
Chicago

Indiana
Gary
Indianapolis

Iowa
All Locations

Kansas
All locations

Kentucky
Louisville

Louisiana
New Orleans

Maine
Portland

Maryland
Baltimore

Massachusetts
Boston

Michigan
Detroit

Grand Rapids

Minnesota
Minneapolis

Mississippi
Jackson

Missouri
All locations

Montana
Billings

Nebraska
All locations

Nevada
Las Vegas

New Hampshire
Portsmouth

New Jersey
Newark
Trenton

New Mexico
Albuquerque

New York
Albany
Buffalo
New York
Rochester
Syracuse

North Carolina
Charlotte

North Dakota
Fargo

Ohio
Akron
Cincinnati
Cleveland

Columbus
Dayton
Toledo

Oklahoma
Oklahoma City
Tulsa

Oregon
Portland

Pennsylvania
Philadelphia
Pittsburgh

Rhode Island
Providence

South Carolina
Greenville

South Dakota
Sioux Falls

Tennessee
Chattanooga
Memphis
Nashville

Texas
Austin
Dallas
Fort Worth
Houston
San Antonio

Utah
Salt Lake City

Vermont
Burlington

Virginia
Norfolk
Richmond
Roanoke

Washington
Seattle
Tacoma

West Virginia
Huntington

Wisconsin
Milwaukee

Wyoming
Cheyenn

FEDERAL EXECUTIVE BOARDS (FEB)

Federal Executive Boards are composed of the heads of federal field offices in metropolitan areas to help disseminate information about Federal policies and activities. If you live in one of over 100 metropolitan areas, you can reach your local board at these telephone numbers:

Albuquerque–Santa Fe, NM (505) 262-6113
Atlanta, GA (404) 331-4400
Baltimore, MD (410) 962-4047
Boston, MA (617) 565-6769
Buffalo, NY (716) 551-5655
Chicago, IL (312) 353-6790
Cincinnati, OH (513) 684-2101
Cleveland, OH (216) 433-9460
Dallas–Ft. Worth, TX (214) 767-0766
Denver, CO (303) 676-7009
Detroit, MI (313) 226-3534
Honolulu, HI (808) 541-2637
Houston, TX (713) 209-4524
Kansas City, MO (913) 551-7100

Los Angeles, CA (310) 980-3445
Miami, FL (305) 536-4344
New Orleans, LA (504) 255-5420
New York, NY (212) 264-1890
Newark, NJ (201) 645-6217
Oklahoma City, OK (405) 231-4167
Philadelphia, PA (215) 597-2766
Pittsburgh, PA (412) 664-6607
Portland, OR (503) 326-3010
St. Louis, MO (314) 539-6312
San Antonio, TX (512) 826-7209
San Francisco, CA (510) 637-1103
Seattle, WA (206) 220-6171
Twin Cities (Minneapolis–St. Paul), MN (612) 725-368

APPENDIX B

DIRECTORY OF MONEY PROGRAMS

Chapter 1. HOW TO COLLECT FAMILY ASSISTANCE AND SUPPORT

Welfare—for Poor Families with Children
Child Care for Low-Income Families
Hot Meals—for Senior Citizens
In-Home Services for Frail Seniors
Job Training—If You Are Receiving Welfare
Help in Collecting Child Support
Head Start
Money and Help—for Refugees
Low–Income Home Energy Assistance
Money—for Refugees to Start a Small Business
Money—to Americans Returning to the U.S. from
    Overseas Broke
Money—to Help You Adopt Children with Special Needs
Free Job Training For Teens in Foster Care
Food Stamps
Free Food
Free Breakfasts for School Children
Free Lunch for School Children
Free Milk for Children
Free Food for Infants, Tots and Pregnant Women
Free Meals to Children and Senior Citizens
Summer Food Service Program for Children
Free Food Commodities—to Pregnant Women, Children,
    Seniors
$83 a Month—to Needy in Puerto Rico to Buy Food
Free Food Commodities—to Needy Native Americans
Free Emergency Food Commodities to Needy Persons
Additional Food Coupons to Pregnant Women Already
    Receiving Food Stamps—to Use at Farmers Markets
Free Meals—for Homeless Children
Construction Job Training for Youth
Money—for the Disadvantaged to Study Community

Development
Work-Study Programs at Hispanic-Serving Community
    Colleges
Salaried On-the-Job Training
Free Job Placement Services
Money—if You Lose Your Job
Part-Time Jobs for Low-Income Seniors
Free Assistance/Training If You lose Your Job Because of
    Imports
Free Training—for Dislocated Workers
Free Job Training for Migrant Workers and Farmworkers
Free Job Training for the Severely Disadvantaged
Free Training for Teens and Unemployed Adults
Job Corps
Money—to Victims of Violent Crimes
Emergency Food and Shelter
Emergency Grants for Disaster Victims
Emergency Housing Grants for Disaster Victims
Part-Time Jobs For Senior Citizens
Part-Time Companion Jobs for Low-Income Seniors
Negative Income Tax (Earned Income Tax Credit)
Money When You Stay Home and Take Care of Your Kids
Federal Money—For Childcare
General Assistance from Your State
General Medical Assistance
Free Local Hospital Care
Free Educational Support for Homeless Children
Free On-the-Job Literacy Training
Free Basic Adult Education for Parents
Free Help for Migrant Workers to Get High School Degrees
Free Legal Help
Free Medicare

Chapter 2. HOW TO COLLECT MONEY TO START A BUSINESS

Money—for Businesses Owned by Low-Income
MicroLoans: $100-$25,000
Assistance to Disadvantaged Business Owners
Money—from Small Business Investment Companies
Business Development Assistance To Small Business
Money—for Businesses that Suffered Due To a Natural
    Disaster
Assistance for Disadvantaged Businesses
Money—for Victims of Physical Disasters
Help for Businesses to Get Government Contracts
Money—from Local Development Companies
Help for Small Contractors to Get Bonded
Free Business Counseling
Help in Getting Contracts
Free Business Counseling and Training
Money—from Certified Development Companies
Money—for Women-Owned Businesses from Dev. Org.
Free Assistance For Vets Who Want to Start a Business
Free Advice on Export Trade Promotion
Free Assistance if You're in Exporting
Help for Businesses Hurt By Military Base Closings
Minority-Owned Business Help Centers
Help for Native Americans to Start Their Own Businesses
Support to Help Minority-Owned Businesses Expand

Money—from Community Development Block Grants
Money—from Development Block Grants for NY/HI
Money—from Develop. Block Grants for Pacific Islands
Money—from Development Block Grants/State's Program
Money—to Become a Landlord
Money—to Start a New Business In a Rural or Small Town
Money—to Run a Farm or Start a Teenage Farm–Related
    Business
Farm Operating Loans
Money—to Buy or Operate a Farm
Money—to Farmers Who Can't Get Credit
Money—to Expand Businesses in Rural Areas
Money—for Small Rural Businesses
Money—for Wind Erosion
Small Business Innovation Research
Money—for Rural Businesses
Money—to Native Americans for Business Development
Money—for Bus Companies
Money—for Minority Transportation-Related Businesses
Money—to Provide Transportation Services for Elderly,
    Disabled
Loans—and Assistance to Women, Minority Businesses
Disadvantaged Businesses—Bonding Assistance Program
Money—for Disadvantaged Businesses

Free Counseling on Doing Business with the Govt.
Money—From a Federally-Sponsored Credit Union
Assistance to Businesses in the Tennessee Valley Region
Money—For Disabled Vets to Start a Business
Money—for Projects Overseas
Foreign Investment Insurance
Free Rights to Government-Owned Energy Patents

Money—to Work On Energy-Related Inventions
Money—to Work On Energy-Related Science
Management and Assistance for Minority Businesses
Money—to Businesses that Employ the Disabled
Money—for Refugees to Start a Small Business
Purchasing Specialist

Chapter 3. HOW TO COLLECT MONEY FOR HOUSING

Money for Low/Moderate Income Housing in Small Towns
Money—for Very Low-Income to Fix Up/Repair a House
Money—To Fix Up Your Home in the Country
Money—for Conserving Water
Money—to Build Farm Labor Housing
Money—to Build Rental Housing in Small Towns
Money—to Buy a Home
Money—to Buy Fixer-Uppers More Than One Year Old
Money—to Fix Up Your Home
Money—to Buy a Trailer
Rent Assistance Checks for Needy Families in Private Housing
Loans—So Disaster Victims Can Buy Homes
Money—for Construction/Rehab of Condominium Projects
Get a Home at Half Price
Money—for Medical Facilities
Money—So Families Hurt By Disaster or Urban Renewal Can Buy a Home
Money—To Buy a Home in an Outlying Area
Money—To Buy/Fix Up Homes in Urban Renewal Areas
Money—to Buy/Rehab Homes in Older Sections of Town
Money—To Buy A Trailer Park
Money for Homeowners to Buy "Fee-Simple Title"
Money—to Finance Rental Housing
Money—to Invest in Rental and Cooperative Housing for Moderate Income Families and Elderly

Mortgages for Home Buyers With Bad Credit
Money—To Fix Up Multifamily Rental Housing
Money to Buy a Home With Graduated Mortgage Payments
Money—to Buy a Trailer and Trailer Lot
Money—to Buy Home in Areas Hurt by Military Cutbacks
Money—for Service Persons to Buy Homes
Housing—for Persons with AIDS
Rent Assistance for the Low Income in Public Housing
Reverse Mortgages So Seniors Can Get Monthly Income
Money—to Invest in Single Room Occupancy Housing
Money—from Local Development Organizations for Housing/Business
Money—from Local Devel. Orgs. for Projects in NY/HI
Money—from Local Development Organizations for Projects in US Possessions
Money from Local Devel. Orgs. for Projects in Small Cities
Money—to Invest In Low-Income Rental Housing
States Subsidized Housing Programs for Moderate Income Persons
Weatherization Assistance for Low-Income Persons
Subsidized Flood Insurance for Homeowners
Money—for Veterans to Buy Housing
Money—for Disabled Veterans to Buy a Home
Money—for Veterans to Buy Manufactured Mobile Homes
Loans—to Native American Veterans to Acquire a Home
Low-Income Home Energy Assistance
Homesteading Programs

Chapter 4. HOW TO GET MONEY FOR EDUCATION

Money—to Needy Undergrads
Money—So Needy Undergrads Can Continue in College
Student Loans
Low-Interest College Loans
Work-Study Program to Pay for College
Money—for Teachers to Attend Overseas Seminars
Free Adult Basic Education
Money—for Professors to Do Research Overseas
Money—for Ph.D. Students to do Research Abroad
Get Help to Study
Get Help to Go On to College
Support for Needy Students
Money—from Your State to Go to College
$24,000 a Year—for Eligible Ph.D. Students
$1,500 a Year—to Eligible Undergrads
Fellowships—for Study in Areas of National Need
Money—for Undergrads Who Want a Career in Public Service
$6,200/Year—for Studying Math, Science, Engineering
Money—for Environmental and Native American Scholars
Fellowships—to American History Teachers

Fellowships—to Study Food and Agriculture
Money—to Study Mathematics
$14,700—to Become a Nurse Anesthetist Nurse
$18,000—for Disadvantaged Medical and Dental Students
Federal Money for Health Professionals to Repay Ed. Loans
State Money—for Health Professionals to Repay Ed. Loans
Scholarships—to Disadvantaged Undergrads if They Agree to Work for the National Institutes of Health
Scholarships—to Health Services Students Who Agree to Work for the National Health Service Corps
Health Professions Student Loans
Money—to Study to be a Professional Nurse
Nursing Student Loans
$18,000 a Year—to Needy Health Professions Students
Scholarships—to Disadvantaged Health Professions
Summer Govt. Jobs for College and High School Students
Money—to Graduate Students to Study Abroad
Earn Money for College as a Volunteer
Army, Navy & Marine, and Air Force ROTC
Social Security Checks for Students 18 to 22

Chapter 5. VETERANS BENEFITS

Inpatient Medical Care for Vets
Hospital Outpatient Medical Care for Vets
Veterans Nursing Home Care
Medical and Dental Care for Eligible Veterans
State Veterans' Homes
Nursing Home Care for Vets in State Veterans' Homes
Hospital Care for Vets in State Veterans' Homes

Personal and Medical Services for Blind Vets
Vocational and Rehabilitation Help for Alcoholic Vets
At-Home Medical and Nursing Care for Eligible Veterans
Medical Care for Dependents of Disabled Vets
Health Care for Veterans and Their Families
Veterans Group Life Insurance
GI Life Insurance

Payments—to Vets with Service–Connected Disabilities
Payments—to Eligible Vets with Non-Service-Disabilities
Payments—to Needy Surviving Spouses and Children
Payments—to Surviving Spouses and Dependents
Payments to Spouses/Dependants of Certain Deceased Vets
Money—to Disabled Vets for Specially Adapted Housing
Money—for Veterans to Buy a Home
Money—for Disabled Vet to Buy a House
Money—for Veterans to Buy Manufactured Mobile Homes
Loans to Native American Veterans to Acquire a Home

Money—for Disabled Vets to Go to College, Get Vocational Rehabilitation or Start a Small Business
Money—for Surviving Spouse/Children to Go to College
Money for Post–Vietnam Vets to Go to College
College Money for Recently Retired Vets
$150–$1,500 Burial Allowance for Vets
Free Headstones for Veterans
Free Help with Veterans Benefits
Legal Services for Veterans

Chapter 6. COLLECTING FROM SOCIAL SECURITY, MEDICARE, MEDICAID

Monthly Social Security Checks—to Retired Workers
Monthly Checks—to a Deceased Worker's Dependents
Monthly Payments—if You Become Disabled
Supplemental Security Income (SSI)
State Money for the Disabled
Medicare—to Pay Your Hospital Bills
Medicare—to Pay Your Doctor Bills
Free Medicare
Medicaid: Medical Coverage for the Poor

How a Senior Can Get Medicaid—Even If You Own a Mansion
Longshore and Harbor Workers' Compensation
Coal Mine Workers' Compensation—Black Lung
Special Benefits for Disabled Coal Miners
Pensions and Benefits—for Railroad Workers
Prescription Drugs for Seniors Citizens
Health Insurance If Laid Off— "COBRA"

Chapter 7. SPECIAL BENEFITS FOR WOMEN, MINORITIES, OTHER GROUPS

Money—for Needy Minority and Women Farmers
Free Job Training for Displaced Homemakers, Single Parents, Minorities
Free Help for Minority Businesses
Money for Minority Students in Colorado to Study Science
Free Help for Minorities to Start a Small Business
Money for Minority Transportation-Related Businesses
4-Year Scholarships for Minority Undergraduates
Student Training and Internships
Money—for Women and Minority Businesses
Help for Minority Veterans
Free Job Training for Women
Women's Bureau—Free Employment Assistance
Money for Women–Owned Businesses from Development Organizations
Help for Women Veterans
Money—for Businesses in Rural Areas
Money—to Acquire Land on Indian Reservations

Money—for Native Americans to Attend Graduate School
Free Job Training for Native Americans
Child Care for Needy Native American Children
$5,100 a Year—for Job Training
Cash Payments—to Needy Native Americans
Money—for Native Americans to Go to College
Money—to Native Americans for Business Development
Money—for Needy Native Americans to Build Houses
$175 a Week—for Ironworker Job Training
Free Help for Native Americans to Start a Small Business
Money—for Native Americans to Buy Homes
Free Support to Help the Disabled Be Employed
Government Jobs for Disabled Persons
Free Job Placement Services for Disabled Persons/Others
Supported Job Programs for Disabled Persons
Free Job Training for Disabled Persons
Books for the Blind and Physically Handicapped
Schools for the Deaf: Gallaudet University

18 FREE BONUS REPORTS

Here are your 18 valuable reports — specially bound together.

Bonus Report #1

HOW TO GET THE JOB OF YOUR DREAMS!

Forget classified ads or employment agencies. If you want that job of your dreams, here are the inside job-hunting techniques as revealed by one of New York's top employment *headhunters*.

First, ask your friends for leads. Don't be satisfied with indefinite answers such as I'll let you know if anything comes up. Ask for specific names and for permission to use your friend's name as a reference.

Second, look in the *Wall Street Journal* and Sunday *New York Times* to check out help-wanted job descriptions and titles in order to see how to best package your talents. For example, one firm may be advertising for a Research Director and another for a Grants Administrator and a third for a Program Director, all with the same functions and experience as you. It is important to use the currently marketable title.

Third, rent a mail box under an assumed name to answer these blind help-wanted ads. Have the replies sent there. Once you learn the name of the hiring organization, try to find a friend or a contact within the company to recommend you. Being recommended by an employee will get you much more personal attention.

Fourth, read about prospective corporations in back issues of *Fortune*, *Business Week* and *Forbes* magazines in your public library. Apply only to firms with successful programs exactly suited to your needs and qualifications.

When applying for jobs, it helps if you are still employed. This makes it look as if it is <u>you</u> and not your employer who wants you to move on. If you are not currently working, try to get your former employer to take your calls for a few weeks after you leave. If you cannot arrange this, use an answering service to take your calls. If you are already between jobs, you should display confidence when applying for jobs and act as if are merely "between opportunities."

One other secret. When you locate a suitable company, phone to find out the president's name. Then hang up and call back an hour later, asking to speak to "Mr. Jones" directly. Ask him if you might stop by for a brief interview. Even if he puts you off, there's a good chance he'll refer you to the head of personnel. Being referred to personnel by the head honcho is not the worst of introductions.

GETTING EMPLOYERS TO COME AFTER YOU

If you get the executive recruiters to come after you, you have a much better chance of getting that top job you want.

Study the executive want ads for the names of the leading executive recruiting firms that specialize in your field. Then get the most powerful businessman or banker you can to recommend you. What you are looking for is the most impressive letterhead possible so that it will carry the weight you need. Of course, you will draft the letter yourself; all he has to do is look it over, have his secretary sign it, slip in a copy of your resume, and mail it out.

Your suggested draft should be a short, one-page letter. "It has recently come to my attention that Joann McFadden, a lawyer with wide public experience, is now considering offers for executive positions in private business. McFadden is seeking a challenging corporate job that would capitalize on his background of..." Companies will soon be calling you.

The same technique can be used to get a raise. Say you like the job you've got. When your boss finds out that headhunters are after you, your chances for a raise or a promotion are greatly increased. However, never approach the boss directly about the raise. Instead, tell him instead that you are reaching the age where you have to start thinking about your family's security. When he asks what your driving at, hint that you've had inquiries from several rival firms but that loyalty to his excellent corporation has kept you from considering them more seriously. Then say that, "If I could be assured that I would be in for more responsibility, some possibility of advancement, then..." This roundabout technique is much more likely to get you the raise than straight-out asking for it.

BE THE BOSS IN JOB INTERVIEWS

Ask you own questions. The company needs to fill the job and just as the interviewer hasn't offered it to you yet, you haven't agreed to accept it yet. So you are an equal bargaining partner.

- You feel your strongest talents are so-and-so; does the interviewer think you would really get a good chance to exercise them? How?

- Who would you be working with or under most directly? What are these people like?

- The salary is a little low, but are there fringe benefits to make up for it?

- What avenues are open for rapid advancement?

You ask questions you want to know. Don't rehash or expand on your qualifications; the interviewer has your application and if he has any questions, let him ask them.

GETTING LETTERS OF RECOMMENDATION

As mentioned above, the first trick to really good letters of recommendation is to draft the letter yourself and find the perfect person to sign it. He will actually be pleased at your considerateness when you hand him the draft.

The second trick is to include an irrelevant fault to show that you are not perfect. The principle here is that the letter credits you with attributes that make you a powerhouse candidate for the job you're looking for. But since no one's perfect, and the opinion of the person recommending you won't count for much if he doesn't show some insight into your limitations, the letter consigns your faults to some area that would only be relevant to a job you are not seeking. This makes the letter appear all that more honest.

For example, say you want a job in department store fashion merchandising. You draft something like, "For marketing ability, fashion sense, insight, and drive, Sandra has no equal." Then a little further down, you slip in, "Of course, if you were looking for someone who would also be a computer wizard, she wouldn't be the first person I'd turn to."

GO TO YOUR SCHOOL REUNION A SUCCESS

Almost no one goes to school reunions except to show that they've succeeded, often, the ones classmates picked as losers who go back to show that they are now somebodies.

So if you want to look like you've made it, lose weight, order a custom-made suit, and when you arrive, have a number of falsely modest replies to answer the inevitable question, "What are you doing now?" A stockbroker might say, "I fool around in the market." A small-town lawyer might say, "I'm just a country lawyer." Your classmates will supply their own delusions of your success, whereas if you come right out bragging , they'll likely spot you as a fraud.

Bonus Report #2

HOW TO HAVE $2,500 IN YOUR POCKET BY THIS AFTERNOON!

If you have no job, or have just been laid off, or if you are short of cash and anxious to get your life on a more prosperous track, the following moneymaking plan is the fastest way I know to put money in your pocket. The plan is "Street Corner Retailing" or peddling. Don't scoff. Many a dollar has been made this way. Street corner retailing can be truly lucrative if you are really outgoing and like people

So if you need money, swallow your pride and start selling items from a tote bag or carton or out of the trunk of your car and you'll never be broke again. You need a few buck to buy your initial inventory. Then, keep taking your profits to buy more and more merchandise.

I personally know of peddlers who buy $20 worth of tube sox from a wholesale distributor at 8 o'clock in the morning, sell them a block away for $40, then buy $40 worth of sox, sell them for

$80, and keep on doing it till they quit at 6 in the evening, having made hundreds of dollars or

more profit for the day.

The types of items you can peddle is endless. You can start out, for example, with $20 worth of large balloons in a big paper bag, a few balloons inflated to attract attention, a little sign on the bag reading "2 for $1" and you'll probably earn more money in a couple of hours working any busy area (parks, malls, fairs, public spaces in front of downtown office buildings, parades) then most people make in a day. You don't even have to inflate the balloons you sell: sell them deflated.

Or park your car in front of any factory or construction site, open the trunk and sell jeans or tube socks or tools.

Park in front of any busy supermarket and sell plastic tablecloths or inexpensive leather handbags.

Set up a velvet-covered tray on any busy street corner and sell costume jewelry or leather wallets.

Set up a folding table on any busy sidewalk and sell low-cost books, dictionaries, coloring books, maps. (And your right to peddle these is protected by the First Amendment.)

Another truly low-cost start-up that I recently saw is a mobile juice stand. Buy an inexpensive hand-operated orange juicer, fasten it to a sheet of plywood placed on top of a small shopping cart in which you store oranges and disposable cups. Display a large sign that reads, "FRESH-SQUEEZED ORANGE JUICE." Charge $1 a glass. Again, go where crowds are.

RENT VACANT STREET CORNERS

Many street venders set up their stands on empty street corners. On weekends, for example, you can set up a large stuffed-toy animal display in front of a gas station or vacant lot at any busy intersection. Pay the property owner for the use of this part of his property, perhaps $25 for four weekends.

To find a good location, look for a spot that is highly visible on a busy thoroughfare, with easy access from and back onto the road. An

out-of-business convenience store or gas station is ideal. Most property owners will be happy to rent you the space for just enough money to cover the property tax.

As with ordinary street vending, almost anything can be sold on street corners. But some items sell better than others, especially large items that can be seen by a car's occupants from a distance. Such items include:

- Beach umbrellas
- Stuffed animals, the bigger the better
- Velvet paintings
- Framed prints
- Produce, pumpkins (at Halloween), Christmas trees (before Christmas)
- Children's bicycles
- Lawn furniture and ornaments
- Auto seat covers

I've seen mattresses and sofas and lounge chairs sold this way. And I've seen large sneaker displays, with the open sneaker boxes arranged one after another on a slanting board.

Locate wholesale sources of merchandise in the yellow pages. In addition, most cities have wholesale districts that you can shop around in.

Bonus Report #3

HOW TO EARN MONEY EVERY TIME YOU TRAVEL!

If you're the kind of person who likes to travel, you can travel to your hearts content and actually earn money to do it. There are thousands of people winging their way over the Atlantic, cruising down to the Caribbean or Mexico, or otherwise going exactly where you've been dreaming of going. And getting paid a check while living this good life.

They're traveling for free. And you can, too... if you're willing to do a little work for the privilege. This could mean running around to several dozen offices, or writing and mailing a hundred or so letters, before hitting upon the source that can give you the paying travel you want.

BE A TRAVEL SERVICE EMPLOYEE

The travel agency field can be extremely rewarding. Aside from the opportunity to make good commissions, this field provides employees with chances for free or cut-rate travel. Particularly appealing is the large discount on one or two trips a year, from each airline an agent serves.

To get these benefits, it's necessary to be employed by a travel agency for one year. While no formal training is required, there are numerous home-study and classroom courses which teach the basic skills. And after working with an agency for two years, you can set up your own agency and receive accreditation from domestic and international airlines associations, entitling you to write airline tickets.

In addition to receiving discounts offered by airlines, travel service employees can latch onto free, or cheap travel by taking "familiarization trips" (supposedly to explore travel areas they haven't seen). The host country's tourist bureau foots the air fare and hotel bills. In return, they expect the agents to encourage customers to travel there.

BE A TRAVEL BROKER

There is a way to latch onto some of this paid travel action without becoming an agent. Most travel agencies welcome the services of an experienced, private travel broker who is skilled at generating business... i.e., getting groups of people who wish to travel together. In fact, there are many people who make a living in just this manner and get some free travel to boot. While many agencies pay brokers in commissions only, it's often possible to exchange commissions for travel.

There are travel agencies that recruit travel brokers by periodically offering a free 10-week "professional travel agent training course." While learning the tricks of the trade, participants are encouraged to sell on the outside. (Of course, they must locate their own customers.) Recruits work, on a commission basis, which they split with the agency.

Participants, can continue as independent travel brokers with the agency after the course is finished. But graduates may decide to shop around for agencies that provide better opportunities, especially for complementary travel.

BE A TOUR LEADER

While most travel service employees do some traveling, the only ones *always* on the move are the tour escorts.

As a beginner, there are a number of ways you can get into this field. One is to apply for the position of "tour guide" with a city sightseeing organization like Gray Line. Then, move up to a "tour escort" position with the more extensive, nationwide tours operated by such companies as:

- **Peter Pan Tours**, P.O. Box 1776, Springfield MA; (413) 781-2900.
- **Coach USA**, One Riverway, Ste. 500, Houston TX 77056; (713) 888-0104.
- **Gray Line Tours**, 2460 W. 26 Ave., Bldg. C, Ste. 300, Denver CO 80211; (303) 433-9800.
- **Arrow Bus Lines**, 19 George St., East Hartford CT 06128; (800) 243-9560.
- **Campus Coach Lines**, 545 Fifth Ave., New York NY 10017; 1-212-682-1050.

"After talking yourself into your first job, the rest is easy," says one guide who has traveled free for several years here and abroad by working as a free-lance tour escort. Besides getting free trips (including an African safari and a Greek Islands sojourn), she received a daily allotment plus tips and commissions).

A number of student travel agencies hire tour leaders to conduct student-type tours, both here and abroad. While most organizations don't require previous experience, they'll favor someone who has worked with young people or has traveled extensively.

ORGANIZE YOUR OWN TOURS

If you have a group of people ready to travel, you should try to organize your own tour. A number of transportation companies and hotels will give a tour organizer an entirely free trip if he books the tickets for (and conducts) a party of about 10 to 40 people. To get the best deal, talk things over with a travel agent or travel wholesaler; the commission he hopes to get from your trip will make him quite accommodating.

WORK FOR AN AIRLINE

Many flight and ground airline personnel (and their immediate dependents) can fly for free or at low-cost to most anyplace. Usually, airline employees can travel free on a "Space Available" basis. Or, in a "SUBLO" (Subject to Load) arrangement, the airline you work for will fly you for only a portion of regular fare.

These glamorous benefits have their price tag. Generally, you must be a full-time airline employee for six consecutive months. In some cases, however, part-time workers qualify for these freebies if the sum of their work hours amounts to six months of full-time employment.

Needless to say, competition is keen for such airline jobs these days, but for anyone who loves travel—it's well worth the effort. And remember, airlines hire a wide spectrum of ground employees, for posts ranging from food service personnel (pantrymen, butchers, waitresses, etc.) to sales and office workers (accountants, personnel directors, ticket agents, etc.).

Perhaps one of the easiest ways to break into this field is to apply for the job of sales representative with one of the numerous, small foreign airlines. The job entails covering a certain territory here in which you "sell" the airline to travel agents. This means organizing familiarization trips, etc. Aside from earning the same flight benefits as other airline employees, a sales rep also gets to travel free to the cities in his assigned district.

According to the Air Transportation Association of America, a good, general education in primary and secondary schools is all that's required for most airline jobs, with the exception of a few specialized fields. The airlines provide training at no cost for employees in most fields including sales, reservations and passenger services, as well as flight attendant positions.

A number of privately owned schools teach the special skills needed for such licensed jobs as dispatchers, flight engineers, captains and co-pilots. The Federal Aviation Administration, 800 Independence Ave., SW, Washington, DC 20591, offers a list of such approved schools.

BE A BUS DRIVER

Many long-distance bus lines offer drivers and their immediate dependents free travel on any of their buses. The pay is quite good, too.

They usually require that drivers be at least 24 and at least 5'7", with 20/30 vision in both eyes (or correctable to 20/30), and good driving and health records. In addition, they sometimes hire temporary drivers during the summer travel season. While temporary drivers don't receive the same benefits as full-timers, it's still a good way to see part of the country for free.

BE A TRAVEL WRITER

If you have some writing ability (and sometimes even if you don't), coupled with a bit of nerve and determination, you may be able to get free travel from national tourist bureaus, resorts and airlines—or their public relations agencies, which arrange plenty of free junkets.

When economic conditions are tight, there are many airplane seats going begging, hotel rooms sitting unoccupied, and once-packed tourist hot spots emptying out. Good publicity is worth its weight in gold to the tourist business; that's why free trips are frequently offered to members of the working press... and occasionally to those of the nonworking press.

Airlines offer free trips when they have a new route or service to publicize. FinnAir, for example, gave away a slew of free tickets when they put brand new planes in service flying to Helsinki; excursions to Lapland and Leningrad were thrown in.

Splashy new resorts (as well as fading old ones) are also generous with junkets.

Sometimes tourist bureaus gives free trips to free-lance writers who appear to have a good chance of publishing a travel article... *this* could be where you fit in. First, it's necessary to convince the tourist bureau or PR firm that you can deliver the goods when you get back. Here, an encouraging letter from an editor certainly helps.

Start by contacting travel agents and reading travel magazines thoroughly, to see which areas are currently getting the biggest promotional push. Trade magazines — such as *Travel Agent*, 801 2nd Ave., New York, N.Y. 10017, (212) 370-5050; *Cruise & Vacation News*, 60 E. 42 St., New York NY 10017, (212) 867-7470 (free to the industry); and *Tour & Travel News*, One Penn Plaza, New York NY 10119, (212) 714-1300(free to the industry)—can be quite helpful.

Once you decide on your destination, write to as many travel editors of as many magazines and newspapers as you can. And, if a publication doesn't have a travel editor, write anyway: travel pieces are featured in a wide variety of publications. (The reference department of your library will have a directory—such as the *Working Press of the Nation*—listing the necessary names and addresses.)

Your letter should say that you're going to a certain destination and that you'd like to write an article for publication when you get back; if you can think of a unique article angle, all the better. Hopefully, you'll receive two or three replies.

That's the time to call the appropriate tourist bureau and PR firm for appointments. Show your letters to someone in authority; convince them of your good intentions. With a little persuasion, you'll find yourself whisked away— all-expenses paid.

A great place to check for travel writing assignments is the *TravelWriter MarketLetter*, published by Robert Scott Milne, Waldorf Astoria Hotel, Ste. 1850, 301 Park Ave., New York NY 10022. You can check out their internet site at www.travelwritermn.com. It's an award-winning monthly newsletter ($60 for a year's subscription) that lists travel publications and businesses that are looking for articles on specific subjects. It tells you about new markets, pay scales, editors, specs and informs you about trips for writers. Here are two recent listings:

Small-ship cruises in Mexico. Alaska Sightseeing/ Cruise West would like to invite qualified professional travel writers to consider a press trip to Mexico's Sea of Cortes. The trip is scheduled for Feb. 28 aboard the 96-guest Spirit of '98, & is 8 days, 7 nights, round trip from Cabo San Lucas. This cruise will visit the wilderness desert islands along 400 miles of Baja California's Sea of Cortes coastline, plus ports of call at Loreto, La Paz, Mulege, & Santa Rosalia, plus a day with the gray whales at Bahia Magdalena. Limited

airfare may be available; assignment helps. Contact Floyd Fickle, Public Relations consultant, Alaska....

American Snowmobiler has 6 issues a year, in winter months. Editor Jerry Bassett needs articles on accommodations & restaurants that are friendly to snowmobilers, faster & more comfortable snowmobiles, new places to ride, new trails & conditions. Pays $150-$300, on acceptance, for all rights to articles of up to 1200 words.

Bonus Report #4

HOW TO NEVER BE WITHOUT A JOB!

I know of one job in which you'll never be out of work — short order cook. A fellow I heard about made this discovery in California, but the situation is true in all areas of the United States. After working several years in a dead-end job, he quit and found himself without a job and with no idea what he wanted to do. He checked the help wanted ads. One read "Fry Cook Wanted." Knowing how to make burgers, he thought, "Maybe I'll try it. I might have enough experience." He phoned the place. The owner did everything but beg him to take the job. Not once did he ask about his experience.

He took the job. The pay was small but he enjoyed the work. Then he saw another ad offering more pay — full fledged cook. Then he saw an opening for head cook. Soon, a Manager job opened. All this happened to him within a year, and he had started with the ability to fry hamburgers and nothing else.

Shortage of cooks? I don't know. All I know is that it's practically impossible for a restaurant to find or keep a cook. I have heard of high school kids hired as dish washers and two weeks later start cooking. So you should always be able to get a job as a short-order cook. How can one learn to cook? Make no mistake about it — you don't need to know how to cook. Buy an egg pan and learn to flip eggs. This ability alone will get you a job. You don't have to be a cook—just say you are and you'll never, never be without a job.

Bonus Report #5

HOW TO SAVE UP TO 50% ON YOUR CREDIT CARD INTEREST!

A credit card is vital in today's economy. But some of them charge as much as 22% on unpaid balances. Trade in your high-interest cards for some of these credit card deals and you'll save as much as $1,000 a year in interest on your outstanding balances. These cards are recommended because of their no- or low-annual fees/and the low interest rates they charge for unpaid balances.

AFBA Industrial Bank, PO Box 14107, Colorado Springs CO 80914. (800) 776-2265. Card charges: No fee. 8.5% initially; prime + 2.5% after 6 months.

MBNA America, PO Box 15342, Wilmington DE 19850. (800) 523-7666. Card charges: No fee. 5.9% first 5 months; then prime + 8.99%.

American First Federal Credit Union, PO Box 9199, Ogden UT 84409. (800) 999-3961. Card charges: (1)No fee/12.75% fixed; or (2) $10 annual fee/11.75% fixed.

Bank One Corp., PO Box 8651, Wilmington DE 19899. (888) 221-9067. Card charges: No fee. 4.9% introductory 4-6 month offer; then 9.9% - 22.9%..

Bank Of America, 1825 E. Buckley Rd., Ste. 5060, Phoenix AZ 85034. (800) 678-2632. Card charges: $0-$45 annual fee. Prime + 5.9% to prime + 9.9%.

First Union Corp., 1525 West W.T. Harris Blvd., Charlotte NC 28262. (704) 590-2700. Card charges: No fee standard card. 6.9% initially; then 13.99% after 6 months.

USAA Federal Savings Bank, 10750 McDermott Freeway, San Antonio TX 78288. (210) 498-4673. Card charges: No fee standard card. Prime + 3.9%.

Carolina First Bank, 102 S. Main St., Greenville SC 29602. (864) 255-7900. Card charges: No fee. 1.4% to 22%.

Central Carolina Bank & Trust Co., 111 Corcoran St., Durham NC 27702. (800) 672-5795. Card charges: (1) Gold card–$20 year/prime + 3.5%; or (2) Standard card–$29 year/prime + 2.5%.

First National Bank of Omaha, PO. Box 3128, Omaha NE 68103. (402) 341-0500. Card charges: No fee. 5.9% first 6 months; then 13.9%.

Mellon Bank, Four Station Square, Ste. 300, Pittsburgh PA 15219. (412) 234-5364. Card charges: No fee standard card. 5.9% the first 6 months; then prime + 3.9%.

Commerce Bancshares, 1000 Walnut St., Kansas City MO 64106. (800) 280-0123. Card charges: Gold card–$29 year/prime + 2.9%.

First Virginia Bank Inc., 6400 Arlington Blvd., Falls Church VA 22046. (800) FVB-BANK. Card charges: No fee gold card. Prime + 2.4%.

Fifth Third Bank, 38 Fountain Sq. Plaza, Mail Drop 109051, Cincinnati OH 45263. (888) 797-5353. Card charges: Gold card–$18 year (waived first year)/prime + 6%.

First Union Corp., 301 S. Tryon St., Charlotte NC 28288. (800) 377-3404. Card charges: Gold card–$39 year/prime plus 2.9%.

PNC Bank Corp., 300 Bellevue Pkwy., Wilmington DE 19809. (800) 762-2273. Card charges: $18 year waivable the first 6 months and 4.9% to 7.9%; then 12.49% to 21%.

Bonus Report #6

4 HOME BUSINESSES THAT CAN MAKE YOU RICH!

If you want your own business and don't have much money, here are four great start-ups. Each takes little cash, can be started in your spare time, and has the potential to be very profitable.

PAYROLL AND BOOKKEEPING SERVICE

If you know the principles of bookkeeping, you can start a local bookkeeping or recordkeeping service that can be highly profitable. Most small firms and professional people do not employ full-time bookkeepers, even though accurate bookkeeping is a necessity, especially because of tax regulations.

Essentially, what a bookkeeping service does is keep meticulous business records for its clients. This involves making journal and ledger entrees from the client's daily reports and preparing a monthly trial balance. (Doing payrolls alone can keep you as busy as you like.) You will probably see the client at his place of business once a month; the rest of the time, he mails you weekly the transactions to be entered in books that you keep in your office.

The service can be started very inexpensively using standard bookkeeping journals and ledgers. However, today it pays to do it on computer. Dozens of good bookkeeping software packages exist, including accounts receivable, accounts payable, general ledger, payroll, and integrated combinations of these. There are also unique packages designed for specific trades such as insurance, property management, or medical services.

Only when you know exactly the type of bookkeeping your business will focus on should you select the software that you will use. The software varies tremendously in price, and the cost is not always an indication of quality, dependability or flexibility. Researching the software you will use is very important, so give it a lot of thought and attention. Talk with other users with interests similar to yours. Go to your public library to read reviews of software in the personal computing magazines. Speak to salesmen in the larger stores that sell software.

You will also need forms suitable for your printer, such as fanfold checks. Many of them are custom printed with clients' letterheads and logos. Consider making a deal with a forms salesman for ordering them for your clients at a reasonable markup.

And be careful with those computer file backups. If you are handling figures for other peoples' business, you cannot afford to lose their data.

How to get started

First, learn about the different bookkeeping systems and methods that are available and being used by bookkeeping services in your area. Call a few (posing as a potential client) and ask about their rates, what system they use; hear what they have to say. Base your own basic system and rates on theirs.

There are two basic methods of setting fees.

1. Charge a flat fee. Many clients prefer to pay a monthly flat fee that they know in advance.. This way they know just how much the service is going to cost them. This requires that you estimate how long it will take to attend to the client's bookkeeping.
2. Charge by the hour. Initially, charge a client a little less than the going rate. You can increase it gradually.

Usually it's best, at the start, to quote the client a trial fee, with the understanding that you can adjust the rates after a 2- or 3-month period.

How to get business

Your most likely customers will be local businessmen. Acquire clients by advertising and promoting your service to small businesses—merchants, lawyers, doctors, auto dealers, drug stores, dentists, hotels and motels, restaurants, gas stations and repair shops, other professionals. Advertise in the *Yellow Pages*, and in local newspapers under "Business Services"; perhaps in local business and professional periodicals if any are published in your area. Send announcements to managers of small local business, making known your experience and background in the field, and give personal and professional references.

Send for the booklet, *Starting and Managing A Small Bookkeeping Service*, from the Small Business Administration, Public Communications, 1441 L Street, NW, Room 100, Washington DC 20416, 1-202-653-6365.

MAID AGENCY

Providing much needed maid service to two-income households is one of the hottest business ideas. A maid service supplies house cleaners on a regular basis — from a few hours to full time. If you provide dependable, spotless service, soon clients will be lining up for your service. Cleaning, in order to be done efficiently, is usually a team effort. The maids follow a set routine. Two or three maids come in, each with specific chores, and they quickly do the job.

When first starting out, you may have to be one of the maids. But shortly, you won't be doing the actual physical cleaning yourself: you'll spend your time lining up jobs and providing independent employees to do the actual cleaning. Your cut is as much as forty percent of the take.

Organization is the key to efficient home cleaning. With proper organization, three people working together can clean a home in one-fifth the time it would take one person. Efficiency is necessary in order for your service to make a profit while charging competitively low rates. Homeowners don't like paying more than $75 to $100 for a thorough cleaning, even less if it's done on a regular or weekly basis. So learn as many shortcuts as possible to teach to your maids. Usually, the customer furnishes cleaning supplies and provides a vacuum cleaner and mop.

To get maids, contact your state division of employment; place classified ads in newspapers; post fliers on supermarket bulletin boards; place small ads in shopper or local newspapers; get referrals from other maids (like most people, they like to work with their friends). Pay your maids a decent wage—say $10 an hour—so as to keep turnover low. Worry about maids quitting is probably the biggest negative in this business.

To get clients, place ads in weekly newspapers. Put a listing in the *Yellow Pages*. After a few jobs, word-of-mouth should keep you very busy.

For further information, send for: *Everything You Need To Know To Start A Housecleaning Service*, published by Cleaning Consultant Services, Inc., 1512 Western Avenue, Seattle WA 98101; (206) 682-9748. $14.95.

ADULT TOYS SALES PARTIES

We've all heard of Tupperware, the famous food container brand. Did you know it is sold at home sales parties, by independent sales people? Tens of billions of dollars worth of merchandise of all sorts are sold this way each year.

You can get rich with your own business selling merchandise via the party plan. A year or so ago I heard of a great line of merchandise to sell at home parties—adult sex "toys." I learned of two sisters who are making it big selling "Whipped Cream for Lovers," "Sex Bubbles, the Bubble Bath For Lovers," giant vibrators and sexy lingerie to women at what they called Pajama Parties. This is a great way to make money because women, your intended customers, feel uncomfortable buying such items in stores. It is an ideal business for a woman or for a husband-wife team where the woman takes charge of the sales parties and the husband concentrates on the buying and shipping.

Party plans

Under the party plan form of selling, you arrange with housewives to hold sales parties in their home or office at which you give product demonstrations to a group of her friends. The hostess gets a percentage of the sales. The sales party is a powerful selling tool because it's a special event that brings with it the expectation of buying something, much like going to a fair or mall. In addition, some guests look upon a purchase as the price they pay for an entertaining evening or afternoon.

The festivities often start with refreshments and games or entertainment to loosen up and relax the guests. You then give a short presentation, pass around samples the guests can look at, answer questions, and hand out literature and order forms. You then take the orders, and later ship or personally deliver the orders yourself. A door prize is usually awarded at the end of the party.

At least two or three of the guests will want to sign up as hostesses for future parties. And those future parties will provide still further hostesses. This chain keeps multiplying and can build up as fast as you can keep up with it.

Starting out

Look upon your show as a "Girls' Night Out" party—a party for adult women, usually married, who know very little about sex toys. The party should have a fun, festive atmosphere where they can discover these items, often for the first time, and learn how they can improve their married lives.

The fastest way to get started is to hold a few "Girls' Night Out" parties in your own home. Invite your friends. In fact you can let them know your plans and ask them to let you try your techniques on them as guinea pigs. They won't care if you mess up. This way you'll get a feel for the business and you'll even be able to recruit a few hostesses for future parties. If you've already hosted a few parties at your own home and feel like you'll be imposing by inviting friends and neighbors to yet another party, you may want to arrange with a friend to hold the first couple of parties at her home.

One of the side benefits of these initial parties is that you'll sign up some future hostesses. Encourage guests to sign up by offering them a special "early bird" incentive such as an extra prize or higher commission, especially if they hold their parties as quickly as possible.

Your merchandise

Products you'll be selling include such exotic items as:

- red hot his & her lingerie & sleepwear
- fishnet, lace, shear body stockings
- x-rated chocolates
- lotions & oils
- edible oils & lubricants
- "industrial strength" vibrators
- all types of sexual devices
- erotic novelties
- x-rated ties
- leather goods
- prisoner of love kits
- costumes
- adults-only games
- books
- videos
- floating candles
- panty roses
- glow in the dark condoms

One of the secrets of success in party plan sales is to have a large selection of items to offer the potential buyers. You should have at least forty different items. In order to get enough items, you have to contact enough suppliers who can provide the kind of merchandise your buyers want.

The easiest way to find merchandise is to visit some local "Adult Toy" shops. Such stores may be listed in the *Yellow Pages* under "Novelties." This listing will include a number of different types of stores—visit the ones that sound like they feature adult items. When going there, don't be embarrassed. Just present your business card and explain you are looking for items to sell to your friends. Look around the store. See which products get the most shelf space. Don't tell them that you plan on running professional party plans: you don't want to give them any ideas. Explain that it's just a small side business. While there, see if they can refer you to any suppliers. Or maybe they'll agree to supply merchandise at discount. If so, buy samples—on consignment— to demonstrate at the parties. Then purchase the items from the store to fill your orders.

In any case, buy some items (in the original boxes that have the manufacturers name and address) so that you can write to the manufacturers directly.

After a while, if not right away, you'll want to buy merchandise directly from the wholesalers, importers and manufacturers. Unfortunately the *Yellow Pages* don't have a category listing such wholesale suppliers. You'll have to search them out. Look up "Novelties—Wholesalers & Manufacturers." Such suppliers carry a wide range of merchandise, but each may carry only a handful of adult items. Some firms that specialize in selling adult merchandise for resale advertise in various salesman-type magazines. Send for their catalogs. These companies include:

- **Lotions & Lace Co., Inc.,** 2881 Hulen Place, Riverside CA 92507; (909) 686-5223. Send $2 postage for their wholesale catalog featuring lotions and oils, videos, lingerie, costumes, games and novelties. They'll include their business start up manual. They also have a party plan guide and sales aids.
- **Unique Sales Co.,** PO Box 28432, St. Louis MO 63146. Send $2 for their wholesale "Marital Aids for Lovers" catalog.
- **New Concept,** PO Box 6756, Laguna Niguel CA 92607; (714) 248-5855. They carry an extensive line of his & hers lingerie and novelties items. Complete sales aids are available including party selling instructions. Send $2 for their starter kit or $20 for their complete 70-page kit (refundable with your first order).
- **Lady Tara Lingerie,** 530 Glen Ave., Palisades Park NJ 07650; (201) 947-8877. They charge $9.95 for their wholesale color catalog of lingerie, funwear, jewelry, etc. It comes with printed promotional material. They also have a video for $12.95.
- **Spector's Lingerie Exotique,** McKeesport PA 15134-0502; (412) 673-**3259**. Wholesale exotic intimate apparel.
- **Horton International,** PO Box 2011, Chicago IL 60690; (708) 344-9217. Videos.

Here are some other possible suppliers. Each carries a tremendous assortment of merchandise, only a small portion of which may be of an adult nature. Contact them to see what they have that you can use:

- **Burto Products, Inc.,** 505 Mayrock Rd., Gilroy CA 95020
- **Evergreen Marketing Inc.,** 4 Poinsetta Ct., Ste. 420, Baltimore MD 21209; (800) 296-2596
- **Franco American Novelty Co., Inc.,** 8400 73rd Ave., Glendale NY 11385; (800) 222-JOKE
- **Pressner & Co.,** 99 Gold St., Brooklyn NY 11201; 1-718-858-1000

Organizing the parties

Have hostesses hold their parties in the evening—any evening except on a weekend. Each hostess should make up a list of 20 to 40 women to invite to the party. Friends, neighbors, co-workers, relatives, mothers of their children's friends, members of organizations they belong to.

If you are nervous about selling before groups of people, start with small parties limited to three or four people. Then increase the number by one or two people at each subsequent party. Before you know it, you'll feel completely self-confident and assured.

On the day of the party, get there early so you have time to set up. Set up your items on a sturdy table with a good white or light colored cloth. Arrange them by type—oils together; vibrators together; leather-goods together; and so on. Try to create a playful effect, one that will encourage giggling and fun: not a sordid, dirty atmosphere. Put showmanship, imagination and flair into the display.

All parties need refreshments, so be sure your hostess has provided such. Refreshments usually consist of coffee, tea and soft drinks and cookies or other nibble items. The hostess usually arranges with a friend to help out with the serving.

Try to inspire your hostess, to put her in an enthusiastic mood. After all, she is your sales partner for the evening. Do this by reminding her of what's in it for her—money, free products, discounts, and her enhanced reputation as someone who does a good job.

Making your sales presentation

A simple way to begin your presentation is to thank the hostess, give a warm welcome to the guests and tell about the prizes and money the hostess can earn. Then give a brief outline of the presentation to come, followed by a brief description of how you started the company. Next, ask the guests one at a time to introduce themselves, and then ask them to describe one of the items and how they plan to use it. Involve the members of the group and the hostess in your presentation.

When making your presentation, always emphasize benefits — what the item can do for the buyer — rather than features that describe the product. Guests are moved to making a purchase by hearing that a sexy outfit will pry their husband away from the TV screen, not by learning it is made of lycra spandex and can be washed in hot water. Speak to the individuals in the group. Do this by making eye contact with guests in various parts of the room. Don't neglect any of them. Ask questions and incorporate this feedback into your presentation. Encourage participation from the group.

Follow with a question and answer period before you make your group closing pitch. Ask, "Before I Complete my presentation, does anyone have any questions?"

Closing and taking orders
Signal the close of the showing by saying something like "Our hostess will be serving refreshments in just a moment. I hope you all enjoyed yourselves this evening. Now, before I hand out order forms, I would like to remind you of our guarantee..."

At the close, have each guest write up her order on a standard 2-part order form that you can buy in any stationery store. The customer gets one copy and you keep the other. Reassure hesitant buyers with some comment as simple as "You made a wise purchase" or "This is one of our best-sellers." Accept full payment in advance or a substantial deposit with the balance to be paid on delivery.

Use this phase of the party to book at least two or three hostesses to hold shows of their own. Establish a date for each party, and arrange a time the next day when you can phone the new hostess to explain the steps involved in holding the sales party..

Multi-level marketing
The really big money in party plans comes from setting up a multi-level program. This means that instead of recruiting hostesses, you would recruit independent distributors who then recruit hostesses. This would be a two level program. Under the normal sales party plan previously described, if you recruit enough hostesses so that you can demonstrate the adult toys at, say, 4 parties a week, this would amount to 200 parties a year. But let's say that rather than recruiting hostesses yourself, you recruit 10 independent distributors who in turn each recruit hostesses

who give 200 parties. Then, during the course of a year, your merchandise would be sold through 2,000 parties. On your own you could never reach this volume.

TELEMARKETING SALES
If you have a good telephone voice and a forceful, yet pleasant personality, you can make money in telemarketing sales (telephone selling). This includes selling, and selling-related functions such as setting up sales appointments or interviews.

You can do this work under contract to a sales organization, or you can collect a finder's fee based on confirmed appointments or ultimate sales volume.

And don't just think you have to call for others. You can sell for yourself. The list of items you can sell is practically endless, including books, home products, cosmetics that you buy at wholesale.

Look for opportunities where there is a well defined market and carefully selected leads. If you find yourself calling names listed in a "reverse" phone directory (one that lists consecutive numbers followed by the names attached to those numbers) you'll get a lot of resentful people answering the phone and a lot of rejections.

If you are selling to a phone list compiled from people who have asked to receive more information, you can expect a much higher success rate.

Your best bet is to is offer products and services to the business world. These people are interested in saving money or in providing better products or services. If you can offer them an attractive product and pricing, and you have a thorough understanding of what you have for sale, then your task becomes much easier.

Your sales will be a function of your ability to establish a rapport with the person responsible for making the purchase. By listening to what he says, you'll be able to tailor your conversation so as to address his needs. If he is looking for something cheaper or better than what he currently has, recognizing this tells you what it will take to get his business. He may be very straightforward with you, telling you exactly what he wants and the price expected, leaving you with the choice of meeting the price or not. Or he may describe to you a problem his business is having. If you can offer a solution, you get the sale.

Other business people select what they buy on the basis of personal relationships: if he likes you, he'll give your stuff a try.

Another type of buyer looks for items that he feels will give him prestige. If possible, for example, he drives a German car. But over the phone you can't see his car. You can only listen carefully for cues as to what kind of person he is and try to tailor your sales approach.

Items and services to sell
Here are just some of the products and services you can sell:
- courier services
- cleaning supplies
- maintenance
- specialized books
- magazines
- travel or transportation services
- advertising space
- data security
- employee perks and fringe benefits
- financial services
- retail equipment
- training
- printing services
- forms
- holiday products
- promotions
- work clothing
- tools
- lubricants
- raw materials
- packaging material
- computer services
- phone services

Your sales pitch
To succeed at telephone selling, you should constantly refine and perfect your sales pitch. Put your standard message in outline form so that when you speak to a potential buyer, you don't forget to mention things or meander off

the topic. Write down the answers to typical questions. Experienced callers can make as many as sixty calls an hour (these include no answers which you should hang up on the third ring, to be redialed later in the day). You'll learn not to waste time on uninterested people, and not to take hang-ups or rudeness to heart.

Sales promoter
Here' an interesting segment of the telephone selling business, one that you can start right away. You make phone calls to bring customers into stores. It works like this. Arrange with a local merchant, say a pharmacy, that you will phone everyone in the area and tell them they can save $5 on every prescription they transfer from another drug store in the next 10 days. The pharmacy pays you a commission on every transferred prescription. Make the same deal with five or ten different kinds of businesses at the same time for especially large earnings.

Contacting by phone: best times to call
- housewives: 11:00 AM – noon
- clerical workers: call at home after 6:00 PM
- executives, business owners: 7 – 8:30 AM; after 10:30 AM
- builders, contractors: before 9:00 AM; after 5:00 PM
- dentists: before 9:30 AM
- doctors: 9:00 – 11:00 AM; 4:00 – 9:00 PM
- grocers, food: before 9:00 AM; 1:00 – 2:30 PM
- lawyers: 11:00 AM – 2:00 PM; after 5:00 PM
- clergymen: between Tuesday and Friday
- accountants: anytime other than tax season (January 5 – April 15)
- engineers, chemists: 4:00 AM – 5:00 PM
- pharmacists: 1:00 – 3:00 PM
- teachers, professors: at home 6:00-9:00 PM
- printers, publishers: after 3:00 PM

A 5th PLAN —
MALL PUSHCART VENDING
Technically, this is not a home business. But Pushcart/Kiosk Vending is an ideal low-investment first step toward the American dream and is worth consideration by anyone thinking of starting her own business. These type of stands are increasingly common at shopping malls

across the country. Weekly leases, relatively low rents, and ideal location keep risks low and the potential for profits high.

There are several advantages to operating a kiosk in a mall:

- First, you don't have to invest a lot in store fixtures. Your actual cost will be determined by how elaborate you make your stand, and how much of the work you do yourself.

- Second, you'll need much less inventory to stock a kiosk than a store. The average area may run 100 square feet, and can be stocked for a much smaller investment than a store.

- Third, owning a kiosk in a mall sounds more prestigious than a flea market or street corner stand.

- Fourth, with the vacancy rate in malls way up, many mall managers are willing to negotiate attractive terms.

- Fifth, an indoor mall location can remain open in the winter, or when it rains.

What to sell

There are disadvantages to kiosk retailing of course, and one of them is size. Because of the small retail space involved, your choice of merchandise will be limited to smaller items. Most stands specialize in one product line, but there is a practically limitless number of product lines you can specialize in:

- stuffed animals
- jewelry
- music boxes
- balloons
- flags
- sunglasses
- gift baskets
- key racks
- key chains
- nameplates
- mugs
- gloves
- kitchen utensils
- flowers
- handmade belts and leather goods
- regional souvenirs
- suntan lotions
- hand-crafted wooden toys

- t-shirts and sweat shirts
- cosmetics

And on and on. Fad and impulse items are most popular.

Your cart and display will have to compete with all that's around and catch the shopper's eye. So the key to successful cart merchandising is to carefully choose and display the merchandise so it makes an immediate visual impact. Your product line should be narrow in scope, focusing on a specific product line designed to create a strong visual identity for your kiosk. If selling jewelry, for example, is should be all gold, or all shell, or all silver.

Mall policies

Kiosk policies vary from mall to mall. Some provide ready-to-use stands or booths, complete with electricity. In other malls, you'll have to supply or build your own. Lease arrangements vary too. Some malls give only short term leases.

Generally, malls want kiosks to sell items that fit the mall's image. Check out the retail shops in the mall to see that you don't compete with the regular stores; if you do, most malls won't rent you space.

Bonus Report #7

BILLS IT'S OK TO PAY LATE

If you've hit a brick wall and owe more at the end of the month then you have money to pay, there are certain bills you can pay a little late and not damage your credit rating. That's because they give you a grace period.

Generally, electric utilities give you a ten day grace period, telephone companies give you eight days, and banks and finance companies give you ten days. Oil company bills are also usually alright to defer. If you can't pay these bills by the grace period and a late charge is imposed, your credit rating should be okay for 30 days.

Professionals, physicians, dentists and hospitals usually don't file credit reports with credit rating services at all, so these are bills you can put off, too.

Bills you absolutely have to pay when due include credit cards from banks (Mastercard, Visa, etc.) and credit cards from department stores. They file credit reports on all customers every month to credit-rating bureaus. So pay these vital bills first.

Bonus Report #8

HOW TO COLLECT MONEY YOU KNOW NOTHING ABOUT!

You may be one of millions of Americans that have money owed to them that they know nothing about. This money could come from forgotten bank accounts, life insurance proceeds, unclaimed inheritances, old utility deposits, unpaid tax refunds, wages from past jobs and dozens of other sources. This is money waiting to be claimed by you if you are the direct owner or heir to this money.

This is money that has "fallen through the cracks." You change your address or change your name, computers bury your file, and without warning, a company that holds assets that belong to you can't find you. After three to five years, the company gives up and turns the assets over to the state. The state is supposed to track you down but most states don't make any effort.

Here's how to see if there is any money waiting for you. Call the "Unclaimed Property" Division of your state's Treasurer's Office and any other states where you or your family have lived, went to school, or been in business. When you call, give your name, address and Social Security number to the unclaimed–property agent. The agent will then check the records to see if you are due anything. Many state's even pay annual interest. So, for example,

if you had a $100 electric company deposit from 1960, it could be worth over $500 today.

Here's a list of each state's Unclaimed Property Division. Phone or write to find out what is due you.

Alabama State Treasury, Unclaimed Property Division, PO Box 302520, Montgomery AL 36130. (334) 242-9614.

Alaska Department of Revenue, Unclaimed Property Unit, P.O. Box 11405, Juneau AK 99811. (907) 465-4653.

Arizona Dept. of Revenue, Unclaimed Property Unit, P.O. Box 29026, Phoenix AZ 85038. (602) 364-0380.

Arkansas Auditor of State, Unclaimed Property Division, 1400 W. 3rd St., Ste. 100, Little Rock AR 72201. (501) 682-9174.

California Division of Collections, Bureau of Unclaimed Property, PO Box 942850, Sacramento CA 94250-5873. (916) 445-8318.

Colorado Unclaimed Property Division, 1560 Broadway, Ste. 1225, Denver CO 80202. (303) 894-2443.

Connecticut Unclaimed Property Division, Dept. of Treasury, 55 Elm Street, Hartford CT 06106. (800) 833-7318.

Delaware Bureau of Abandoned Property, PO Box 8931, Wilmington DE 19899. (302) 577-3349.

District of Columbia, Office of Finance & Treasury, Unclaimed Property Unit, 810 1st Street NE, Room 401, Washington DC 20004. (202) 727-0063.

Georgia Dept. of Revenue, Property Tax Division, Unclaimed Property, 270 Washington St., Room 404, Atlanta GA 30334. (404) 656-4244.

Hawaii Unclaimed Property Section, PO Box 150, Honolulu HI 96810. (808) 586-1589.

Idaho Unclaimed Property Division, PO Box 36, Boise ID 83722. (208) 334-7623.

Illinois Unclaimed Property Division, PO Box 19495, Springfield IL 62794. (217) 782-6992.

Indiana Attorney General's Office, Unclaimed Property Division, 402 W. Washington, Ste. C-531, Indianapolis IN 46204. (800) 447-5598.

Iowa Treasurer, Unclaimed Property Division, State Capitol Building, Des Moines IA 50319. (515) 281-5368.

Kansas Unclaimed Property Div., 900 SW Jackson, Ste. 201, Topeka KS 66612. (800) 432-0386.

Kentucky Unclaimed Property Branch, Kentucky State Treasury Department, Ste. 183, Capitol Annex, Frankfort KY 40601. (502) 564-4722.

Louisiana Office of the State Treasurer, Unclaimed Property Section, PO Box 44154, Baton Rouge LA 70804. (888) 925-4127.

Maine Treasury Department, Abandoned Property Division, 39 State House Station, Augusta ME 04333. (207) 624-7477.

Maryland Unclaimed Property Section, 301 W. Preston St., Baltimore MD 21201. (800) 782-7383.

Massachusetts Abandoned Property Division, 1 Ashburton Place, 12th Floor, Boston MA 02108. (617) 367-0400.

Michigan Dept. of Treasury, Unclaimed Property Division, Lansing MI 48922. (517) 335-4327.

Minnesota Minnesota Commerce Department, Unclaimed Property Section, 133 E. 7th St., Ste. 600, St. Paul MN 55101. (800) 925-5668.

Mississippi Unclaimed Property Division, PO Box 138, Jackson MS 39205. (601) 359-3600.

Missouri Missouri State Treasurer, Unclaimed Property Division, PO Box 1004, Jefferson City MO 65102. (573) 751-0840.

Montana Dept. of Revenue, Attn: Unclaimed Property, P.O. Box 5805, Helena MT 59604. (406) 444-6900.

Nebraska Unclaimed Property Division, PO Box 94788, Lincoln NE 68509. (402)471-2455.

Nevada Dept. of Business & Industry, Unclaimed Property Division, 2501 E. Sahara Ave., Ste. 304, Las Vegas NV 89104. (800) 521-0019.

New Hampshire Abandoned Property Division, Treasury Department, 25 Capitol St., Rm. 205, Concord NH 03301. (603) 271-2619.

New Jersey Department of the Treasury, Property Administration, P.O. Box 214, Trenton NJ 08695 (609) 984-8234.

New Mexico Dept. of Revenue & Taxation, Special Tax Programs & Services, PO Box 25123, Santa Fe NM 87504. (505) 827-0767.

New York Office of Unclaimed Funds, Alfred E. Smith Building, Albany NY 12236. (800) 221-9311.

North Carolina Dept. of State Treasurer, Escheat & Unclaimed Property Section, 325 N. Salisbury St., Raleigh NC 27603. (919) 508-5979.

North Dakota Unclaimed Property Division, State Land Dept., PO Box 5523, Bismarck ND 58506. (701) 328-2805.

Ohio Division of Unclaimed Funds, 77 S. High St., 20th Fl., Columbus OH 43215. (614) 466-4433.

Oklahoma State Treasurer Office, Unclaimed Property Section, 4545 N. Lincoln Blvd., Oklahoma City OK 73105. (405) 521-4275.

Oregon Unclaimed Property Unit, 775 Summer St., NE, Salem OR 97301, (503)378-3805 x283.

Pennsylvania Pennsylvania State Treasury, Office of Unclaimed Property, PO Box 1837, Harrisburg PA 17105. (800) 222-2046.

Rhode Island Unclaimed Property Division, PO Box 1435, Providence RI 02901. (401) 222-6505.

South Carolina Office of the State Treasurer, Unclaimed Property Division, PO Box 11778, Columbia SC 29211. (803) 737-4771.

South Dakota Unclaimed Property Division, 500 E. Capitol Ave., Pierre SD 57501. (605) 773-3379.

Tennessee Unclaimed Property Division, Andrew Jackson Bldg., 10th Floor, Nashville TN 37243. (615) 741-6499.

Texas Unclaimed Property Division, Texas State Comptroller's Office, Box 12019, Austin TX 78711. (800) 654-3463.

Utah State Treasurer s Office, Unclaimed Property Div., 341 S. Main St., 5th Floor, Salt Lake City UT 84111. (888) 217-4096.

Vermont Abandoned Property Division, State Treasurer s Office, 133 State St., Montpelier VT 05633. (802) 828-2407.

Virginia Division of Unclaimed Property, Dept. of Treasury, PO Box 2478, Richmond VA 23218. (804) 371-6244.

Washington Unclaimed Property Section, Dept. of Revenue, PO Box 448, Olympia WA 98507. (800) 435-2429.

West Virginia Unclaimed Property Division, One Players Club Dr., Charleston WV 25311. (800) 642-8687.

Wisconsin Unclaimed Property Division, State Treasurer s Office, PO Box 2114, Madison WI 53701. (608) 267-7977.

Wyoming Unclaimed Property Division, 2515 Warren Ave., Ste. 502, Cheyenne WY 82002. (307) 777-5590.

Bonus Report #9

MILLIONAIRES WHO HELP PEOPLE IN NEED!

Many millionaires have private charitable foundations that give millions of dollars to persons in need. The reason they do it, whether out of feelings of guilt, to honor a loved one, or to save on taxes, is not important.

Each has different eligibility requirements, so contact the ones that meet your needs.

Emma J. Adams Memorial Fund, Inc., 860 Park Ave., New York NY 10021. Welfare assistance, primarily through institutions, to the elderly and indigent gentlemen and gentlewomen in the New York City metropolitan area.

Dorothy Ames Trust, c/o Key Trust Co. of Maine, P.O. Box 1054, Augusta ME 04330. Aid to hearing-impaired children.

William Babcock Memorial Endowment, 305 San Anselmo Ave., Suite 219, San Anselmo CA 94960. (415) 453-0901. Assistance for medical costs to residents of Marin County, CA who lack the financial resources to pay for exceptional medical, surgical, and hospital expenses not covered by insurance or other community agencies.

The James Gordon Bennett Memorial, c/o New York News, 220 E. 42 St., New York NY 10017. Pecuniary aid to needy journalists who have been employees for ten or more years on a daily Newspaper in New York City. Acceptance is based on need and is to be used for "the physical needs of persons who, by reason of old age, accident or bodily infirmity, or through lack of means, are unable to care for themselves."

Ingeborg A. Biondo Memorial Trust, 605 Pennsylvania Ave., Matamoras PA 18336. (914) 856-4484. Grants to orphaned and physically, mentally and emotionally handicapped individuals.

Thomas C. Burke Foundation, 804 Cherry St., Ste. B, Macon GA 31201. (912) 738-9955. Medical assistance to cancer patients in the Macon-Bibb county, Georgia, area.

Ina Calkins Board, c/o Bank of America, 14 W. Tenth St., Kansas City MO 64141. (816) 979-7481. Welfare assistance to elderly needy residents of Kansas City, Missouri.

The Elizabeth Church Clarke Testamentary Trust/Fund Foundation, c/o U.S. Bank, NA, P.O. Box 3168 Trust Division, Portland OR 97208. Grants to individuals for medical assistance and bodily rehabilitation. Recipients must be Oregon residents.

Maxwell M. Corpening, Jr. Memorial Foundation, P.O. Box 2400, Marion NC 28752. Grants to needy residents of McDowell County, North Carolina, for rent, medicine and other necessities.

Josiah H. Danforth Memorial Fund, 8 Fremont St., Gloversville NY 12078, (518) 725-0653. Grants for residents of Fulton County, N.Y., for medical assistance.

George W. Davenport Charitable Trust, c/o Fleet Investment Management, One Monarch Pl., MA SP M21 TRU, Springfield MA 01144. Financial assistance to needy elderly who live in Bernardston, Leyden, or Greenfield MA.

The de Kay Foundation, c/o Chase Manhattan Bank, 270 Park Ave., 21st Floor, New York NY 10017. (212) 270-9077. Financial assistance to needy elderly persons "of culture or refined heritage" in New York, New Jersey and Connecticut.

Sarah W. Devens Trust, c/o Rice, Heard & Bigelow, 50 Congress St., Ste. 1025, Boston MA 02109. (617) 557-7413. Financial assistance for elderly women living in Massachusetts.

Alfred I. duPont Foundation, 1650 Prudential Dr., Ste. 400, Jacksonville FL 32207. (904) 858-3123. Financial assistance to the elderly indigent who live in the southeastern U.S. who are in a very distressed situation and require health, economic or educational assistance.

Blanche Fischer Foundation, 7912 SW 35 Ave., Ste. 7, Portland OR 97219. (503) 246-4941. Grants for needy Oregon residents who are physically disabled.

Zachary and Elizabeth Fisher Armed Services Foundation, c/o Fisher Bros., 299 Park Ave., New York NY 10017. Aid to individuals whose spouses or parents served in the U.S. Armed Services.

C.E. Gibbs Memorial Fund Trust, c/o The Honesdale National Bank, 733 Main St., Honesdale PA 18431. (717) 253-3355. Financial assistance to persons who are or were employed in the publishing or periodical distribution industry.

Addison H. Gibson Foundation, One PPG Place, Ste. 2230, Pittsburgh PA 15222. (412) 261-1611. Hospital and medical costs for self-supporting residents of western Pennsylvania who have correctable medical conditions but cannot afford the necessary treatment. Applicant must be referred by medical professional.

Gilmore Foundation, c/o Old Kent Bank, 300 Old Kent Bank Building, Grand Rapids MI 49503. Financial assistance to extremely low-income residents of the Kalamazoo, Mich., area who cannot care for themselves due to physical limitations or old age.

Gore Family Memorial Foundation, c/o SunTrust Bank, 501 East Las Olas Blvd., Fort Lauderdale FL 33301. Grants to assist needy residents of Broward County, FL, with medical expenses, housing, and transportation costs.

Marion D. and Maxine C. Hanks Foundation, Inc., 8 E. Broadway, Ste. 405, Salt Lake City UT 84111. (801) 364-7705. Grants and support for medical expenses to needy individuals.

Teresa F. Hughes Trust, c/o Pacific Century Trust, P.O. Box 3170, Honolulu HI 96802. (808) 566-5570. Assistance to Hawaiian children who are orphans, neglected, abused, or born out-of-wedlock, and indigent or infirmed adults over age 50. Applicant should be recommended by a professional in the community.

Mary J. Hutchins Foundation, 45 John St., New York NY 10038. Welfare assistance to indigent people in the NYC metropolitan area.

William B. Lake Foundation, c/o First Union National Bank, Broad and Walnut Streets, Phila. PA 19109. Assistance to Philadelphia-area residents suffering from diseases of the respiratory tract or pulmonary disease.

George A. Laughlin Trust, c/o WesBanco, Trust Dept., 1 Bank Plaza, Wheeling WV 26003. (304) 234-9400. Interest-free loans to Ohio County WV residents with three or more children to purchase homes.

Pearle Vision Foundation, 2534 Royal Ln., Dallas TX 75229. (972) 277-5993. Financial assistance for eye surgery, treatment, and low vision equipment.

Edwin Phillips Foundation, Fleet Investment Management, Charitable Unit, 75 State St., MA BO F07 B, Boston MA 02109. Medical and living expenses to financially needy, blind residents of Peoria County, Illinois.

Katharine C. Pierce Trust, c/o State Street Corp., P.O. Box 351, M-3, Boston MA 02101. Financial relief for needy, deserving "gentlewomen" in reduced circumstances, so that "their lives may be made more comfortable."

Fannie B. Pratt Trust, c/o Dane & Howe, 45 School St., 4th Floor, Boston MA 02108. (716) 227-3600. Assistance to financially needy widows in Boston.

The Presser Foundation, c/o Institutional Services, Presser Place, Bryn Mawr PA 19010. (610) 525-4797. Emergency aid to music teachers in need.

Agnes C. Robinson Trust, c/o Crestar Bank, Trust Tax Services, P.O. Box 27385, Richmond VA 23261. (202) 879-6339. Financial aid to needy persons in the metropolitan Washington DC area.

Jasper H. Sheadle Trust, c/o Key Trust Co, Trust Tax Dept., 800 Superior Ave., 4th Floor, Cleveland OH 44114. Payments to American-born elderly couples or elderly women living in Cuyahoga or Mahoning counties, OH.

Fred B. Sieber Foundation, 17820 Lee Ave., Redington Shores FL 33708. Grants for general welfare and medical expenses.

Otto Sussman Trust, P.O. Box 1374, Flushing NY 11370. Assistance to residents of New York, New Jersey, Oklahoma and Pennsylvania in need because of death or illness in their family or some other unfortunate circumstance.

Anna Emory Warfield Memorial Fund, c/o Anne S. deMuth, P.O. Box 674, Riderwood MD 21139. (410) 494-0808. Relief assistance to aged, dependent women in the Baltimore area.

Carrie Welch Trust, Rt. 5, Box 240, Walla Walla WA 99362. Aid to needy or worthy aged individuals living in Washington, with preference to the Walla Walla area.

Werner Wilhelm Charitable Foundation, 32300 Northwestern Hwy., Ste. 200, Farmington Hill MI 48331. General welfare assistance to needy individuals.

Bonus Report #10

"LAST CHANCE" CREDIT CARD SECRETS!

These days, it is important to have credit cards, especially one or two Visa or MasterCards. Even if you have no or poor credit, you can get a card.

The secret is to get your first charge card. Once you have that card, and have promptly made the monthly payments owed on it, you can leverage it into as many cards as you want or need. If you have poor credit, start with the easiest card you can get, and then expand from there.

Before applying for any credit cards, get a copy of your credit report to make sure it is accurate. Get a free copy by contacting TRW Consumer Assistance, PO Box 2350, Chatsworth CA 91313; (800) 682-7654. The report comes with a booklet explaining how to read it, and steps to take in case of mistakes.

There are two principal ways to get that first card: (1) Get a secured card; (2) Get a department store or major oil company card.

GETTING A SECURED CREDIT CARD
Secured credit cards are intended for people with poor credit histories, or none at all. Here's how it works. You deposit, say, $500 as collateral into a standard interest-paying savings account at a bank that offers secured credit cards. Typically, you agree to keep the $500 on deposit for one year. The bank then issues you a secured credit card with a $500 spending limit. In other words, the bank lends you your own money. The cards usually have a 25-day grace period, after which they charge approximately 18% interest.

Use the card regularly for a year or so, never letting the credit card balance rise above $350. If need be, you can get a cash advance up to the $500 limit. After the year, apply for a regular bank card and request that your $500 collateral be released plus any accumulated interest.

Many banks offer secured credit cards, and the interest rates paid on deposits and charged on purchases vary widely. Here are the twelve largest secured card issuers.

Providian Financial Corp., 201 Mission St. San Francisco, CA 94105. (415) 543-0404. Market served: national.

First National Bank of Marin, PO Box 150540, San Rafael CA 94915. (415) 459-6100. Market served: national.

First Consumers National Bank, 9300 SW Gemini Dr., Beaverton OR 97005. (800) 876-3262. Market served: national.

Bank of America, 1825 E. Buckeye Rd., Ste. 5060, Phoenix AZ 85034. (800) 678-2632. Market served: western states.

First Premier Bank NA, 900 W. Delaware, Sioux Falls SD 57104. (800) 987-5521. Market served: national.

Wells Fargo Bank, 1220 Concord Ave., Concord CA 94520. (800) 642-4720. Market served: Western U.S.

United National Bank, 675 Franklin Blvd., Somerset NJ 08873. (732) 937-4600. Market served: national.

Key Bank and Trust, 626 Revolution St., Havre De Grace MD 21078. (800) 539-5398. Market served: national.

The Chase Manhattan Corp., 100 Duffy Ave., Hicksville NY 11801. (800) 46-CHASE. Market served: national..

First Union Corp., 1525 West W.T. Harris Blvd., Charlotte NC 28262. (704) 590-2700. Market served: national.

California Commerce Bank, 2029 Century Park East, Los Angeles CA 90067. (310) 203-3472. Market served: California, Mexico.

First National Bank In Brookings ,700 22 Ave. South, Brookings SD 57006. (800) 658-3660. Market served: national.

Beginning with a department store or oil company card

Another method to get that first card is to apply to local department stores or to major oil companies like Exxon, Sunoco or Mobil. Because the companies want your business, their requirements are less stringent than the major credit card issuers, and most of them will issue a card quickly. At least one credit expert suggests that you apply to the more prestige department stores, not the Macy's, Sears and Penny's that cater to the masses. Why? Because prestige stores are more likely to assume that if you're a customer, you must be well-off, and therefore their credit personnel are less likely to make a perfunctory negative decision.

Once you've established credit by making purchases and paying them off, you're ready to apply for bank cards like Visa and MasterCard.

INCREASING YOUR CREDIT LINE

Your first card will typically have a $1,000 or so credit line. When you get your first card, borrow against this credit line. Pay it off over a 3 or 6 month period. The bank will then increase the credit limit. Repeat the process, borrowing against the higher credit limit, to increase your credit line a second time. Before you know it, you'll have anywhere from a $3,000 to $10,000 line of credit.

GET ALL THE CREDIT CARDS YOU WANT

Once you've received your first regular Visa or MasterCard using one of the methods shown above, and then proceeded to increased the credit limit, you can begin applying for as many credit cards as you want.

If you apply for and receive twenty different cards, each with a $5,000 credit line, you'll have $100,000 in working capital to go into business or for some other purpose. Try to apply for cards that have special low-interest promotions.

PHONE NUMBERS FOR BEST CREDIT
See Bonus Report 5.

CARDS CREDIT CARD TIED TO HOME EQUITY LINE OF CREDIT

You can get a credit card with a very high line of credit by using the equity in your home to secure the debt. Under such a plan, you get a credit limit equal to approximately 70% of the appraised market value of your home minus what you still owe on your mortgage. So, for example, if you have a home assessed at $100,000 and you still owe $55,000 on the mortgage, you can get a $15,000 line of credit.

One advantage of such a line of credit is that the interest is deductible when figuring your income tax. The disadvantage is if you can't repay over a specific number of years, you can lose your house. Contact local banks for details on the programs they offer. Shop around for the best terms.

HELP IF YOU'RE IN DEBT

If you're in debt and over your head in bills you can't pay, the first thing you should do is get counseling/negotiating help.

A *consumer credit counselor* will help you review your situation. If you have enough income to cover your minimum payment each month but can't seem to manage to pay off any balances, the counselor will help you devise a sound monthly payment plan.

If you're unable to pay even a small monthly payment, the counselor will negotiate directly with your creditors to arrange a payment plan you can manage. This arrangement may include getting creditors to accept canceling late payment charges, waiving interest charges over a certain level, and even agreeing to a balance you can realistically settle.

The nonprofit **National Foundation For Consumer Credit** (8611 2 Ave., Ste. 100, Silver Spring MD 20910; 1-800-388-2277) is highly recommended. It is a national organization of more than 700 Consumer Credit Counseling Offices throughout the country. And it's services are free.

Bonus Report #11

SECRETS OF THE INSIDERS!

Want to join the upper crust. Here are inside secret you can use to stop envying and start being envied.

GET INVITED TO THE WHITE HOUSE

Every year the White House hosts scores of dinner parties, special dinners, luncheons, receptions, afternoon teas and assorted other events to honor people or organizations. Most seats will go to various officials and VIPS, but a good number may still go to citizens from around the country who have presented themselves as the right Americans to throw into the mix.

The first step to get an invite is to find out the White House social schedule a few months in advance. Once you spot upcoming events, you have to figure—what possible connection do you have with the guest of honor, their countries, organizations, personal lives, etc. This kind of built-in pipeline to the guest of honor, especially from a newer and small country, is a natural ticket to an invitation.

Write to the President's social secretary and mention that you've learned there to be a dinner or event for Mr. X on such and such a date, that you were planing a trip to Washington around then, that you have special interest in Mr. X or his country, cause, industry, etc., because (state the reason), and that you'd be more than happy to help honor him. The key factor in getting invited is the special interest you have in the guest of honor or his affiliations.

If you ever had your photo taken with the guest of honor, had your name printed in connection with his, etc., send a copy along with your letter as a reminder. Also include some facts about yourself — both professional and personal.

GET VIP TREATMENT IN A HOSPITAL

It is scary being in hospital. First of all, you're there because you are not well or are having some type of operation or procedure. Secondly, hospitals seem like impersonal laces where you are just a patient with a number on a plastic wrist band.

Fortunately, there are steps you can take to be get VIP-like treatment that will make your hospital stay more comfortable, human and personal. Here's what you can do:

Have the right doctor
Before being admitted, get a doctor who's on the hospital's board of directors, or who's on the teaching staff—a doctor with clout in the hospital.

Speak with the hospital administrator
When you know you'll be going to the hospital, make an appointment to speak with the hospital

administrator. Introduce yourself and tell her that you're going to be a patient, that you're concerned about your hospital stay, and that you'd appreciate if she'd take a personal interest in your case.

During the admission procedure ask what rooms are available and ask about your potential roommate's medical status to be sure you can deal with his illness. If you are not physically up to it, your spouse, friend or relative can ask for you.

Get the nursing staff on your side
Go out of your way to be polite. You want them to take an interest in you.

Know your rights when entering a hospital
There are certain rights and courtesies you are entitled to as a patient. You're entitled to privacy in all examinations and consultations. If you're in a teaching hospital, for example, and there's a class of medical students watching while the doctor examines you, you can refuse permission for them to be there.

You can have curtains drawn around your bed while being examined.

You're entitled to be included in conversations about your case. You have the authority to refuse treatment if not convinced of its necessity.

When your child is a patient, and you want to stay with him, if the hospital discourages it, get the doctor to write a note advising it. Argue that you can't give fully informed consent to the child's treatment if you can't be there to monitor reactions and make proper judgement. If you're insistent, most hospitals won't refuse doctors' orders.

ADD A TITLE TO YOUR NAME
Every body loves a title after their name. Just think of the lawyer who served as a judge for a few months. He can call himself "Judge" the rest of his life. This being America, there are not too many barons and countesses. But there are plenty of occupational titles you can use, especially on business cards which supply not only your name and address, but also a title. So if you show apartments, call yourself a Real Estate Broker. If you like to cook, call yourself a Culinary Consultant. Similarly, if you like to rearrange your furniture, can call yourself an Interior Designer.

If your occupation doesn't lend itself to a title, you can always denote yourself with a generic title such as business consultant, sales representative, marketing consultant, public relations consultant, free-lance writer, and so on.

Get good quality business cards; they won't cost you much. On the cards, your title should be centered, in somewhat smaller letters, directly under your name.

GET A CAB DURING A DOWNPOUR
If you need a cab, you should remember two things: One: empty cabs head toward the center of town on the biggest or fastest roads possible. Two, cabs head towards major hotels.

So if you can't get a cab on a rainy day, get on the downtown side of a street that cab drivers would normally take back toward the center of town. And then walk in this direction yourself until you reach a hotel whose doorman is vigorously haling taxis for hotel guests. Slip inside the hotel through a side door, go to a rest room to dry and refresh yourself. Then ask a bellperson or clerk the name of the doorman. You then rush out, slipping him a buck or five-spot and say, "John, could you get me a cab as fast as possible. I'm late for a meeting."

CONTACT CELEBRITIES
How'd you like to reach Pamela Anderson, Cher, Bill Gates, George Bush, Alyssa Milano, Natasha Henstridge, David Schwimmer? The directory that follows will help you do it.

Here are some tips when writing celebrities. When sending a letter, be polite and courteous. Handwritten letters sometimes get better responses then typed ones — they can seem more personal. Always include a self addressed stamped envelope. You don't necessarily have to send a picture for the celebrity to sign. If you don't send your own picture, you will probably get back a black and white picture, it may be pre-signed, or even pre-stamped with an autograph. Sending your own picture is a more trustworthy way to ensure an authentic autograph. Make sure you ask the celebrity to sign the picture if you're enclosing one.

Another great way to get autographs is to check who's performing on Broadway. When you write her "Care of' the theatre," you normally reach the celebrity directly.

Abdul-Jabbar, Kareem 1436 Summitridge Dr., Beverly Hills CA 90210

Abdul, Paula 14755 Ventura Blvd., #1-710, SO, CA 90212

Ackroyd, David 273 N. Many Lakes Dr., Kalispell MT 59901

Adams, Don 2160 Century Park East, Los Angeles CA 90067

Adjani, Isabella 2 Rue Gaston de St Paul, 75016 Paris France

Aerosmith 1776 Broadway, 14th Floor, NY, NY 10019

Agassi, Andre 6739 Tara Ave., Las Vegas NV 89102

Aiello, Danny 4 Thornhill Dr., Ramsey NJ 07446

Alda, Alan 641 Lexington Ave., #1400, New York NY 10022

Alexander, Jason 6230-A Wilshire Blvd., Ste. 103, Los Angeles CA 90048

Alexis, Kim 343 N. Maple Dr., #185, Beverly Hills CA 90210

Ali, Muhammad P.O. Box 187, Berrien Springs MI 49103

Allen, Tim 7920 Sunset Blvd., Ste., 400 Los Angeles CA 91521

Allen, Woody 930 Fifth Ave., New York NY 10018

Alley, Kristie 4526 Wilshire Blvd., Los Angeles CA 90010

Allman, Greg PO Box 12932 Birmingham, AL 35202

Alt Carol 111 East 22 St. Ste. 200 New York NY 10010

Amanpour, Christiane CNN Center, P.O. Box 105366, Atlanta GA 30348

Ambrosia 77 W 55th St., NY, NY 10019

Anderson, Gillian 250 North Robertson Blvd., Ste. 518, Beverly Hills CA 90211

Anderson, Harry 9830 Wilshire Blvd., Beverly Hills CA 90212

Anderson, Juliet P.O. Box 3040786, Milwaukee WI 53234

Anderson, Loni 20652 Lassen Ste., #98, Chatsworth CA 91311

Anderson, Lynn 4925 Tyne Valley Blvd., Nashville TN 37220

Anderson, Pamela 31342 Mulholland Hwy., Malibu CA 90265

Anderson, Richard Dean 1824 Courtney Ave., Los Angeles CA 90046

Andrews, Julie 135 Copley Place, Beverly Hills CA 90210

Anka, Paul 10100 Santa Monica Blvd., Los Angeles CA 90067

Anniston, Jennifer 5750 Wiltshire Blvd., Ste. 580, Los Angeles CA 90036

Arkin, Adam 1999 Avenue of the Stars, Ste. 2850, Los Angeles CA 90067

Arnold, Tom 12424 Wilshire Blvd., #740, Los Angeles CA 90025

Arquette, David 8942 Wilshire Blvd., BH, CA 90211

Arquette, Patricia 9560 Wilshire Blvd., Ste. 500, Beverly Hills CA 90212

Arquette, Roseanne 8899 Beverly Blvd., Los Angeles CA 90048

Assante, Armand 335 North Maple Dr., Beverly Hills CA 90210

Atkins, Chet 1096 Lynwood Blvd., Nashville TN 37215

Aykroyd, Dan 8455 Beverly Blvd., Los Angeles CA 90048

Babcock, Barbara 530 West California Blvd., Pasadena CA 91105

Babilonia, Tai 13889 Valley Vista Blvd., Sherman Oaks CA 91423

Babyface 8255 Beverly Blvd., Los Angeles CA 90048

Bacall, Lauren 1 W. 72 St., Ste. 43, New York NY 10023

Bacon, Kevin 9830 Wilshire Blvd., Beverly Hills CA 90212

Baez, Joan P.O. Box 818, Menlo Park CA 94026

Bailey, F. Lee 1400 Centre Park Blvd., Ste. 909 West, Palm Beach, FL 33401

Baio, Scott 4333 Forman Ave., Toluca Lake CA 91602

Bakula, Scott 9560 Wilshire Blvd., Ste. 500, Beverly Hills CA 90212

Baldwin, Alec 132 S. Rodeo Dr., #300, BH, CA 90212

Baldwin, Stephen 8730 Sunset Blvd., #490, LA, CA 90069

Bancroft, Anne 2301 La Mesa Dr., Santa Monica CA 90405

Banderas, Antonio 132 S Rodeo Dr., #300, BH, CA 90212

Banks, Tyra Box 36 East 18, Los Angeles CA 90036

Bardot, Bridgitte La Madrague, F-83990, St. Tropez France

Barker, Bob 1851, Outpost Dr., Los Angeles CA 90068

Barrymore, Drew 9560 Wilshire Blvd., 5th Floor, Beverly Hills CA 90212

Baryshnikov, Mikhail 157 W. 57 St., #502, New York NY 10019

Bassett, Angela 9911 West Pico Blvd., Ste. PH1, Los Angeles CA 90035

Bassinger, Kim 11288 Ventura Blvd., Ste. 414, Studio City CA 91604

Bateman, Justine 11268 Ventura Blvd., Ste. 190, Studio City CA 91604

Bates Kathy, 121 N. San Vincente Blvd., Beverly Hills CA 90211

Baxter, Meredith 10100 Santa Monica Blvd., Ste. 700, Los Angeles CA 90067

Bay, Susan 801 Stone Canyon Rd., Los Angeles CA 90077

Beatty, Warren 13671 Mulholland Dr., Beverly Hills CA 90210

Begley, Ed Jr. 1900 Ave. of the Stars, #1640, Los Angeles CA 90067

Belafonte, Harry 1133 Ave. of the Americas, New York NY 10036

Belafonte, Shari 28600 Pacific Coast Hwy., Malibu CA 90265

Belushi, Jim 8033 Sunset Blvd., Ste 88, Los Angeles CA 90046

Benedict, Dirk P.O. Box 634, Bigfork MT 59911

Bening, Annette 232 North Canon Dr., Beverly Hills CA 90210

Bennett, Tony 130 W. 57 St., #9D, New York NY 10019

Benjamin, Richard 719 N. Foothill Rd., Beverly Hills CA 90210

Bergen, Candice 955 South Carrillo Dr., Ste. 200, Los Angeles CA 90048

Bergen, Polly 1400 Devin Dr., Los Angeles CA 90069

Berry, Halle 1122 S. Robertson Blvd., #15, Los Angeles, CA 90035

Bertinelli, Valerie 12711 Ventura Blvd., Ste. 490, Studio City CA 91604

Blige, Mary J 40 W 57th St., NY, NY 10019

Boyz II Men 6244 Sunset Blvd., #1700, LA, CA 90028

Branagh, Kenneth 302-308 Regent St., London W1R 5AL, England

Bridges, Jeff 9560 Wilshire Blvd., Suite 500, Beverly Hills, CA 90212

Brinkley, Christie 2124 Broadway, #104, New York NY 10023

Broderick, Matthew 17 Charlton St., New York NY 10004

Brokaw, Tom 941 Park Ave., #14C, New York NY 10025

Bronson, Charles P.O. Box 2644, Malibu CA 90265

Brooks, Mel 2301 La Mesa Dr., Santa Monica CA 90405

Buffet, Jimmy 424A Fleming St., Key West, FL 33040

Burnett, Carol c/o Bill Robinson, ICM, 8942 Wilshire Blvd., 2nd Fl., Beverly Hills CA 90211

Bush, George W. The White House, Washington, D.C. 20500

Caan, James P.O. Box 6646, Denver, CO 80206

Cage, Nicholas P.O. Box 69646, Los Angeles CA 90069

Cain, Dean 1103 North El Centro Ave., Los Angeles CA 90038

Caine, Michael Rectory Farm House, North Stoke, Oxfordshire, England

Cameron, Kirk P.O. Box 8665, Calabasas CA 91372

Campbell, Neve 101-1184 Denman St., Box 119, Vancouver BC V6G 2M9, Canada

Cannon, Dyan 10351 Santa Monica Blvd., Ste. 211, Los Angeles CA 90025

Carey, Drew 400 Warner Blvd.,B, CA 91522

Carey, Mariah P.O. Box 4450, NY, NY 10101

Carey, Jim P.O. Box 57593, Sherman Oaks CA 91403

Carlin, George 901 Brigham Ave., Los Angeles CA 90049

Carlisle, Belinda 3907 West Alameda Ave., Ste. 200, Beverly Hills CA 91505

Carlisle, Kitty Hart 32 East 64th St., New York NY 10021

Carpenter, Mary-Chapin 7003 Carroll Ave., Silver Spring, MD 20212

Carpenter, Richard P.O. Box 1084, Downey CA 90240

Carradine, David 9753 La Tuna Canyon Road, Sun Valley CA 91352 - 2235

Carreras, Jose Via Augusta 59 E-08006, Barcelona, Spain

Carrere, Tia 8228 Sunset Blvd., Ste. 300, Los Angeles CA 90046

Carrey, Jim P.O. Box 57593, SO, CA 91403

Carson, Johnny 6962 Wildlife, Malibu CA 90265

Caruso, David 270 N. Canon Dr. #1508,BH,CA,90210

Carvey, Dana 17333 Rancho St., Encino CA 91316

Cash, Johnny 711 Summerfield Dr., Henderson TN 37075

Cassidy, David 8721 Sunset Blvd., Penthouse Ste. 7, Los Angeles CA 90069

Cates, Phoebe 9560 Wilshire Blvd., Ste. 500, Beverly Hills CA 90212

Ceasar, Sid 1910 Loma Vista Dr., Beverly Hills CA 90210

Chan, Jackie Waterloo Road, Ste. 145, Kowloun, Hong Kong

Channing, Stockard 10390 Santa Monica Blvd., Ste. 300, Los Angeles CA 90028

Charisse, Cyd 10724 Wilshire Blvd., #1406, LA CA 90024

Charles, Ray 2107 West Washington Blvd., Ste. 200, Los Angeles CA 90018

Chase, Chevy 9830 Wilshire Blvd., Beverly Hills CA 90212

Cher P.O. Box 960, Beverly Hills CA 90213

Chlumsky, Anna 151 El Camino Dr., Beverly Hills CA 90212

Christie, Julie 23 Linden Gardens, London W2 England

Chung, Connie 524 West 57th St., New York NY 10112

Clancy, Tom c/o Putnams, 200 Madison Ave., New York NY 10016

Clapton, Eric 18 Harley Ave., Regents Park, London NW1 England

Clark, Dick 3003 West Olive Ave., Burbank CA 91505

Cleaver, Eldridge 935 NW 15 Ave., Miami, FL 33125

Clooney, George 8817 Lookout Mountain Ave., Los Angeles CA 90046

Close, Glenn 9830 Wilshire Blvd., Beverly Hills CA 90212

Collins, Jackie 13701 Riverside Dr., Ste. 608, Sherman Oaks CA 91423

Collins, Joan 15 Bulbecks Walk, South Woodham, Ferners, Chelmsford, Essex CM3 5ZN, England

Cooper, Alice 4135 East Keim Dr., Paradise Valley AZ 85235

Copperfield, David 515 Post Oak Blvd., Ste. 300, Houston TX 77027

Coppola, Francis Ford 916 Kearny St., San Francisco CA 94133

Cosby, Bill P.O. Box 4049, Santa Monica CA 90411

Costner, Kevin P.O. Box 275, Montrose CA 91021

Couric, Katie 320 Central Park W., #19B, New York NY 10025

Cox, Courtney 1122 S. Robinson Blvd., S. 15, Los Angeles CA

Crawford, Cindy 132 South Rodeo Dr., Ste. 300, Beverly Hills CA 90212

Cruise, Tom 14755 Ventura Blvd., #1-710, SO, CA 91403

Crystal, Billy c/o Creative Artists Agency, 9830 Wilshire Blvd., Beverly Hills CA 90212

Dafoe, William 33 Wooster St., #200, New York NY 10013

Dangerfield, Rodney 530 East 76 St., New York NY 10021

Daniels, Jeff 137 Park St., Chelsea MI 48118

Danson, Ted 1033 Gayley Ave., Ste. 208, Los Angeles CA 90024

Danza, Tony 25000 Malibu Rd., Malibu CA 90265

Dash, Stacey Box 800487, Santa Clarita CA 91380-0487

Day, Doris P.O. Box 223163, Carmel CA 93922

De Niro, Robert c/o Tribeca Products, 375 Greenwich St., New York NY 10013

De Vito, Danny c/o Jersey Films, Sony Studios, 10202 Washington Blvd., Culver City CA 90232

DeBakey, Michael c/o Baylor College of Medicine, 1 Baylor Plaza, Houston TX 77030

DeGeneres, Ellen 1122 S. Roxbury Dr., Los Angeles CA 90035

Dempsey, Patrick 431 Lincoln Blvd., Santa Monica CA 90402

Deneuve, Catherine 76 Rue Bonaparte, Paris F-75006 France

Depardieu, Gerald 4 Place de la Chapelle, Bougival France

Depp, Johnny 8942 Wilshire Blvd., Beverly Hills CA 90211

Dern, Laura 2401 Main St., Santa Monica CA 90405

Devane, William 15511 Decente Dr., Studio City CA 91604

Diamond, Neil 904 Glen Way, Beverly Hills CA 90210

Diaz, Cameron 955 S. CarnilloDr., # 300, Los Angeles CA 90036

Dicaprio, Leonardo 955 S. Carillo Dr., #300, Los Angeles CA 90048

Dickinson, Angie 9580 Lime Orchard Rd., Beverly Hills CA 90210

Dixie Chicks 1450 Preston Forest Square, #212. Dallas, Texas. 75230

Doherty, Shannon 1033 Gayley Ave., #208, LA CA 90024

Donahue, Phil 420 E. 54 St., #22F, New York NY 10022

Donaldson, Sam 4452 Volta Place NW, Washington D.C. 20007

Douglas, Kirk 805 North Rexford Dr., Beverly Hills CA 90210

Douglas, Michael P.O. Box 49054, Los Angeles CA 90049

Drescher, Fran 232 N. Cannon Dr., Beverly Hills CA 90210

Dreyfus, Julia Louis 9560 Wilshire Blvd., 5th Floor, Beverly Hills CA 90212

Dreyfuss, Richard 2809 Nichols Canyon, Los Angeles CA 90046

Duchovny, David 8942 Wilshire Blvd., Beverly Hills CA 90211

Dukakis, Micheal & Kitty 85 Perry St., Brookline MA 02146

Dukakis, Olympia 222 Upper Mountain Road, Montclair NJ 07043

Dunaway, Faye P.O. Box 15778, Beverly Hills CA 90209

Duval, Robert P.O. Box 520, Plains VA 22171

Dylan, Bob P.O. Box 870, New York NY 10276

Easton, Shenna 151 El Camino Dr., Beverly Hills CA 90212

Eastwood, Clint P.O. Box 4366, Carmel CA 93921

Eden, Barbara 9816 Denbigh, Beverly Hills CA 90210

Elfman, Jenna c/o More-Medavoy Mgmt., 7920 Sunset Blvd., Los Angeles CA 90046

Eisner, Michael 500 S Buena Vista, Burbank CA 91521

Elliot, Chris 151 El Camino Dr., Beverly Hills CA 90210

Elliott, Sam 33050 Pacific Coast Hwy, Malibu CA 90265

Estefan, Gloria P.O. Box 4447, Miami FL 33269

Estevez, Emilio P.O. Box 4041, Malibu CA 90264

Everhart, Angie 115 E. 57 St., #1540 New York NY 10022

Evigan, Greg 5472 Winnetka Ave., Woodland Hills CA 91364

Fairchild, Morgan 2424 Bowmont Dr., Beverly Hills CA 90210

Falk, Peter 1004 N. Roxbury Dr., Beverly Hills CA 91522

Farrahkhan, Louis 4855 S. Woodlawn Ave., Chicago, IL 60615

Fawcett, Farrah 3130 Antelo Rd., Los Angeles CA 90077

Feinstein, Michael 8942 Wishire Blvd., Beverly Hills CA 90211

Fields, Sally 12307 7th Helena Dr., Los Angeles CA 90049

Fierstein, Harvey 1479 Carla Ridge Dr., Beverly Hills CA 90210

Fiorentino, Linda 9830 Wilshire Blvd., Beverly Hills CA 90212

Fisher, Carrie 1700 Coldwater Canyon, Beverly Hills CA 90210

Fleiss, Heidi 505 South Beverly Dr., Ste. 508, Beverly Hills CA 90212 - 4542

Flowers, Gennifer 13834 Magnolia Blvd., Sherman Oaks CA 91423

Flynt, Larry 9211 Robin Dr., Los Angeles CA 90069-1146

Fonda, Bridget 9560 Wilshire Blvd., Ste. 500, Beverly Hills CA 90212

Fonda, Jane 1050 Techwood Dr. NW, Atlanta GA 30318

Fonda, Peter RR Ste. 38, Livingston MT 59047

Forbes, Steve 60 Fifth Ave., New York NY 10011

Ford, Gerald R. 40365 San Dune Rd., Rancho Mirage CA 92270

Ford, Harrison 10279 Century Woods Dr., Los Angeles CA 90067

Foster, Jodie 10900 Wilshire Blvd., #511, Los Angeles CA 90024

Fox, Michael J. 3960 Laurel Canyon, Ste. 281, Studio City CA 91604

Foxworthy, Jeff 8380 Melrose Ave., #310, Los Angeles CA 90069

Franken, Al c/o Saturday Night Live, 30 Rockefeller Plaza, New York NY 10112

Franklin, Aretha 16919 Stansbury, Detriot MI 48213

Franz, Dennis 11805 Bellagio Rd., Los Angeles CA 90049

Fraser, Brendan 2210 Wilshire Blvd., Ste. 513, Santa Monica CA 90403

Freeman, Morgan 3077 Saxon Ave., 2B, Bronx NY 10463

Fuentes, Daisy 2200 Fletcher Ave., Fort Lee, NJ 07024

Funicello, Annette 16102 Sandy Ln., Encino CA 91316

Garcia, Andy 4323 Forman Ave., Toluca Lake CA 91602

Garner, James 33 Oakmont Dr., Los Angeles CA 90049

Garofalo, Janeane 9560 Wilshire Blvd., Ste. 500, Beverly Hills CA 90212

Garr, Teri 9150 Wilshire Blvd., Ste. 350, Beverly Hills CA 90212

Gates, Bill 10700 Northrop Way, Bellevue WA 98004

Gayle, Crystal 51 Music Square East, Nashville TN 37203

Gellar, Sarah Michelle 11350 Ventura Blvd., #206, Studio City CA

George, Phyllis Cave Hill Box 4308, Lexington KY 40503

Gere, Richard 9696 Culver Blvd., Ste. 203, Culver City CA 90232

Gershon, Gina 9560 Wilshire Blvd., Ste. 500, Beverly Hills CA 90212

Gertz, Jami 8942 Wilshire Blvd., Beverly Hills CA 90211

Gibbons, Leeza 5555 Melrose Ave., Ste. L, Los Angeles CA 90038

Gibson, Mel 4000 Warner Blvd., #P3-17, Burbank CA 91522

Gifford, Kathy Lee 625 Madison Ave., Ste. 1200, New York NY 10022

Gilbert, Melissa 151 El Camino Dr., Beverly Hills CA 90212

Glenn, John 1000 Urlin Ave., Columbus, OH 43212

Glover, Danny c/o Carrie Productions, 41 Sutter St., Ste. 1648, San Francisco CA 94104

Goldberg, Whoopi 555 Melrose Ave., Ste. 114, Los Angeles CA 90038

Gooding, Cuba Jr. 8942 Wilshire Blvd., Beverly Hills CA 90211

Goodman, John 5180 Louis Ave., Encino CA 91316

Gorbachev, Mirhail Leningradsky Prospekt 49, Moscow Russia

Gossett, Louis Jr. P.O. Box 6187, Malibu CA 90264

Gottfried, Gilbert 1350 Ave. of the Americas, New York NY 10019

Goulet, Robert 2700 East Sunset Rd, # C-27,LV, NV 89120

Grammer, Kelsey 3266 Cornell Rd., Agoura Hills CA 91301

Grant, Amy 9 Music Square, Ste. 214, Nashville TN 37203

Grant, Hugh 36 Redcliff Rd., London SW10 JNJ, England

Greenwood, Lee 1311 Elm Hill Pike, Nashville, TN 37214

Gretzky, Wayne P.O. Box 17013, Inglewood CA 90308

Grieco, Richard 15263 Mulholland Dr., Los Angeles CA 94188

Griffith, Andy P.O. Box 1968, Manteo NC 27954

Hackman, Gene 118 South Beverly Dr., Ste. 1201, Beverly Hills CA 90212

Haggard, Merle P.O. Box 536, Palo Cedro CA 96073

Haig, Alexander 1155 15 St. NW, #800, Washington DC 20005

Haim, Cory 233 S St. Andrews Pl., Los Angeles CA 90004

Halen, Eddie Van 31736 Broad Beach Rd., Malibu CA 90265

Hall, Arsenio 10987 Bluffside Dr., Ste. 4108, Studio City CA 91604

Hall, Jerry 308 W. 81 St., New York NY 10024

Hall, Monty 519 N. Arden Dr., Beverly Hills CA 90210

Hannah, Daryl 8306 Wilshire Blvd., Ste. 535, Beverly Hills CA 90211

Harrelson, Woody 10780 Santa Monica Blvd., Ste. 280, Los Angeles CA 90025

Harris, Emmylou P.O. Box 158568, Nashville, TN 37215

Hasselhoff, David 11342 Dona Lisa Studio City CA 91604

Hatcher, Teri 151 El Camino Dr., Beverly Hills CA 90212

Hawke, Ethan 9830 Wilshire Blvd., Beverly Hills CA 90212

Hayek, Salma 151 El Camino Dr., Beverly Hills CA 90212

Heche, Anne C/O Paradigm, 10100 Santa Monica Blvd., #2500, L.A. CA 90067

Hefner, Hugh 10236 Charring Cross Rd., Los Angeles CA 90077

Henderson, Florence Box 11295, Marina Del Rey CA 90295

Henstridge, Natasha 151 El Camino Dr., Beverly Hills CA 90212

Hoffman, Dustin 540 Madison Ave., Ste. 2700, New York NY 10022

Hogan, Hulk 4505 Morella Ave., Valley Village CA 91607

Hogan, Paul 55 Lavender Place, Milson's Pt., Sydney NSW 2060 Australia

Holbrook, Hal 9000 Sunset Blvd., #1200, Los Angeles CA 90069

Holly, Lauren 13601 Ventura Blvd., Ste. 99, Sherman Oaks CA 91423

Hopper, Dennis 330 Indiana Ave., Venice CA 90291

Horne, Lena 23 E. 74th St,. New York NY 10021

Howard, Ron 1925 Century Park E.,# 2300, LA CA 90067

Hunt, Helen 9630 Wilshire Blvd., Beverly Hills CA 90212

Huston, Angelica 74 Market St., Venice CA 90291

Idol, Billy 8209 Melrose Ave., Los Angeles CA 90046

Ice Cube 6809 Victoria Ave., Los Angeles CA 90043

Ice-T 2287 Sunset Plaza Dr., Los Angeles CA 90069

Iglesias Julio 5 Indian Creek Dr., Miami, FL 33154

Iman 111 E. 22nd St., #200, New York NY 10010

Indigo Girls 315 Ponce de Leon Ave., #755, Decatur, GA 30030

Ireland, Kathy 1900 Ave. Of The Stars, Ste.793, Los Angeles CA 90067

Jackson, Janet 338 N. Foothill Rd., Beverly Hills CA 90210

Jackson, Jesse 400 T St., Washington, DC 20001

Jackson, Kate 1628 Marlay Dr., Los Angeles CA 90069

Jackson, Michael c/o Neverland Ranch, Los Olivos CA 93441

Jackson, Reggie 305 Amador Ave., Seaside CA 93955-4725

Jackson, Samuel L. 955 S. Carillo, #300, Los Angeles CA 90048

Jagger, Mick 304 W 81st St., New York, NY 10024

Jennings, Peter 7 W. 66th St., New York NY 10023

Jennings, Waylon 1117 17th Ave. S., Nashville TN 37212

Jewel P.O. Box 33494, San Diego CA 92163

Jillian, Ann 4241 Woodcliff Rd., Sherman Oaks CA 91403

Joel, Billy c/o Maritime Music Inc., 280 Elm St., 2nd Fl., Southampton NY 11968

John, Elton 1249 Stillwood Dr. NE, Atlanta GA 30307

John, Olivia Newton P.O. Box 2710, Malibu CA 90265

Jolie, Angelina 955 S. Carrillo Dr. 3rd Floor, Los Angeles, CA 90048

Jones, George 1005A Lavergne Circle, Hendersonville, TN 37075

Jones, James Earl P.O. Box 610, Rawling NY 12564

Jones, Quincy 3800 Barham Blvd., # 503, Los Angeles CA 90068

Jones, Tom 363 Copa De Oro Rd., Los Angeles CA 90077

Jones, Tommy Lee 8942 Wilshire Blvd., Beverly Hills CA 90211

Jordan, Michael 1 Magnificent Mile, 980 N. Michigan Ave., Chicago IL 60611

Judd, Ashley P.O. Box 680339, Franklin TN 37068

Judd, Naomi P.O. Box 17087, Nashville TN 37217

Judd, Wynonna 1321 Murfreesboro Rd., Ste. 100, Nashville TN 37217

Kazan, Elia 174 E. 95th St., New York NY 10128

Keaton, Michael 9830 Wilshire Blvd., Beverly Hills CA 90210

Keitel, Harvey 110 Hudson Ave., Ste. 9A, New York NY 10013

King, B.B. P.O. Box 4396, Las Vegas NV 89107

King, Larry CNN, 820 First St. NE, Wash. DC 20002

Kinski, Nastassja 11 W. 81 St., New York NY 10024

Kissinger, Henry 350 Park Ave., New York NY 10022

Kitaen, Tawny P.O. Box 16693, Beverly Hills CA 90209

Klein, Calvin 205 W. 39th St., New York NY 10018

Klein, Robert 67 Ridge Crest Dr., Briarcliff NY 10510

Klugman, Jack 22548 Pacific Coast Hwy., Malibu CA 90265

Koch, Ed 1290 Ave. of the Americas, New York NY 10104

Koppel, Ted P.O. Box 234, New York NY 10023

Korman, Harvey 1136 Stradella, Los Angeles CA 90077

Kudrow, Lisa 8722 Burton Way, Ste. 402, Los Angeles CA 91505

Labelle, Patti 1212 Grennox Rd., Wynnewood PA 19096

Lamas, Lorenzo 6439 Reflection Dr., Ste. 101, San Diego CA 92124

Lansbury, Angela 635 Bonhill Rd., Los Angeles CA 90049

Larroquette, John P.O. Box 6910, Malibu CA 90265

Latifah, Queen 151 El Camino Dr., Beverly Hills CA 90212

Lauper, Cyndi 2211 Broadway, # 1, New York NY 10024

LeBlanc, Matt 9150 Wilshire Blvd., Ste. 350, Beverly Hills CA 90212

Lee, Spike 124 Dekalb Ave., 2 Floor, Brooklyn NY 11217

Leigh, Jennifer Jason 2400 Whitman Place, LA CA 90068

Leno, Jay c/o NBC, 3000 W Alameda Ave., Burbank CA 91523

Leonard, Nimoy c/o The Gersh Agency Inc., 232 Canon Dr., Beverly Hills CA 90210

Leoni, Tea 248 Horizon, Ste. 1, Venice CA 90291

Letterman, David c/o Late Night Show, 1697 Broadway, New York NY 10019

Lewis, Juliette 151 El Camino Dr., Beverly Hills CA 90212

Liddy, G. Gordon 9112 Riverside Dr., Fort Washington MD 20744

Lithgow, John 1319 Warnall Ave., Los Angeles CA 90024

Locklear, Heather 151 El Camino Dr., Beverly Hills CA 90212

Lopez, Jennifer 8560 Wilshire Blvd., Ste. 500, Beverly Hills CA 90212

Lords, Traci 3349 Cahuenga Blvd. W., #28, LA CA 90068

Loren, Sophia c/o La Concordia Ranch, 1151 Hidden Valley Rd., Thousand Oaks CA 91361

Lovitz, Jon 9200 Sunset Blvd., Ste. 428, Los Angeles CA 90069

Lucas, George 3270 Kerner Blvd., Ste. 1730, San Rafael CA 94912

MacNicol, Peter c/o Ally McBeal Show, 10201 W. Pico Blvd., Los Angeles CA 90035

MacPherson, Elle 414 E. 52nd St., #PH13, New York NY 10022

Madonna 75 Rockefeller Plaza., New York NY 11746

Manilow, Barry 5443 Beethoven St., Los Angeles CA 90066

Margret, Ann 3111 Bel Air Dr., Ste. 20H, Las Vegas, NV 89109

Marsalis, Wynton c/o Wynton Marsalis Enterprises, 70 Lincoln Center Plaza, New York NY 10023

Marshall, Penny 7150 La Presa Dr., Los Angeles CA 90068

Martin, Ricky 8439 Sunset Blvd., #405, Los Angeles, CA 90069

Martin, Steve P.O. Box 929, Beverly Hills CA 90213

McCarthy, Jenny 2112 Broadway, Santa Monica CA 90404

McCoo, Marilyn P.O. Box 7905, Beverly Hills CA 90212

McEntire, Reba 1514 South St., Nashville, TN 37212

McMahon, Ed 12000 Crest Dr., Beverly Hills CA 90210

McNamara, William P.O. Box 25148, Farmington NY 14425

Merchant, Natalie 9830 Wilshire Blvd., Beverly Hills CA 90212

Michener, James 4650 54 St., Saint Petersburg, FL 33711

Midler, Bette 9701 Wilshire Blvd., 10ᵗʰ Fl., Beverly Hills CA 90212

Milano, Alyssa 151 El Camino Dr., Beverly Hills CA 90212

Minnelli, Liza 1776 Broadway, New York NY 10019

Mizrahi, Isaac 133 South Swall Dr., Beverly Hills CA 90211

Modine, Matthew 151 El Camino Dr., Beverly Hills CA 90212

Moore, Demi 9830 Wilshire Blvd., Beverly Hills CA 90212

Moore, Dudley 5505 Ocean Front Walk, Marina Del Rey CA 90291

Moore, Mary Tyler 510 E. 86 St., #21A, New York NY 10128

Moreno, Rita 9000 Sunset Blvd., #1200, Los Angeles CA 90069

Morrisette, Alanis 119 Rockland Center, Ste. 350, Nanuet NY 10954

Moss, Kate 205 West 39th St., New York NY 10018

Murphy, Eddie 2727 Benedict Canyon, Beverly Hills CA 90210

Murray, Bill RFD 1 Box 573, Palisades NY 10964

Newhart, Bob 420 Amapola Lane, Los Angeles CA 90077

Newman, Paul 9830 Wilshire Blvd., Beverly Hills CA 90212

Newton, Wayne 6629 S. Pecos, Las Vegas NV 89120

Newton-John, Olivia P.O. Box 2710, Malibu, CA 90265

Nicholson, Jack 9544 Lime Orchard Dr., Beverly Hills CA 90210

Nielsen, Leslie 1622 Viewmont Dr., Los Angeles CA 90069

Nimoy, Leonard 801 Stone Canyon Rd., Los Angeles CA 90077

Nolte, Nick 6174 Bonsail Dr., Malibu CA 90265

Norris, Chuck P.O. Box 872, Navasota TX 77868

North, Oliver RR 1 Box 560, Bluemont VA 22012

O'Brien, Conan c/o Late Night Live, 30 Rockefeller Plaza, New York NY 10012

Olin, Lena 9560 Wilshire Blvd., Ste. 500, Beverly Hills CA 90212

Olmos, Edward James 18034 Ventura Blvd., Ste. 228, Encino CA 91316

Osmond, Marie 1420 East 800 N., Orem, UT 84059

Ovitz, Micheal 9830 Wilshire Blvd., Beverly Hills CA 90212

Pacino, Al 350 Park Ave., Ste. 900 New York NY 10022

Palminteri, Chazz 375 Greenwich St., New York NY 10013

Paltrow, Gwyneth 9830 Wilshire Blvd., Beverly Hills CA 90212

Parker, Sarah Jessica P.O. Box 69646, Los Angeles CA 90069

Parton, Dolly Attn: Dunice Eledg, 700 Dollywood Parkway, Pidgeon Forge, TN 37863

Pavarotti, Luciano 941 Via Giardini, 41040 Saliceta S. Guiliano, Modena Italy

Perot, H. Ross 1700 Lakeside Square, Dallas TX 75251

Perry, Luke 19528 Ventura Blvd., Ste. 533, Tarzana CA 91356

Pesci, Joe P.O. Box 6, Lavallette NJ 08735

Peters, Bernadette 323 W. 80 St., .Y. NY 10024

Pfeiffer, Michelle 231 N. Orchard Rd., Burbank CA 91506

Philbin, Regis 955 Park Ave., New York NY 10028

Pierce, David Hyde c/o Grub Street Productions, 5555 Melrose Ave., Wilder Bldg. 101, Los Angeles CA 90038

Pitt, Brad 9150 Wilshire Blvd., Ste. 350, Beverly Hills CA 90212

Porizkova, Paulina 9830 Wilshire Blvd., Beverly Hills CA 90212

Povich, Maury 250 W. 57 St., Ste. 26W, New York NY 10019

Powell, General Colin 1663 Prince St., Alexandria, VA 22314

Presley, Priscilla 151 El Camino Dr., Beverly Hills CA 90212

Priestly, Jason 1033 Gayley Ave., #208, Los Angeles CA 90024

Quaid, Dennis 9665 Wilshire Blvd, Ste. 200, Beverly Hills CA 90212

Quaid, Randy P.O. Box 17372, Beverly Hills CA 90209

Quayle, Dan 201 N. Illinois St., # 350, Indpls. IN 46204

Queen Latifah 1325 6 Ave,, N.Y., NY 10019

Raitt, Bonnie P.O. Box 626, Hollywood CA 90078

Randall, Tony 1 West 81st St., New York NY 10024

Rather, Dan 524 West 57th St., New York NY 10019

Reagan, Nancy 2121 Ave. Of The Stars, Los Angeles CA 90067

Redford, Robert 1101 E. Montana Ave., Santa Monica CA 90403

Reeves, Keanu 7920 Sunset Blvd.,#350, Los Angeles CA 90046

Reynolds, Burt 16133 Jupiter Farms Rd., Jupiter FL 33458

Richards, Michael 4024 Radford Ave., Bldg. 5 Ste. 102, Fullerton CA 92632

Ritter, John 15030 Ventura Blvd., Ste. 906, Sherman Oaks CA 91403

Rivers, Joan 1 East 62nd St., New York NY 10021

Rock, Chris 151 El Camino Dr., Beverly Hills CA 90212

Rodman, Dennis 4809 Seashore Dr., Newport Beach, CA 92663

Roseanne 151 El Camino Dr., Beverly Hills CA 90212

Ross, Diana P.O. Box 11059, Glenville Station Greenwich, CT 06813

Rourke, Mickey 9150 Wilshire Blvd., Ste. 350, Beverly Hills CA 90212

Russo, Rene 8046 Fareholm Dr., Los Angeles CA 90046

Ryder Winona 240 Centre St., New York NY 10013

Sabato, Antonio Jr. 13029 Mindanao Way, Ste. 5, Marina del Rey CA 90292

Adam, Sandler 9000 Sunset Boulevard, Suite 1200, Los Angeles, CA 90069

Sarandon, Susan 40 West 57th St., New York NY 10019

Schroder, Rick 9560 Wilshire Blvd., Ste. 500, Beverly Hills CA 90212

Schwimmer, David 232 N. Canon Dr., Beverly Hills CA 90210

Schwarzenegger, Arnold 3110 Main St., Santa Monica CA 90405

Selleck, Tom 331 Sage Ln., Santa Monica CA 90402

Seymour, Jane Box 548, Agoura CA, 91376 CA 90212

Shatner, William 3674 Berry Dr., Studio City CA 91604

Shaver, Helen 9171 Wilshire Blvd., Ste. 436, Beverly Hills CA 90210

Sheen, Martin 6916 Dume Dr., Malibu CA 90265

Sheridan, Nicollette 8942 Wilshire Blvd., Beverly Hills CA 90211

Shields, Brooke 431 Beloit Ave., Los Angeles CA 90049

Shue, Elizabeth 1146 Sierra Alta Way Los Angeles CA 90069

Silverstone, Alicia 8890 Beverly Blvd., Ste. 102, Los Angeles CA 90048

Simon, Carly 135 Central Park 2, #6-S, New York, NY 10023

Simon, Neil 10745 Chalon Rd., Los Angeles CA 90077

Simon, Paul 1619 Broadway, #500, New York NY 10019

Slater, Christian 8007 Highland Terrace Los Angeles CA 90046

Smith, Anna Nicole 200 Ashdale Ave., Los Angeles CA 90049

Smith, Will 330 Bob Hope Dr., Burbank, CA 91523

Smits, Jimmy P.O. Box 49922, Los Angeles CA 90049

Sorvino, Mira 41 W. 86th St.,NY, NY 10024

Spacey, Kevin 200 E. 58th St., Ste. 7H, New York NY 10022

Britney, Spears Box 250, Osyka, MS 39657

Spelling, Tori 5700 Wilshire Blvd., #575, Los Angeles CA 90036

Springsteen, Bruce 1224 Benedict Canyon, Beverly Hills CA 90210

Stallone, Sylvester 8942 Wilshire Blvd.. Beverly Hills, CA 90211

Stamos, John 151 El Camino Dr., Beverly Hills CA 90212

Steenburgen, Mary 320 E Ojai Ave., Ojai CA 93023

Stern, Howard c/o K-ROCK FM, 600 Madison Ave., New York NY 10022

Stone, Sharon P.O. Box 7304, North Hollywood CA 91603

Strait, George 1000 18th Ave., South Nashville TN 37212

Streep, Meryl P.O. Box 105, Taconic CT 06079

Streisand, Barbra 301 N. Carolwood Dr., Los Angeles CA 90077

Sutherland, Kiefer 1033 Gayley Ave., Ste. 208, Los Angeles CA 90024

Swayze, Patrick 132 S. Rodeo Dr., #300, Beverly Hills CA 90212

Tarentino, Quentin 151 El Camino Dr., Beverly Hills CA 90212

Taylor, Elizabeth 700 Nimes, Bel Air CA 90213

Thomas, Marlo 420 E. 54 St., #22F, New York NY 10022

Tomei, Marisa 120 W. 45 St., Ste. 3600, New York NY 10036

Tomlin, Lily 2014 Demille Dr., Hollywood CA 90027

Travolta, John 12522 Moorpark,Ste. 109, Studio City CA 91604

Trump, Donald c/o The Trump Corporation, 725 Fifth Ave., New York NY 10022

Trump, Ivana 725 Fifth Ave., New York NY 10022

Turner, Kathleen 163 Amsterdam Ave., #210, New York NY 10169

Turner, Ted 1050 Techwood Dr. NW, Atlanta, GA 30318

Twain, Shania 410 W Elm St., Greenwich, CT 06830

Van Dyke, Dick 23215 Mariposa De Oro St., Malibu CA 90265

Vila, Bob 20 Rascilly Rabbit Rd., Box 749, Marston Mills, MA 02648

Voight, Jon 13340 Galewood Dr., Sherman Oaks CA 91423

Wahlberg, Mark 63 Pilgrim Rd., Braintree MA 02184

Wallach, Eli 90 Riverside Dr., New York NY 10024

Walters, Barbara c/o 20/20, 147 Columbus Ave., 10th Floor, New York NY 10023

Washington, Denzel 4701 Sancola Ave., Toluca Lake CA 91602

Welch, Raquel 540 Evelyn Pl., Beverly Hills CA 90210

White, Betty P.O. Box 491965, Los Angeles CA. 90049

Williams, Robin 1100 Wall Rd., Napa CA 94550

Williams, Vanessa 2070 Stanley Hills Dr., Los Angeles, CA 90046

Willis, Bruce 1122 S. Robertson Blvd., Ste. 15, Los Angeles CA 90035

Winfrey, Oprah 110 N. Carpenter St., Chicago IL 60607

Winslet, Kate 31/32 Soho Square, London, W1V 5DF England

Woods, Tiger 6704 Teakwood St.., Cypress, CA 90630

Yeager, Chuck P.O. Box 128, Cedar Ridge CA 95924

Yearwood, Tricia P.O. Box 65, Monticello GA 34064

Young, Sean P.O. Box 20547, Sedona, AZ 86341

JOIN EXCLUSIVE CLUBS

The secret to joining an exclusive, upper-crust club is to practice well-bred inconspicuousness. You don't want to be black-balled by any member. Since nobody in such clubs will be impressed by mere money, you should never appear like a social climber. If you are seen as a fast-talking, flashy dresser, chances are you will be rejected.

The secret to getting into such a club is to realize that many established, older clubs are always short of money, which means they are always quietly looking for new members. To get in, timing is very important. You should make a move to join when you are young or have just moved into town, before you have irked any older members by besting them in business deals, or giving better parties, or whatever.

Get to know someone you know is a member. Work on school or business connections. Eventually you will find a member to sponsor you. At the initial interviews, keep a low profile and avoid overt attempts to impress the club officers. Let them do most of the talking. Suggest interest without letting them know of your eagerness to join.

GET DRINKS ON THE HOUSE

There are a number of ways to get drinks on the house. The most popular is to frequent a neighborhood or working-class "Irish" bar. It is customary practice there that for every three or four drinks you buy, the bartender will buy you a complementary round.

One of the most outrageous methods I've heard of for getting free drinks is that of the fellow who, when eating in a better restaurant, would call over first the waiter and then the maitre d' to complain about some debris he found in his food and complain loudly about the sorry state of the kitchen. The maitre d' would inevitably offer to give him another entrée. But the patron would shake his head and say he lost his appetite. "Just give me a drink."

And finally, another method that often works in a good restaurant is to ask the waiter if the chef would mind autographing the menu so that you can keep it as a memento of a fabulous dining experience. Such flattery often gets you a drink on the house.

CRASH EXCLUSIVE PARTIES

There is a whole underground of party crashers in New York and Los Angeles. They don suitable attire and attend the most exclusive of gatherings. You too can crash these receptions. It just takes nerve.

At every social event, there are bound to be some empty seats. Here's how to get in. Put on formal attire or clothing appropriate to the event. Wearing a tuxedo, for example, with a button that says "Host" or "Finance Committee" will always convince the door guards to let you in. When crashing, always assume the attitude that you belong and know what you are doing. Look like you belong.

When walking in, Do Not Stop. Look straight ahead and walk with determination. Don't run. Remember, you outrank the guards. No shifty eyes or ogling the guests — you don't want to give the guards any reason to question your presence.

GET A GOOD TABLE IN A CROWDED RESTAURANT

If you don't wish to wait an hour for a good table and want to break through all the people ahead of you, bribery almost always works.

Quietly slip the maitre d' an envelope with a twenty or fifty dollar bill in it. Then wait until he comes up to nod you to the front. Such tips are bread-and-butter for the maitre d' and his assistant.

If you're reluctant to tip, you can try titles. "The Judge's eyes are failing. Could we please have a front table." Or try, "The Ambassador's hearing's not too good. We need a table closer to the front."

GO TO EXCLUSIVE RESTAURANTS AND NOT LOOK LIKE A TOURIST

Tourists are everywhere these day, in all our major cities. They are easy to spot — shorts, sneakers, tee shirts and cameras. And wherever they go they are treated like tourists. They don't get into top restaurants. Or they're seated in outer Siberia. They don't get good service because they are not perceived as regulars.

The secret to good service is to dress conservatively. Men should wear dark business suits or blazer and gray trousers. Women should wear business attire. This way you'll look like a top big-city executive.

To be "in" at New York's "21" Club, you have to realize that there are places to see and be seen. At lunch time, try to get a table on the second floor in front. After theater, you want to sit downstairs in the grille next to the bar.

Bonus Report #12

RX: SAVE UP TO HALF ON ALL YOUR PRESCRIPTIONS!

Filling your prescriptions by mail can save you as much as 50 percent or more. Contact these companies to compare prices.

- **AARP**, (800) 456-2277
- **Diversified Prescription Delivery**, (800) 452-1976
- **Medi-Mail Pharmacy**, (800) 331-1458

- **Members Services Systemed Pharmacy,** (800) 247-1003.

Make sure your doctor writes out your prescriptions using the generic name instead of the brand name of each drug. Generic drugs are just as good and cost much less.

HOW YOU CAN GET FREE PRESCRIPTION DRUGS

When your doctor gives you a prescription for a drug you haven't had before, ask for lots of free samples. Explain that this way you can make sure you are not allergic to the drug before you pay for a prescription you might not use.

Then, every time your doctor writes a refill on the medication, ask for more free samples. Just explain that your budget is tight and you would appreciate the help. Doctors get these samples for free from the drug companies so it doesn't cost them anything.

FREE PRESCRIPTION DRUGS FROM THE DRUG MAKER

Hoecht Marion Russell, the large pharmaceutical house, has a program that distributes free prescription drugs manufactured by the company to individuals who fall below the federal poverty level and who have no prescription reimbursement coverage or third party payment plans.

Initial inquiry can be made by the patient, the patient's family, doctor, or social service worker. Once accepted, individuals may continue indefinitely as long as they are in financial and medical need.

You can call the Hoecht Marion Russell Patient Assistance Program toll-free at (800) 221-4025.

Bonus Report #13

GREATEST SECRET OF BECOMING RICH!

The greatest secret to getting rich is to make use of what is known as "The One Percent Solution." This method, together with the wonders of compound interest, can make you rich.

HOW IT WORKS

The method does nothing less than make you move at a steady pace towards your ultimate goal. Here is how it works.

Starting with your next pay check, save one percent from each paycheck you receive in the next two months. So, if your weekly check is for $750, save $7.50 (one percent) every payday. That's right, just $7.50. After a few weeks, you won't even miss the $7.50. Open an interest paying bank account in which to save the money each week.

After two months, raise the amount by one percent so that you now save two percent, (an additional $7.50 for a total of $15 in our example). You'll feel like you only have $7.50 less to spend each week because you already got accustomed to the first $7.50.

Now, repeat this procedure every two months so that you keep raising your savings by one percent. Do this until your reach a savings rate of ten percent. This will be your ultimate savings goal.

Listen. Saving is like jogging. You work yourself up gradually to the rate you desire. If you start out at the ultimate rate right away, you won't be able to handle it and you'll drop out. So you build up your savings abilities gradually, till you are able to handle the ten percent rate.

REACHING YOUR GOAL

Having money in your pocket is like having candy. If you have candy, you will eat it. In the same way, the average person spends whatever he earns, no matter how much, or even more. So unless you have disciplined yourself to save some, you will spend it. With the One Percent method, you gradually train yourself to spend only what you have left in your pocket after savings.

One of the best ways to save is to have your savings deducted automatically from your paycheck and put into your One Percent savings account. Set this up with your employer and your bank.

Don't touch this account for anything. If an unexpected bill pops up, realize that before your One Percent account, you somehow took care of unexpected bills. Do so now.

Similarly, reduce your reliance on credit cards, on credit, and on installment buying. This will help you take control of your spending.

4 SIMPLE IDEAS TO KEEP ON BUDGET

- Don't borrow to buy something that loses value. Don't borrow for a car unless you have to since it will go down in value. It is smarter to borrow for a house, college education or other appreciating item. And when you borrow, do so at the lowest rate possible for the shortest period possible.

- Borrow at the lowest possible interest rate. That's often a home loan. The rates are low; the interest deductible. When you buy your house, don't pay down the loan below 80% unless you are otherwise debt free or need to for credit reasons. Use the money instead to pay off other higher interest non-deductible debt.

- Don't be tempted by low monthly payments. Even if those monthly payments on a 60 month car loan look low, you'll wind up paying a tremendous amount in interest. So, if you can afford a 36 or 24 month car loan, do so.

- Don't prepay your mortgage if you have high-interest credit card balances or car loans due. If you have extra money to pay down your mortgages, use it to pay down or pay off their car loans, furniture/appliance loans and credit cards.

MORE THAN A MILLION DOLLARS BY AGE 55

It's possible through this regular and simple savings plan to have more than a million dollars by age 55. Begin by saving money in your One Percent account and then transferring to growth mutual funds or higher-paying money market accounts or CDs and let it accumulate.

Suppose you start this plan when you are 25 years old. While we can't predict future interest rates, at a modest 13 percent accrued yield, by the time you're 55, you'll have accumulated a nest egg of $1,421,312.

If you keep saving till you are 65, you'll have accumulated a nest egg worth an astounding $5,258,196.

Bonus Report #14

HOW TO MAKE A FORTUNE WITH A MAIL-ORDER BUSINESS YOU CAN START WITH $100!

There' a woman in Maryland with the last name of Fox who sells only to other people named Fox. She sells only items that have a direct connection with the animal fox, or perhaps a type of foxiness. For example, Christmas (and every other kind of) greeting cards, bookplates, novelties, stationery, birth notices, mailboxes, gadget jewelry, Shakespearean quotations about foxes, lapel pins and other items — each incorporating the picture of a fox.

Her first mailing piece was headed "Calling All Foxes," and today she has tens of thousands of buyers on her customer list. It is estimated that there are perhaps 80,000 families in the U.S. with the name "Fox," so she had a wonderful chance to expand the business into something really big with the possibilities of making a fortune out of the clever idea.

A similar type of business is run by Ray Melissa, owner of the Melissa Catalog, a catalog of items personalized with the name "Melissa." He states he gets 30 to 40 calls a day from young girls with the first name Mellisa—junior high to high school age. Personalized clothing sells best.

There are many,.many names with which you could duplicate these businesses. Here are examples of last names that should provide good size markets:

Ace	Fountain	Poole
Adam	Flagg	Park
Ash	Flowers	Payne
Appleton	Foote	Post
Armstrong	Ford	Press
Baker	Gardner	Price
Ball	Gold	Rainwater
Barker	Grant	Redman
Bass	Gray	Reed
Beard	Green	Rhodes
Bell	Hall	Rich
Bird	Hart	Rice
Birch	Hill	Robin
Black	Hunter	Rose
Blackman	Jackson	Sands
Blue	Jefferson	Savage
Block	Johnston	Shoemaker
Brook	Katz	Shepherd
Brown	King	Snow
Butler	Knight	Stone
Bull	Lamb	Storm
Carpenter	Lemon	Summers
Castle	Monroe	Taylor
Cook	Moss	Walker
Copper	Lincoln	Warden
Crane	Little	Washington
Crown	Love	Webb
Davenport	Mann	White
Diamond	Miller	Winters
Drake	Moon	Wise
Fish	Moore	Wolf
Fisher	Nichols	Wood

For example, there are 260,000 Smith families in the United States, and thousands and thousands of slight variations of the name Smith, such as Schmidt, Smyth, etc. There are 170,000 Brown families in the country with thousands more with the name Browne. 160,000 Jones families await a Jones mailorder service. There are 126,000 Michelle's. And so on down the line with many first and last names.

There are many variations of some of these names. such as Cooke, Horne, Wolfe, Wolff, etc. These variations would run into hundreds of thousands of extra names.

And you don't have to actually have one of these names to run such a business. Just sign all letters to customers using a "stage" name.

Mark Twain dedicated one of his early books to "John Jones" with this observation: "I know there are a great many John Jones in America and I also realize that people who have books dedicated to them usually buy those books." He figured that if every John Jones bought the book, he could retire.

ITEMS, GIFTS AND GADGETS TO SELL

Here are just some of the items you can sell:

Appliqués	Napkins
Awards	Paperweights
Balloons	Pencils
Balls	Pens
Belt buckles	Pins
Bumper stickers	Playing cards
Buttons	Post-it notes
Calendars	Rulers
Decals	Scarves
Emblems	Shoe laces
Frisbees	Shopping bags
Glasses	Socks
Hats	Stationery
Headbands	Styrofoam cups
Key tags	Ties
Letter openers	Tote bags
Luggage tags	Towels
Magnets	T-shirts
Markers	Visors
Mugs	Wristbands

Some names lend themselves to a line of jewelry. Others lend themselves more to novelties. Some names would have to settle for a color, others for pictures and printed items. Many have an exact identity—such as Baker, Ball, Bird, Bull, Fish, King, Moon, Robin, Wolf . Color names would include Black, Brown, Gold, Green, Gray, White. Some names would call for imaginative thinking—Bass, Birch, Carpenter, Copper, Love, Vine, and so on.

Local suppliers of imprinted, stamped or marked items are listed in the *Yellow Pages*. Here are some nationwide suppliers. Contact them for their catalogs.

- **Gemini Co.**, 810 S. Maumee, Tecumseh MI 49286. (800) 788-3891.
- **Morgan/Artcraft Screenprint**, 460 W. Canfield, Detroit MI 48201. (800) 786-0687.

- **New Image, Inc.**, 2401-B Ogletown Rd., Newark DE 19711. (800) 836-0523.

WHERE TO GET NAMES

The beauty of the business is it is easy to get mailing lists of people to mail to. Almost any list broker (look in the *YELLOW PAGES*) could get you lists of people with the names you want. They rent for about $80 a thousand. You can even compile names yourself right from phone books, or from phone directories on the internet.

Bonus Report #15

HOW YOUR HOME VIDEO CAMERA CAN MAKE YOU RICH!

I've probably received more inquiries about this moneymaker — insurance videotaping — than about any other business opportunity.

HOW IT WORKS

Insurance companies like detailed information regarding property and possessions before they settle claims for fire, theft or other loss or damage. The more specific proof a claimant can provide, the better his chances of effecting a favorable settlement. But, most people cannot readily remember what they own and its value after a loss occurs.

A videotape, however, of the insured possessions, can be excellent evidence when a claim is made. The insurance videotaping business is a simple field to get into, and aside from acquiring the necessary video equipment, a low-cost business to start. Potential clients include homeowners and business people. You go to homes, apartments, offices, businesses, and factories to photograph entire rooms and areas, individual items, valuable objects, closet and drawer contents, merchandise inventories and equipment.

Your can charge by the hour or by the job. Try to estimate how long a job will take so that you average at least $50 an hour. The normal home should take one or two hours. Businesses are more complicated, take a lot more time, and therefore command higher fees.

Before doing any jobs for money, practice on your own home and those of friends and relatives. Then, when you've got the techniques down pat, you can videotape for money. Use your best tapings as sample videos to show prospective clients.

GETTING CLIENTS

- Word-of-mouth referrals, distributing flyers, and getting referrals from insurance agents who then get a commission, are the best ways to get business. The flyer should point out that even though many homeowners think they can do it themselves, the services of a professional videographer are essential because—
  1. The average homeowner never gets around to it.
  2. He cannot do a thorough job of documentation.
  3. A complete, professionally-made video can pay for itself a thousand-fold when a claim is made.

- Go through the *Yellow Pages* and make a list of insurance agents. Then contact each one, explaining how they can increase their incomes by offering inventory videotaping to their clients. You could either phone or write the agents. Explain that they contact their clients on their own letterhead to recommend your service. When a client buys the service, the insurance agent gets a commission. Prepare a flyer that the agent can print under his own name to send out to his clients.

- As an inducement to homeowners, offer, at no additional charge, to tape their children for a permanent record , thus helping with the problem of missing children.

- Call your clients back each year to see if there are new purchases to be added to the videotape.

TAPING HOUSEHOLD INVENTORIES

The purpose of the video is to help determine the value of the objects by establishing exactly what is lost, and the value and purchase dates for major items.

- Go through the home, room by room, taking both close-ups and long shots of the valuables. Tape labels inside suits and on the back of china plates. Tape close-ups of registration, serial or model numbers on appliances and other equipment.

- Have the client narrate the taping by telling about the possessions — purchase price, when purchased, condition, whether or not they've been damaged, modernized or upgraded, or altered in any significant manner.

- Gather all stock certificates, bonds, deeds, insurance policies, any important contracts, health records, bank documents, purchase receipts, every potentially important piece of paper. Tape them face-up on a table and have the client flip them over while you hold the camera.

- Videotape the garage and cars or other vehicles, including the mileage on the odometer and any stereo equipment or other improvements which contribute to the value.

- Tape the building exterior, recording all repairs, improvements, and defects. Move slowly around the building, scanning every part of it including roof and chimney.

- Have the homeowner narrate the tape, describing each item in detail. Have him provide information about when the items were purchased and the original prices, and take close-up shots of receipts.

The finished tape should be from 20 to 60 minutes of nonstop display and nonstop talk. Make a backup copy and give the finished tapes to the client so they can store one copy in a safe deposit box or other off-premises location.

TAPING BUSINESS PREMISES

Tape the business premises and its furnishings and equipment in the same way you would tape a home, with the business client or some other official narrating the tape.

- Tape the office, factory, warehouse, selling area. Start with wide shots. Then go from area to area, corner to corner, taping everything you see including machinery, display fixtures, shelves, carpeting, light fixtures, heating and air-conditioning equipment.

- Tape cars, trucks, forklift trucks, conveyers and other materials-handling equipment.

- Tape merchandise inventories. Usually, inventories consist of manufactured items packed in cases; for instance, one dozen pairs of sneakers per case. To tape the inventoried stock of each item, pan the entire area, showing the quantity of cartons. Then, unpack a representative case and tape its contents.

Give the client two to four days to review the tape for errors. You should be under no obligation if they have omitted something, but if your camerawork was faulty, they deserve a retaping at no charge.

EQUIPMENT AND TECHNIQUE

The most expensive investment will be the purchase of video equipment. Initially—especially if you will start out doing just residential jobs—your ordinary home camcorder will do the job. But if you plan on doing business-related taping, you'll need better equipment.

Home systems use ½-inch videotape; professionals use ¾-inch tape which gives a better quality picture. The ideal situation, at least when starting out, would be to rent the equipment when you have a taping assignment. Some video professionals never buy their equipment. They rent so that they are always assured of getting the most up-to-date apparatus.

Some manufacturers offer training courses where you can have the opportunity to use their products. Sony, for example, has a program called Sony Video Utilization Services which provides training for both beginners and experienced video people. If a local college or high school has a video program, contact the instructor for his recommendations as to what equipment to buy, and where to buy it.

When the client narrates the tape, describing each item, be sure he covers the following details:

1. Make/manufacturer:

2. Model:
3. Serial number:
4. Purchased on_____, from_____, for $_____:
5. Purchase documented by "receipt," "canceled check," "credit card statement," or "video/photographs."
6. Current value according to "client's estimate" or "an appraisal."

Bonus Report #16

How to get your creditors off your back—for good!

If your debts are out of control and you can't pay off your bills, there are a number of steps you can take to get your creditors off your back. Sometimes using these techniques will buy you some extra time. Sometimes, your creditors will forgive your debts for a fraction on the dollar or even altogether.

SEND AN ANGUISHED LETTER

One technique is to make the first move—contact the businesses you owe money to tell them that you can't make payments right now because of sudden or unusual circumstances. Send them an anguished letter telling them your payments will be late, but try not to give them a fixed date when you will pay.

This technique will often get you as much as six months relief. It gives the impression of tremendous financial hardship due to some personal catastrophe. Your creditors will feel you are sincere because you contacted them to admit your inability to pay on time, and they'll usually be more lenient and understanding.

When writing your letter, paint the bleakest possible picture of your finances. Be honest, but play up illnesses, accidents, job layoffs, car repossessions, major back taxes that you owe, and the like. Never disclose where you work or bank. If you send a payment, don't send a check from your bank—send a postal money order.

Collections Dept.
ABC Appliance Store
340 Main St.
Smithville IN 46507

Re: Acct. No. 46582

Dear Sir:

I've received your notice stating that my account is past due.

I would like to pay but in the last few months my family and I have been hit by a number of monetary and health setbacks.

My wife, whose earnings contributed half the family income, has recently had a serious illness and won't be able to return to work for some time.

In addition, my job has recently been cut back to 25 hours a week.

And a fire destroyed my kitchen, garage and car.

Notwithstanding these and other problems, we would like to resume payments as soon as we are able.

I thank you for your consideration in this matter.

Sincerely yours,

Your Name

SEND A LETTER TO THE COLLECTION AGENCY

If a creditor gives your debt to a collection agency, this means you've done a good job so far of avoiding paying the bill. When all collection efforts fail, the original creditor and the collection agency will decide whether to give the debt to an attorney for collection. The risk of such an action depends on how much you owe, are you currently employed or likely to become employed, the likelihood of their winning, whether or not you recently filed for bankruptcy (you have to wait 7 years to file again).

Your most powerful weapon against a collection agency is your right to tell it to leave you alone. Simply send a letter to the agency to cease all communication with you. Here's such a letter to send to a collection agency to get it off your back.

```
Persistent Collection
Service
98 Shylock St.
Pinehill NY 10298

Re: Mr. I.O. Zilch
    Acct. No. 46582

Gentlemen:

    For three months now, I've
received phone calls and
letters from you concerning
my outstanding debt to Omega
Jewelers.

    As I have informed you, I
cannot pay this bill.

    Accordingly, under 15
U.S.C. § 1692c, this is my
formal notice to you to
cease all further
communications with me
except for the reasons
specifically set forth in
the federal law.

    Sincerely yours,

    Your Name
```

After you send such a letter, under the Federal Fair Debt Collections Practices Act (FDCPA), a collection agency can only contact you to tell you that collection efforts against you have ended; or that the collection agency or original creditor will invoke a specific remedy against you, such as suing you. If they continue to harass you, you can sue them.

THREATEN BANKRUPTCY

A third step you can take is to send a letter to your creditors threatening bankruptcy; a calm, business-like letter that just "incidentally" mentions that you have consulted a lawyer about the possibility of bankruptcy. The mere mention of this possibility often makes creditors hesitant about insisting on immediate payment.

Normally, a creditor's only legal means of collecting an unsecured debt is to sue you, win a court judgment, and then try to collect the amount of the judgment out of your property and income. Much of your property, furnishings, clothing, personal effects, even food, is exempt from being taken to pay a court judgment. And your nonexempt personal property may not be worth enough to tempt a creditor to go to the legal expense and hassle of going after it.

Creditor's usually first go after your wages and other income. But only 25% of your net wages can be taken to satisfy a court judgment, except if the judgment is for back alimony or child support. In addition, creditors usually can't touch public benefits such as unemployment insurance, AFDC welfare payments, disability insurance or Social Security.

Here's an example of a such a letter threatening bankruptcy:

```
Collections Dept.
ABC Appliance Store
340 Main St.
Smithville IN 46507

Re: Acct. No. 46582

Gentlemen::

    In the last few months my
family and I have been hit
by a number of monetary and
health setbacks.

    My wife, whose income
contributed half the family
income, has recently had a
```

serious illness and won't be able to return to work for some time.

In addition, my job has recently been cut back to 25 hours a week.

And a fire destroyed my kitchen, garage and car.

Notwithstanding these and other problems, we would like to resume payments as soon as we are able.

I have consulted an attorney about the possibility of declaring bankruptcy. But I would rather resume payments as soon as our circumstances permit.

I thank you for your understanding in this matter.

Sincerely yours,

Your Name

FILE A CHAPTER 13 WAGE EARNER PLAN

Chapter 13 of the Federal Bankruptcy Act is especially designed for the debt relief of people who earn a living from salaries, wages, or commissions. Known as the Wage Earner Plan, it is an installment payment plan administrated by the same branch of our courts that handles regular bankruptcy. You must be a wage-earner to use the law. That is the primary requirement.

Under a Chapter 13 bankruptcy, you keep your assets, but, in exchange, you agree to pay off your creditors (sometimes in part, sometimes fully) over 3 to 5 years. Your residence can be exempted from any levy to the extent determined by local law.

To initiate a Chapter 13 bankruptcy, you fill out a pack of forms listing your income, property, expenses and debts, and file them along with a filing fee—a few hundred dollars— with the bankruptcy court. In addition, you must file a workable plan to repay your debts based on your income and expenses.

The Wager Earner plan does not in itself "wipe out" debts, but a little known proviso of your filing requires your creditors to file a claim within 6 months. Many fail to file, in which case those debts are indeed "wiped out." In some cases, none file, which enables you to wipe out all your debts without bankruptcy. If creditors do appear, then the court allows you to spread your payments out over a 3 to 5-year period in smaller amounts that you can afford to pay, whether weekly, monthly, or bimonthly.

Once you file, you stop bill collectors, lawsuits, judgments, assignments, seized bank accounts, and other actions against you. There is a 3-month grace period between the date of filing and your court date, time in which no payments are required. And to top it off, in many cases your credit rating is improved because you made an honest effort to work with the lending firms.

In addition, if the seller used deceptive trade practices to induce your purchase, your debt may be wiped out under the provisions of the Uniform Commercial Code.

There are any number of books at your local library that give instructions on how to file for Chapter 13 bankruptcy. "Repay Your Debts" by Robin Leonard is one such recommended book.

Bonus Report #17

HOW TO BUY AIRLINE LOST– AND–FOUND ITEMS FOR PENNIES ON THE DOLLAR!

Here's a little-known fact: Airlines send lost, unclaimed luggage to the Unclaimed Baggage Center, a center for lost possessions located in Scottsboro, Alabama. The lost bags and cargo are sent their unopened so the center never knows what it is going to receive. To pick up bargains on lost treasures, you don't have to physically travel to this store in Scottsboro. You can get on the center's web site at www.unclaimedbaggage.com.

About one billion passengers check two billion bags every year. So even though just a miniscule percentage gets lost and is never claimed, you can see how stuff gets lost. Millions of items a year.

About half the stock is clothing, but you can also find jewelry, laptop computers, CD players, sporting goods, camera equipment, and all kinds of miscellaneous trinkets.

Bonus Report #18

WHO TO CALL: TOLL-FREE HELP LINES FOR FREE ASSISTANCE!

Whether you need help caring for an ill relative, dealing with a drub problem, living with an abusive spouse, collecting from Social Security, or you have some other problem that is making life miserable, here are phone numbers you can call to get assistance.

Abortion National Abortion Federation, (800) 772-9100. Offers information about aboetion and provides details about funding sources and qualified abortion providers.

Adoption Gladney Center, (800)-GLADNEY. Comprehensive services to adoptive parents, birth parents, children.

Aging (1) Communicating for Seniors, (800) 432-3276. Answers questions for the elderly on health-related matters and Medicare; (2) Eldercare Locator, (800) 677-1116. Nationwide directory assistance to help older persons and care givers locate support services for the elderly. Provides information on how to locate services such as meals, home care, recreation, community services, etc.

AIDS CDC National AIDS Hotline, (800) 342-AIDS. Information and referrals to physicians, support groups, legal help, home care services, housing agencies, etc.

Alcoholism AL-ANON Family Group, (800) 356-9996. A self-help recovery program with over 30,000 local groups.

Alcoholism Mothers Against Drunk Driving, (800)-GET-MADD. Offers services, emotional support and victim support groups to victims of this violent crime through 500 chapters.

Allergy Asthma and Allergy Foundation of America, (800) 7-ASTHMA. Offers information and has support groups throughout the nation.

Alzheimer's Disease (1) Alzheimer's Disease and Related Disorders Association, (800) 272-3900. Provides phone numbers of local support groups; (2) American Health Assistance Foundation, (800) 437-2423. Emergency financial help for treatment of Alzheimer's patients and to caregivers.

Animal Welfare Petfinders, (800) 666-5678. Functions as a national lost and found pet service. Also offers assistance to owners traveling with their pets.

Arthritis Arthritis Foundation, (800) 283-7800. Provides information on support groups, exercise classes and more.

Attention–Deficit Disorder National Attention-Deficit Disorder Association, (800) 487-2282. Gives support to persons suffering from ADD and their families.

Au Pairs Au Pair in America, (800) 9AU-PAIR. The oldest and largest au pair program in America. Call for information on how to host an au pair and get 45 hours of child care weekly.

Autism Autism Society of America, (800) 328-8476. Provides information and referrals.

Autoimmune Diseases American Autoimmune Related Diseases Association, (800) 598-4668. Support services to individuals and families.

Automobile Safety Auto Safety Hotline, (800) 424-9393.

Birth Defects (1) Association of Birth Defect Children, (800) 313-ABCD. Information and support to families of children with birth defects caused by their mother's exposure to environmental agents such as drugs, chemicals, radiation, etc.; (2) March of Dimes Resource Center, (888) 663-4637. Provides information on issues relating to pregnancy, childbirth, and birth defects, and offers referral service.

Blindness (1) American Foundation for the Blind, (800) 232-5463; (2) Job Opportunities for the Blind, (800) 638-7518. Career counseling, job listings and referrals to blind individuals seeking employment.

Bones Osteoporosis and Related Bone Diseases National Resource Center, (800) 624-BONE.

Brain Tumor Patient Information Line of the National Brain Tumor Foundation, (800) 934-CURE. Provides information about specific brain tumors and treatments. Provides a listing of support groups throughout the nation.

Breast Cancer Y-ME Breast Cancer Organization, (800) 221-2141.

Cancer (1) CancerConnection, (800) 678-9990. Specially trained oncology nurses answer questions on prevention, diagnosis and treatment. (2) CHEMOcare, (800) 55-CHEMO. One-to-one emotional support on the telephone or in person to cancer patients undergoing treatment.

Cerebral Palsy United Cerebral Palsy Associations, (800) 872-5827. Nationwide information/referral service plus local affiliates that provide services in the areas of family support and employment development.

Child Abuse Childhelp/National Child Abuse Hotline, (800) 4-A-CHILD. Trained crisis counselors provide crisis intervention, information and referrals for anyone with concerns about child abuse.

Child Care Child Care Aware, (800) 424-2246. Puts parents in touch with referral services in their area.

Child Welfare Children's Defense Fund, (800) CDF-1200.

Chronic Fatigue Syndrome CFIDS Association of America, (800) 442-3437.

Civil Rights Civil Rights Hotline, US Dept. of Health and Human Services, (800) 368-1019. To report abuse of civil rights in programs funded by this government agency.

Cocaine Habit (800) COCAINE. Provides a national drug abuse treatment referral service.

Credit Counseling Consumer Credit Counseling Service National Referral Hotline, (800) 388-2227. 1,000 local non-profit offices provide credit counseling assistance and referrals.

Crime Wetip Hotline, (800) 78-CRIME. Pays rewards up to $1,000 for tips and leads.

Diabetes Juvenile Diabetes Foundation, (800) 533-2873. Local family support groups.

Disaster Relief American red Cross, (800) HELP-NOW. Disaster relief.

Domestic Violence National Domestic Violence Hotline, (800) 799-SAFE. Crisis intervention, information about sources who can provide emergency assistance.

Down Syndrome National Down Syndrome Society, (800) 221-4602. Provides information on Down syndrome; referrals to parent support groups.

Drug Abuse Samaritans Behavioral Helpline, (800) 253-1334. Information and referrals about cocaine, alcohol, prescription drug dependency.

Eating Disorders National Eating Disorder Hotline, (800) 248-3285. Referrals service and on-line therapists.

Education National GED Information Hotline, (800) 62-MYGED. Referrals to local GED testing centers and class sites.

Employment Women in Community Service, (800) 562-2677. Programs and support services for at-risk women and low income youth.

Epilepsy Epilepsy Foundation of America, (800) 332-1000. Provides referrals and information.

Eyes National National Eye Care Project, (800) 222-EYES. Participating doctors provide medical eye exams and treat the disadvantaged elderly.

Family Family Service America, (800) 221-2681. Assists families and individuals in solving problems involving marital troubles, parent-child tensions, family abuse, aging parents.

Funeral Funeral Service Consumer Assistance Program, (800) 662-7666. Provides information and acts as a go-between or arbitrator in problems involving funeral homes.

Gambling National Council on Problem Gambling, (800) 522-4700. **Grief Recovery** Grief Recovery Helpline, (800) 445-4808.

Hair Care Sebastian's Hotline, (800) 829-7322. Stylists and colorists give advice on hair care and disaster solutions, and recommend local salons.

Handicapped (1) Abledata Database of Assistive Technology, (800) 227-0216. Database listing 23,000 assistive products and rehabilitation equipment for people with disabilities; (2) HEATH Resource Center, (800) 544-3284. National clearinghouse for disabled persons seeking education or training after high school.

Handicapped Travel National Tour Association, Handicapped Travel Division, (800) NTA-8886. Referrals to tour companies that can accommodate the handicapped on escorted tours, or experienced at dealing with disabilities.

Headache National Headache Foundation, (800) 843-2256.

Health (1) National Health Information Center, (800) 336-4797. Information referral system that refers inquiries to the most appropriate source; (2) National Organization for Rare Disorders, (800) 999-6673. Provides information on 3,000 rare diseases; (3) Well Spouse Foundation, (800) 838-0897. Local support groups offer support to partners of the chronically ill or disabled.

Hepatitis Hepatitis Foundation International, (800) 891-0707. Telephone support, information about viral hepatitis, and physician referrals.

Hospices HospiceLink, (800) 331-1620. Information, informal support, and referrals to local hospices and bereavement support groups.

Hospitals Hill-Burton Free Hospital Care, (800) 638-0742. Information and referrals to hospitals that provide free and/or below cost hospital care for low income people.

Incontinency National Association for Continence, (800) BLADDER.

Kidneys American Kidney Fund, (800) 638-8299. Offers financial assistance to persons with chronic kidney failure.

Literacy National Literacy Hotline, (800) 228-8813. Offers referrals to nationwide literacy programs for persons who want to learn to read.

Lupus American Lupus Society, (800) 331-1802. Patient support groups; doctor referrals.

Medical Housing National Association of Hospital Hospitality Houses, (800) 542-9730. Provides family-centered lodging and support services to families and their loved ones who are receiving medical treatment far from home.

Medical Transport (1) AirLifeLine, (800) 446-1231. Free air transportation to ambulatory patients traveling to and from medical treatment and in financial need; (2) National Patient Air Transport Helpline, (800) 296-1217. Referrals to charitable and commercial services for patients needing transport to distant specialized treatment facilities.

Mental Health National Foundation for Depressive Illness, (800) 248-4344. Referrals to doctors who specialize in treating depression, and local support groups.

Migrant Workers BOCES Geneseo Migrant Center, (800) 245-5681. Health and educational services and referrals for migrant workers.

Missing Children (1) I Am Lost Hotline, (800) I AM LOST. Parents can call to register missing children; lost children can call for help. Also offers counseling services for parents of missing children; (2) Missing Children Help Center, (800) USA KIDS. Serves as a coordinating agency between parents, missing children and law enforcement and guides parents through the legal system.

Motorcycles Discover Today's Motorcycling, (800) 833-3995. Information to persons interested in buying a motorcycle or learning how to ride one, including referrals to nearest instruction location.

Muscular Dystrophy MDA Lifeline—Voice of Hope, (800) 572-1717. Information and referrals to local support groups, clinics, summer camps.

Nursing Visiting Nurse Associations of America, (800) 426-2547. Refers callers to the nearest Visiting Nurse Association, non-profit organizations that provide all aspects of home health care including general nursing, adult day care, care for the dying, friendly visit services, and Meals on Wheels.

Panic Disorders National Institute of Mental Health Information service, (800) 64 PANIC. Information and referrals to local organizations.

Parental Kidnapping A WAY OUT, (800) A WAY OUT. Confidential counseling and advice for parents considering abducting or who have taken their children.

Parents (1) Parents Anonymous, (800) 421-0353. Information and referrals to 2,000 local support groups where parents meet weekly to discuss parenting problems; (2) Toughlove, International, (800) 333-1069. Self-help materials to parents and kids in trouble, and referrals to local parent support groups.

Parkinson Disease American Parkinson Disease Association, (800) 223-2732. Provides information and referrals to local health services and physicians.

Radon EPA Radon Info. Line, (800) 767-7236. Information on radon safety in the home.

Recreation Areas National Recreation and Park Association, (800) 626-6772. Information on recreation areas, including services for the elderly and handicapped.

Relief CARE, (800) 521-CARE. The largest private relief organization.

Runaways Covenant House Ninepin, (800) 999-9999. Telephone Crisis intervention, referrals, information, and message relay services to homeless, runaway and other troubled youth and their families.

Safety Education National Safety, (800) 621-6244. Referrals to defensive driving courses and first aid/CPR classes.

Social Security (1) National Organization of Social Security Claimants, (800) 431-2804. A referral service to lawyers who handle Social Security disability cases. (2) Social Security Administration, (800) 772-1213.

Spinal Injury National Spinal Cord Injury Hotline, (800) 526-3456. Information, referrals and support to the paralyzed and their families.

Strokes Stroke Connection of the American Heart Association, (800) 553-6321. Referrals to 1,000 local stroke support groups for stroke survivors and their families.

Student Aid Federal Student Aid Information Center, (800) 433-3243. Answers technical questions and assists with applications.

Stuttering Stuttering Foundation of America, (800) 992-9392. Information and referrals to speech pathologists.

Substance Abuse (1) Cottage Program International, (800) 752-6100. Counseling to alcoholics and drug abusers and their families, referrals and in-home visits. Special services for Vietnam vets. (2) National Clearinghouse for Alcohol & Drug Information, (800) 729-6686. The world's largest substance abuse information and referral clearinghouse.

Sudden Infant Death Syndrome SIDS Alliance, (800) 221-7437. Support to SIDS families.

Taxation IRS Assistance, (800) 829-1040.

Tourette Syndrome Tourette Syndrome Association, (800) 237-0717. Helps patients who have been undiagnosed or misdiagnosed by publicizing and distributing information; referrals to support groups.

Trade Unions National Right to Work Legal Defense Foundation, (800) 336-3600. Information and advice to workers abused by compulsory unionism.

Veterans Veterans of the Vietnam War, (800) VIETNAM. Advice on veterans issues; Find-A-Vet computerized locator service; United Veterans Beacon House projects for homeless vets and their families.